A CHARLTON STANDARD CATA

WADE WHIMSICAL
COLLECTABLES

EIGHTH EDITION

By
PAT MURRAY

Editor
JEAN DALE

Publisher
W. K. CROSS

The Charlton Press

TORONTO, ONTARIO • PALM HARBOR, FLORIDA

PRODUCTION

Editor	Jean Dale
Graphic Technician	Davina Rowan
Pricing Co-ordinator	William T. Cross
Photography	Gordon Murray
Cover Illustration	Gingerbread Man

ACKNOWLEDGMENTS

The Charlton Press wishes to thank those who have assisted with the eighth edition of the *Wade Whimsical Collectables* – A Charlton Standard Catalogue.

Special Thanks

To my husband Gordon for his help and encouragement, and his time devoted to taking thousands of photographs for the Charlton Library of Wade Catalogues.

Also to Wade Ceramics and their staff for providing information on the manufacture of Wade porcelain. Many thanks to The Official International Wade Collector's Club, and to Jenny Wright the Club Manager.

Contributors to the Eighth Edition

The Publisher and the Author would like to thank the following collectors and dealers for their assistance in supplying photographs, measurements, and backstamp details:

Andrew Barfoot; Helen Barker; Val Baynton; Sara Bernotas; Paul Birdsall; Elizabeth Bowden; Lyn and Ian Bowman; Sue Braithwaite; Linda Bray; Margaret Brebner; Peter Brooks; Alan Burgess; Lisa Burlington; Mary Carter; Lizzi Chambers (Tetley GB); Elizabeth and John Clark; Mark Colclough; Tess Contois; Sue Cooper; Joyce and David Divelbis; Kathryn Ellison; Sandy Elphick; Elizabeth Everill; Jean-Pierre Gauthier; Bill Gibson; Kerrie and Stewart Glenard; Betty and Dennis Hannigan; Vince Harvey; Jean and Rachel Higham; Brenda Hochreiter; Brenda Holdom; Marion Hunt; Sue and Brian Hunter; Mandi, Sydney and Rob Jaques; Dennis Johnson; Peg and Roger Johnson; Pat and Gary Keenan; Donna Kinder; Esther and Gene Kramer; Diane LeBlanc; Dave Lee; James Lyttle; Sheila McEwan; Sue McLeod; Mr MacGregor; Mr. McEwean; Barbara Mabey; Reva and Michael Matthew; Valeries and Wayne Moody; Judi and Brian Morris; Rose and Chand Muniz; Carole and John Murdock; Helen and Bob Murfet; Daniel Murray; Molly Newman; Mrs. H. Palmer; Phyllis Palvio; Margaret Parsons; JoAnn Postlewaite; Margaret and Graeme Remihana; David Rigg, Redco Foods Inc.; Betty Ann and Monroe Robbins; Janet and Brian Robinson; Ed and Bev Rucker; Sarah Smith; Terry Smith; Saxon Stoof; Stuff-N-Nonsense; Annabel and Keith Sutherland; Dawn Sutton; Thelma and Jedd Swinhoe; T&A Collectables; Michelle Tenty; Val Tolfrey; Jeremy and George Wade; Naseem Wahlah; Dennis Watson; Eva Widda; Joyce Walker; Sue Williams; Annie and Steve Windsor; Sandra Wood; John Wright; Sandy and Bob Wright; Mary and Steve Yager

And many thanks to all those who have helped with information and photographs for this book and preferred to remain anonymous.

A SPECIAL NOTE TO COLLECTORS

We welcome and appreciate any comments or suggestions in regard to *Wade Whimsical Collectables*. If you would like to provide new information or corrections, or participate in pricing, please contact Jean Dale at the Charlton Press.

Printed in Canada
in the Province ofQuebec

The Charlton Press

Editorial Office
P.O. Box 820, Station Willowdale B
North York, Ontario M2K 2R1, Canada
Telephone: (416) 488-1418   Fax: (416) 488-4656
Telephone: (800) 442-6042   Fax: (800) 442-1542
www.charltonpress.com   e-mail: chpress@charltonpress.com

A RESOUNDING THANKS TO PAT AND GORDON MURRAY

Pat Murray has retired. The work that Pat and her husband Gordon have accomplished over the past twenty five years in chronicling the history of Wade laid the foundation for all Wade catalogues and books. Without this dedication the Wade collector would be at a loss as to which direction to travel. We at the Press wish to thank Pat and Gordon for all their efforts over the years, and to wish them a happy retirement.

The Press will continue to research, compile, price and publish *Wade Whimsical Collectables* and *Wade Collectables*. Our work will not match the calibre of the Murrays', but they are "Standards" and we will strive to achieve it. It is without question we will need your help, for while the Murrays devoted all their spare time to Wade collectables, we are unable to do likewise, due to the weight of other books we publish. So if we miss information, are incorrect in our pricing, please take the time to help set us right.

Please do not write or email the Murrays, correspond with us for we are responsible for all mistakes.

We need your help.

Jean Dale / Bill Cross

HOW TO USE THIS CATALOGUE

THE PURPOSE

As with the other catalogues in Charlton's Wade reference and pricing library, this publication has been designed to serve two specific purposes: first to furnish the collectors with accurate and detailed listings that will provide the essential information needed to build a rich and rewarding collection; second, to provide collectors and dealers with an indication of the current market prices on Wade Whimsical Collectables.

THE LISTINGS

This guide is divided into three main sections. The first section includes models produced for the Wade product line (for example *Wade Whimsies*), which are listed alphabetically. The second section focuses on models produced for fairs, events, and membership exclusives, and is listed alphabetically. The third section includes models produced by Wade under commission for other corporations. These are listed alphabetically according to the issuing company.

STYLES AND VERSIONS

STYLES: A change in style occurs when a major element of the design is altered or modified as a result of a deliberate mould change. An example of this is *Goldilocks and the Three Bears*, 1953-c.1958 (style one) and *Goldilocks and the Three Bears*, 1996 (style two).

VERSIONS: Versions are modifications in a minor style element of the figures, such as the open- and closed-eared rabbits in the Red Rose Tea series.

TECHNICAL INFORMATION

The whimsical Wades in this book were produced in the George Wade Pottery, the Wade Heath Pottery and in the Wade Ireland Pottery between the 1930s and 2007, For each model, the name of its series, the year of production, the model's name, its size (the height first, then the width in millimeters), the colours and its present value are presented. All known backstamps of the models are listed above the tables. If the figures can be found with a variety of backstamps, then each backstamp is followed, in a parenthesis, by the model numbers applicable to it. For a few listings, only approximate dates of issue are given, as they could not be confirmed by Wade. When known, the year the model was discontinued and its original issue price is also given.

WADE COLLECTOR'S CLUB

The Official International Wade Collector's Club, run by Wade Ceramics, was founded in 1994. Members receive an annual Wade membership model upon joining and the opportunity to purchase club limited edition models. The full-colour quarterly magazine has information on new and old Wade models, dates and locations of Wade shows and exhibitions, and much more. To join the club, write to: The Official International Wade Collector's Club, Royal Victoria Pottery, Westport Road, Burslem, Stoke-on-Trent, ST6 4AG, Staffordshire, England.

CONTENTS

COMIC ANIMALS AND BIRDS
Donkeys 2
Duck Family 4
Frog Family 5
Penguin Family. 6
Pig Family 8
Rabbit Family 9
Rabbit (Little Laughing Bunny) 11

HAPPY FAMILIES
Cat Family 14
Dog Family 14
Elephant Family. 15
Frog Family. 15
Giraffe Family. 16
Hippo Family 16
Mouse Family 17
Owl Family 18
Pig Family 18
Rabbit Family. 19
Tiger Family 20

NOVELTY ANIMALS AND BIRDS
Baby Bird 22
Cheeky Duckling 22
Duckling, Head Back, Beak Closed 23
Duckling, Head Forward, Beak Open 23
Laughing Rabbit 24
Laughing Squirrel 24
Old Buck Rabbit 25
Pongo 26

STORYBOOK FIGURES
Alice and the Dodo 28
Bengo and His Puppy Friends, TV Pets. 29
Butcher, The Baker and The Candlestick Maker. . 30
Dismal Desmond 31
Goldilocks and the Three Bears 32
Jumbo Jim 33
Noddy Set 33
Nursery Favourites 34
Nursery Miniatures 36
Nursery Rhymes 37
Nursery Rhyme Blow Ups 38
Sam and Sarah (Mabel Lucie Attwell Figures) . . . 39
Thomas the Tank Engine. 40
Tinker, Tailor, Soldier, Sailor 41
Tom and Jerry 42
Wynken, Blynken, Nod and I've a Bear Behind . . . 43
Yogi Bear and Friends 44

WHIMSIES, 1954-2007
Christmas Crackers, Safari Whimsies 46
Collectable Limited Edition Crackers. 47
Comical Whimsies 48
Cool Cats 48
Dinosaur Collection 49
Dogs and Puppies. 50
English Whimsies 54
Family Pets. 62
Farmyard Whimsies 62
First Whimsies 63

First Whimsies Blow Ups 77
Nativity Whimsies Set 78
New Colourway Whimsies 79
Pearl Lustre Whimsies 82
Polar Bear Blow Ups 83
Tetley Tea Folk Whimsies 84
Whimsie-land 85
Whimsey-in-the-Vale 89
Whimsey-on-Why 91
Whoppas 95

MISCELLANEOUS SETS
Alphabet and London Trains 98
Angels 99
Bear Ambitions 102
Betty Boop 102
British Character Set 103
Child Studies 104
Circus Set 105
Drum Box Set 105
Felix the Cat 106
Fish Waiter 107
Flying Birds 108
Goodie Boxes 109
Honey Bunch Bears 110
Horse Sets 111
Kissing Bunnies 112
Minikins 114
Mr Men and Little Miss 119
Mr Snowflake and His Family 120
My Pet 121
Pocket Pals 122
Pokemon 124
Rule Beartannia 125
Snippets 126
Tony the Tiger 128
Tortoise Family 129
Treasures Set 131
Various Novelty Models 132
Water Life Collection 133
Zoo Mazing 134

FAIRS AND EVENTS
U.K. Fairs
    Alexandra Palace, 1998 136
    Alton Towers Fair, 1998 137
    Arundel
        Christmas Bonanza, 1999-2006 138
        Collectors /Swap Meets, 2001-2006 143
    Birmingham Fairs, 1994-1996 148
    Collect It! Fairs
        Newark, 1998 149
        Stoneleigh, 1998 149
    Dunstable Fairs, 1996-2006 150
    Olympia Incentive Exhibition, 1998 153
    Ripley Village Fete and Teddy Bears' Picnic, 1998 154
    Stoke Fairs
        1997, Trentham Gardens 155
        1998, Trentham Gardens 155
        1999, Trentham Gardens 156
        2000, Trentham Gardens 156
        2000, Stratford Show Grounds 157
        2001, Trentham Gardens 158
        2002, Kings Hall Civic Centre 159
        2003, North Staffordshire Hotel 160
        2004, North Staffordshire Hotel 161

2005, Kings Hall Civic Centre 161
2006, Kings Hall Civic Centre 162
2007, Discover Trentham. 162
Wade Christmas Extravaganza, 2000 163
U.S.A. Wade Collectors Shows
Seattle, WA, 1996 164
Oconomowoc, WI, 1997. 164
Buffalo, NY, 1998 164
San Antonio, TX, 1999 164
Kansas Wade Show, 2000-2001. 165
Red Rose Tea Fair, CT, 2006 166
Rosemont Trade Show, Rosemont, IL, 1999. 167
Mini Wade Fair, York, PA, 1999 167
Summer Wade Fest, Harrisburg, PA, 2000-2006. 168
West Coast Wade Collectors Fair, WA, 2002-2003 175
One-of-a-Kind Models. 177

THE OFFICIAL INTERNATIONAL WADE COLLECTOR'S CLUB FIGURES
Membership Figures 184
Enrol a Friend 185
Membership Series 185
Christmas Models 198

COMMISSIONERS ISSUES
Ameriwade 203
Arthur Price of England 204
Balding and Mansell 206
BJ Promotions. 208
Blyth Ceramics 209
Brighton Corporation 209
Brooke Bond Oxo Ltd., England 210
C&S Collectables Direct 211
Cadbury World. 234
Camtrak 235
Carryer Craft of California 237
Ceramica 238
CIBA Geigy 238
Collect It! Magazine 239
Collector (The). 242
Cotswold Collectables 242
Cricket Design Incorporated (CDI Imports) 243
David Trower Enterprises 247
E. and A. Crumpton 249
Father's Collection and Wades by Peg 250
Frisco Coffee 250
Fudge Collectables. 251
G&G Collectables 252
Gamble, Peggy (formerly Gamble and Styles) 254
General Foods. 255
Gold Star Gifthouse 256
Granada Television. 256
Great Universal Stores 257
James Robertsons & Sons 261
K.P. Foods Ltd. 262
KS Wader / Happy Wad-ing 263
Keenan, Patty. 268
Key Collectables. 269
King Aquariums Ltd 279
Langford, Keith 280
Latka, Sharon 281
Lever Rexona 282
Lux Soap 283
Memory Jars 283
New Victoria Theatre 284
Out of the Blue Ceramics 285
Pos-ner Associates. 287

R & M Collectables 287
Red Rose Tea (Canada) Ltd. 288
Red Rose Tea U.S.A. Ltd. (Redco Foods Ltd) 298
Robell Media Promotions Ltd. 307
St. John Ambulance Brigade (U.K.) 308
Salada Tea Canada 308
Sharps Chocolate 309
Simons Associates Inc. 310
Spillers Dog Foods Ltd. 312
Staffordshire House Gifts 312
Thomas Waide & Sons Ltd. 313
Tom Smith and Company Ltd. 314
Traufler 333
21st Century Collectables. 334
21st Century Keepsakes 335
UKI Ceramics Ltd. 336
Wade Watch USA 340
WadeUSA.com 2003 340
Warner Brothers 341
Whimsal Waders 341
Williamson, Robert and Peter Elson 342
Unknown Company 343

INDEX 347

INTRODUCTION

WHIMSICAL WADES

By the early 1950s, the Wade Potteries had filled the demand to replace industrial ceramics damaged in the war, and there was not sufficient work to keep the employees busy. This was when Sir George Wade decided to produce his now world-famous miniature animals—the *First Whimsies* — which he referred to as his "pocket money toys." They first appeared in spring 1954 at the British Industries Fair. The miniatures were intended for school children, but they soon attracted the attention of adults and became very collectable.

George Wade's policy was to limit the number of whimsical models produced, so they would not flood the market and lose their appeal. Models of the early 1950s were produced in sets, usually of five, and most sets were in production for only a year or two, some for as little as a few months. Whenever a large industrial order was received, the whole pottery would revert to the production of industrial wares, leaving some sets or series unfinished. Perhaps the pottery intended to go back to unfinished series, but because of slow sales, high production costs, copyright laws, or a new interest by the public, they were never completed.

In some of these cases there were only a few thousand models made, usually as a test run, and therefore they were not issued for nationwide sale. To recoup production costs, some models may have been sold only in one area of the United Kingdom.

In 1958 the three English Wade Potteries were restructured under the name Wade Potteries Ltd., later renamed Wade PLC. Wade (Ulster) Ltd. was renamed Wade Ireland Ltd. in 1966.

Sir George Wade died in 1986 at age 95, to be followed a year later by the untimely death of his son Tony. With their passing, 120 years of Wade family involvement in ceramics came to an end.

In 1989 Wade PLC was taken over by Beauford PLC and renamed Wade Ceramics Ltd., which is still in production today. Wade Ireland was renamed Seagoe Ceramics and continued to manufacture domestic table wares until 1993, when it reverted back to the production of industrial ceramics.

THE PRODUCTION PROCESS

The Wade Pottery manufactures a particularly hard porcelain body which has been used in many different products. It consists of a mixture of ball clays, china clay, flint, feldspar, talc, etc., some ingredients imported from Sweden, Norway and Egypt. These materials are mixed in large vats of water, producing a thick sludge or "slip." The slip is passed into a filter to extract most of the water, leaving large flat "bats" of porcelain clay, approximately two feet square and three inches thick. The clay bats are dried and then ground into dust ready for the forming process. Paraffin is added to the dust to assist in bonding and as a lubricant to remove the formed pieces from the steel moulds.

Once pressed into the required shape, the clay articles are dried, then all the press marks are removed by sponging and "fettling," which is scraping off the surplus clay by hand, using a sharp blade. From the early 1960s, a new method of fettling was used, whereby the base of the model was rubbed back and forth on a material similar to emery paper. This resulted in a lined or ribbed base, which is the best method of identifying the majority of post-1960 Wade figures.

One or more ceramic colours are applied to the clay model, which is then sprayed with a clear glaze that, when fired, allows the colours underneath to show through. This process is known as underglaze decoration. On-glaze decoration is also used by Wade, which includes enamelling, gilding and transfer printing, and is done after the article has been glazed and fired.

Some whimsical Wades are hollow, usually because they were prototype models that were discarded or removed from the pottery by workers. Other models may be found in different colour glazes than the originals, due to one or more of the following reasons:

1. The first colour glaze was laid down for a test run, but when the models came out of the kiln at the end of the firing period (sometimes as long as three days), it was either too light or too dark. This occurred in the case of the black *English Whimsies* "Zebra," which was so dark when it emerged after its run through the kiln that the striped pattern could not be clearly seen. The colour glaze was then changed to beige.

2. When the model was shown to the client he did not like the initial colour, so another was chosen.

3. Some models were reissued in different colour glazes for use in promotions for Red Rose Tea and for Tom Smith Christmas crackers.

WADE MODELLERS, 1954-1994

Listed below are the modellers who helped to create whimsical Wade figures. The year that each modeller started working at Wade is given and, if known, the year he or she left.

After leaving Wade, many modellers went on to work for Royal Doulton, Szeiler, Sylvac, Dilsford Studio and other well-known British potteries. This accounts for the great number of other collectable models that bear a distinctive and characteristic likeness to Wade models.

Robert Barlow, Late 1930s
  Comic Duck Family
  Tinker, Tailor, Soldier, Sailor

Nancy Great-Rex, Late 1930s-Early 1940s
  Butcher, Baker and Candlestick Maker

Ken Holmes, 1975 to the present
  Burglar and Policeman Series
  Children and Pets
  Dinosaur Collection

William K. Harper, 1953-1962
  Alphabet Train
  Bernie and Pooh
  Drum Box Series
  Elephant Train
  First Whimsies
  Flying Birds
  Minikins Series
  Noddy Set
  Novelty Models
  Tortoise Family
  TV Pets

Leslie McKinnon, 1959-1961
  The British Character Set
  Happy Families series

Simon Millard
  Thomas the Tank Engine
  Percy Engine

Cyril Roberts
    Henry Engine
    James Engine

Paul Zalman, 1961
    Mabel Lucie Attwell models

MODEL BOXES, 1954-1995

Most collectors have seen or purchased Wade models in their original boxes. In order to catch the eye of a collector, early Wade boxes were made to be just as colourful, appealing and decorative as their contents.

When Wade models were issued in the 1950s, their appeal to collectors was not as avid as it is today; as a result, few boxes from the 1950s were kept by the original purchasers. Models in their boxes can command a higher price than a model alone, and depending on the age and condition of the box, the price of the model may increase by 30 to 50 percent.

In the 1970s the rising cost of paper and the fact that Wade produced an established collector's product caused the company to produce less appealing containers. But by the 1980s, the boxes again became colourful and eye-catching, although they had lost the old-world charm of the boxes of the 1950s.

Box designs and colours can vary depending on the year of issue and the length of the production run. Some popular models that were reissued two or more times can be found in two, and at times three, different box sizes and colours (as in the *Happy Families* series, which were issued and reissued in three different box designs).

WADE MARKS, 1930s-1998

Wade Heath Ltd. and George Wade and Son Ltd. not only shared their pottery moulds, they also shared the Wade trademark during the late 1940s and into the 1950s. This makes it difficult to distinguish which pottery a particular model came from. As a general guide for those models produced in both potteries, the Wade Heath postwar novelty models have a green or greenish brown "Wade England" mark on their bases, and the postwar George Wade figures have a black or blue "Wade England" transfer on their bases.

Later, with the addition of Wade Ireland, it became even more difficult to determine the origin of a model. The potteries had a habit of helping each other out in order to speed up production. These figures all had the mark of the originating pottery on their bases and were packed in boxes from that pottery, even though they may have been made in another location.

A good example of this practice is the 1977 *Bisto Kids* set. During one of our conversations, Tony Wade told me that, although they were marked "Wade Staffordshire" on their bases, these models were in fact produced in the Wade Ireland Pottery. The George Wade Pottery had another large order to complete, so Wade Ireland took over.

Similarly, some of the 1950s *First Whimsies* are believed to have been produced by Wade Ireland, although none of the models have a Wade Ireland mark, and the entire series of ten sets was packed in Wade England boxes.

Many small open-caste models (models with no bases and standing on thin legs) do not have enough space on them for a Wade label or an ink stamp. They were originally issued in boxes with "Wade England" clearly marked on the box or packet front.

Once removed from their container, however, these models are hard to identify without the aid of Wade collector books (the *First Whimsies* is a good example of this).

Larger, more solid-based models were marked with a Wade ink stamp or with a black and gold label on their bases. But over the years the label or the ink stamp can wear off or be washed off by previous owners, leaving them unmarked.

Wade Heath

Ink Stamps

1. Black ink stamp "Flaxman Ware Hand Made Pottery by Wadeheath England," 1935-1937.
2. Black ink stamp "Flaxman Wade Heath England," 1937-1938.

3. Black ink stamp "Flaxman Wade Heath," 1937-1938.
4. Black ink stamp "Wadeheath Ware England," 1935-1937.
5. Green-brown ink stamp "Wade England," late 1940s-early 1950s.
6. Green ink stamp "Wade England [name of model]," late 1940s-early 1950s.

7. Black ink stamp "Wadeheath by permission Walt Disney England," 1937-1938.
8. Black ink stamp "Wade" and red ink stamp "Made in England," 1938.
9. Black ink stamp "Wade England," late 1940s-early 1950s.

WADE

Hand-painted Marks

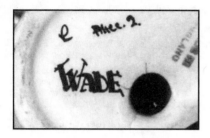

1. Black hand painted "Wade Alice 2," with black ink stamp "Made in England," 1930s.
2. Black hand painted "Wade Alice 7" and red ink stamp of leaping deer, 1930s.
3. Black hand painted "Hiawatha Wade England," 1937.

Ink Stamps

4. Black ink stamp "Wade England," late 1940s.
5. Black ink stamp "Wade Made in England," 1955.
6. Brown ink stamp "Wade England," with brown cricket in large C. Only seen on some of the *Happy Families* models.

Transfer Prints

7. Small black transfer "Wade England [name of model]," 1950s.
8. Large black transfer "Wade England [name of model]," 1950s.
9a. Black transfer "Wade Snippet No. 1 Mayflower Carried 102 Pilgrims to North America 1620-Real Porcelain-Made In England," 1956.
9b. Black transfer "Wade Snippet No. 2 Santa Maria Flag ship of Columbus 1492-Real Porcelain-Made In England," 1956.
9c. Black transfer "Wade Snippet No. 3 Revenge Flag ship of Sir Richard Grenville 1591-Real Porcelain-Made In England," 1956.
9d. Black transfer "Wade Snippet No. 4 Hansel-Real Porcelain-Made in England," 1957.

9e. Black transfer "Wade Snippet No. 5 Gretel-Real Porcelain-Made in England," 1957.
9f. Black transfer "Wade Snippet No. 6 Gingy-Real Porcelain-Made in England," 1957.
10. Blue transfer "Wade England," 1956-1957.
11. Black transfer "Wade Porcelain England," 1961.
12. Black transfer "Wade Porcelain Copyright Walt Disney Productions Made in England," 1961.

13. Brown transfer "Wade Made in England," 1962.
14. Brown transfer "Copyright RHM Foods Ltd. & Applied Creativity, Wade Staffordshire," 1977.

15. Black transfer "Wade Made in England," 1978-1987.
16. Black transfer "Walt Disney Productions" in an oval shape, with "Wade England" in centre, 1981-1987.
17. Black transfer "Wade Porcelain England S/F [1-6]," 1984-1986.
18. Red transfer "Wade Made in England," 1985, 1994.
19. Black transfer "Harrods Knightsbridge," 1991-1994.
20. Black transfer "Wade Limited Editions Modelled by Ken Holmes [includes model name, series number and limited edition number]," 1993-1994.

21. Black transfer "Arthur Hare [Holly Hedgehog] © C&S Collectables Wade England," 1993-1995.
22. Black transfer "Wade," enclosed in an outline of the Isle of Wight and numbered, 1994.
23. Black transfer "[Limited edition number] © H/B Inc, Scooby-Doo, Limited edition of 2,000, Wade England, G&G Collectables," 1994.

24. Black transfer "1994 [1995] Mirror Group Newspapers Ltd © C&S Collectables Wade England," 1994-1995.

Impressed Marks

25. Impressed "Wade Porcelain Made in England," 1958.

Embossed Marks

26. Small embossed "Wade," 1954-1983.

27. Embossed "'Whimtrays' Wade Porcelain Made in England," 1958-1965.

28. Embossed "Wade Porcelain Made in England," 1958-1984.
29. Embossed "Wade Porcelain - Mabel Lucie Attwell © Made in England," 1959-1961.
30. Embossed "Angel Dish Wade Porcelain Made in England," 1963.
31. Embossed "Robertson," 1963-1965.
32. Embossed "Wade England," 1965-1994.

33. Large embossed "Wade Made in England," 1975-1984.
34. Embossed "Mianco [year of issue] Wade England" on rim of base, 1989-1995.

35. Embossed "Wade England 1990 [1991]," 1990-1991.
36. Embossed "Wade England 1991" on rim of base and ink stamp "GSG," 1991.
37. Large embossed "Wade," 1993-1994.

Labels

38. Small black and gold label "Wade England," 1954-1959.
39. Black and gold label "Genuine Wade Porcelain Made in England," 1959-1965.
40. Large black and gold label "Wade England," early 1970s-1981.
41. Black and gold label "Walt Disney Productions Wade England," 1981-1985.

WADE IRELAND

Ink Stamps

1. Black ink stamp "'Pogo' Copyright, Walt Kelly, Made in Ireland 1959," 1959.
2. Black ink stamp "Made in Ireland," 1974-1985.
3. Purple ink stamp "Made in Ireland," 1974-1985.

Transfer Prints

4. Green transfer "Shamrock Pottery Made in Ireland," 1953-1956.

Impressed Marks

5. Impressed "Shamrock Pottery Made in Ireland," 1953-1956.

6. Impressed "Irish Porcelain Made in Ireland by Wade Co. Armagh," with shamrock, early 1950s.
7. Impressed "Made in Ireland," early 1970s.

Embossed Marks

8. Embossed "Irish Porcelain, Made in Ireland," with a shamrock leaf, 1953-1956.
9. Embossed "Shamrock Pottery Made in Ireland," 1959.
10. Embossed "Wade Porcelain Made in Ireland," 1970s-1980s.
11. Embossed "Made in Ireland, Porcelain Wade, Eire Tir-Adheanta," 1980-1988.
12. Embossed "Wade Ireland," 1984-1987.

MODELS TRANSFERRED

Replacing the four volumes of Charlton Standard Catalogues of Wade and the Wade Whimiscal Book with two user friendly, meaningful catalogues meant rethinking the entire "World of Wade". This resulted in the transfer of the most collectable categories from the four volumes and Wade Whimsicals in to two: *Wade Collectables* and *Wade Whimsical Collectables.* For example, money boxes have been gathered from all volumes and are now together in a money box section in *Wade Collectables.* *Disney*, which is a category in its own right, also has its own section in the Collectables catalogue. The following list will help the collector through this reorganization.

MODELS TRANSFERRED FROM *WADE WHIMSICAL COLLECTABLES,* 7th Edition
to *WADE COLLECTABLES*, 4th Edition

LEPRECHAUNS AND PIXIES

Baby Pixie
    Baby Pixie Derivatives

Large Leprechauns
    Large Leprechaun Derivatives

Larry and Leter, the Leprechaun Twins
    Larry and Lester Derivatives

Leprechaun on Toadstool with Crock of Gold

Lucky Fairy Folk

Lucky Leprechauns
    Lucky Leprechaun Derivatives

Lucky Leprechaun Shamrock Plaque

Shamrock Cottage
    Shamrock Cottage Derivatives

FIGURES

Pogo

MONEY BOXES

Andy Capp Money Box
Bengo Money Box
Bertie the Badger Money Box
Betty Boop Money Box
Fawn Money Box
Harrods of Knightsbridge Doorman Money Box
Kennel Money Boxes
Polacanthus Money Box, The Isle of Wight Dinosaur
Thomas the Tank Engine Money Boxes
    Percy the Small Engine
    Thomas the Tank Engine
Toadstool Cottage Money Box
    Leprechaun Figure
    Noddy Figures
Tony the Tiger Money Box

WALT DISNEY FIGURES

Bulldogs
Disney Blow Ups
Donald Duck
Dopey
Happy Clock
Hat Box Series
    Hat Box Derivatives
Little Hiawatha and his Forest Friends
Mickey Mouse
Pluto
Pluto's Pups
Sammy Seal
Snow White and the Seven Dwarfs
    Style One
    Style Two
Snow White and the Seven Dwarfs Brooches

WADE IRELAND

Bally-Whim Village
English Whimsies on Irish Whimtrays
Flying Birds
Shamrock Pottery
    Irish Comical Pig
    Pink Elephant

COMMISSIONED MODELS

Pex Nylons
    Fairy and Candle Holder

R.H.M. Foods of England
    Bisto Kids

MODELS TO BE TRANSFERRED FROM WADE WHIMSICAL COLLECTABLES, 8th Edition
TO WADE COLLECTABLES, 5TH EDITION

The following models will be incorporated in to the 5th edition of Wade Collectables.

WADE CERAMICS
    Betty Boop
    Children and Pets
    Nativity Set
    Nennie the Scottish Terrier

CERAMICA
    Born Free

C&S COLLECTABLES
    Betty Boop Figures
    Dracula

HARRODS OF KNIGHTSBRIDGE
Cookie Jar
Egg Cuo
Pepper Cruet Saluting
Salt Cruet Holding Package

OUT OF THE BLUE CERAMICS
Batman, Boxed Set
Superman
Tiny Treasuers

RICHLEIGH PROMOTIONS
Children of the World

S & A COLLECTABLES LTD.
Jack the Ripper

UKI CERAMICS
The Flintstones Collection
Taurus the Bull
Wade Classical Collection

WARNER BROTHERS
My Dog Skip

WADE SECTION

COMIC ANIMALS AND BIRDS

Donkeys   2
Duck Family   4
Frog Family   5
Penguin Family   6
Pig Family   8
Rabbit Family   9
Rabbit (Little Laughing Bunny)   11

COMIC ANIMALS AND BIRDS

From the late 1940s to the 1950s, the Wade Heath Royal Victoria Pottery and the George Wade Pottery produced a large series of animal and bird models, some described as comic or novelty. Because the two Potteries produced the same models using the same moulds and both used the "Wade England" mark, it is hard to tell which models were made in which pottery. But it is believed that models stamped "Wade England" in green, brown or black were produced in the Royal Victoria Pottery before 1953, and those models transfer printed with a black or blue "Wade England" mark were produced in the George Wade Pottery in the early to mid- 1950s. The *Comic Families* models have been found with creamy beige background glazes and dark coloured clothing and are also found in white with pastel blue and grey colours.

During this period whenever Sir George Wade would come across surplus models, he would say, "Stick'em on something." The figures would be sent to the Wade Heath Pottery, where they were joined onto surplus bramble-ware mustard pots (minus their lids) or basket-ware eggcups, then mounted on a moulded leaf-shaped base to make a novelty bowl. The finished product was then recoloured and called a "Posy Bowl."

DONKEYS

Circa 1948-1952

The *Comic Donkeys* set is a pair of comic figures, one happy and one sad, which were produced in the Wade Pottery between the late 1940s and the early 1950s. The original price was 2/6d each.

A model of Cheerful Charlie with the words "Cheerful Charlie" hand written on his body and "Montreal" hand written on his ears has been found and is possibly a souvenir model exported to Montreal, Quebec, Canada. For other models with similar hand written souvenir place names please see "Staffordshire House Gifts."

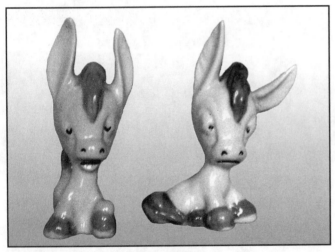

Cheerful Charlie and Doleful Dan

Cheerful Charlie "Montreal"

Backstamp: **A.** Black ink stamp "Wade England"
B. Green brown ink stamp "Wade England"

No.	Name	Description	Size	U.S. $	Can. $	U.K. £
1a	Cheerful Charlie	Beige; coffee mane, tail, hooves	110 x 55	275.	300.	150.
1b	Cheerful Charlie	Pink; coffee mane, tail, hooves; black lettering Montreal	110 x 55	275.	300.	150.
2	Doleful Dan	Beige; coffee mane, tail, hooves	110 x 55	275.	300.	150.

Note: For ease of reference, the models are listed in alphabetical order, not in order of issue.

Donkey Derivatives

Cheerful Charlie and Doleful Dan Salt and Pepper, Circa 1948

Doleful Dan and Cheerful Charlie

Backstamp: Green-brown ink stamp "Wade England"

No.	Name	Description	Size	U.S. $	Can. $	U.K. £
1a	Cheerful Charlie	Pink; beige mane, tail, hooves	110 x 55	175.	200.	100.
1b	Cheerful Charlie	Pink; grey mane, tail, hooves	110 x 55	175.	200.	100.
2	Doleful Dan	Pink; grey mane, tail, hooves	110 x 55	175.	200.	100.

Cheerful Charlie and Doleful Dan Egg-cup / Posy Bowl, Circa 1948

Cheerful Charlie Posy Bowl

Doleful Dan Posy Bowl

Backstamp: Green-brown ink stamp "Wade England"

No.	Name	Description	Size	U.S. $	Can. $	U.K. £
1a	Cheerful Charlie	Blue egg-cup posy bowl	105 x 105	125.	135.	65.
1b	Cheerful Charlie	Cream egg-cup posy bowl	105 x 105	125.	135.	65.
1c	Cheerful Charlie	Multicoloured egg-cup posy bowl	105 x 105	125.	135.	65.
2a	Doleful Dan	Blue egg-cup posy bowl	105 x 105	125.	135.	65.
2b	Doleful Dan	Green egg-cup posy bowl	105 x 105	125.	135.	65.
2c	Doleful Dan	Multicoloured egg-cup posy bowl	105 x 105	150.	165.	85.

DUCK FAMILY

1950s

The *Comic Duck Family* was designed by Robert Barlow. The original price for "Mr. Duck" and "Mrs. Duck" was 2/6d each. "Dack" and "Dilly" each sold for 1/6d.

The Comic Duck Father and Mother are also found marked "Szeiler." Joseph Szeiler worked for the Wade pottery in the early 1950s. Before leaving to start his own pottery, 'Studio Szeiler,' he was given permission by Sir George and Anthony Wade to 'borrow' some of the discontinued Wade moulds to produce models for a limited time, providing these were clearly marked with a Szeiler backstamp. For other Wade/Szeiler models see "Cheerful Charlie and Doleful Dan," "Comic Rabbit," and the "Kissing Bunnies."

Duck Family (Mr. Duck, Mrs. Duck, Dack and Dilly)

Backstamp: **A.** Unmarked (1a, 2)
B. Black transfer print "Wade England" (1b, 1c, 2, 3, 4)

No.	Name	Description	Size	U.S. $	Can. $	U.K. £
1a	Mr. Duck	White; beige beak, tail, feet; blue cap, tie; small eyes	70 x 38	250.	275.	150.
1b	Mr. Duck	White; yellow beak, feet; orange-red cap; small eyes	70 x 38	250.	275.	150.
2	Mrs. Duck	White; yellow beak, feet, bonnet; small eyes	70 x 37	250.	275.	150.
3	Dack	White; yellow beak, feet; blue cap; small eyes	40 x 28	250.	275.	150.
4	Dilly	White; yellow beak, feet; orange tam; small eyes	40 x 27	250.	275.	150.

FROG FAMILY
STYLE ONE
Circa 1948-1952

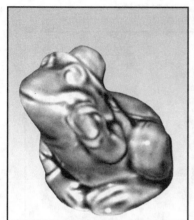

Mr. Frog

Mrs. Frog

Boy Frog

Backstamp: Black ink stamp "Wade England"

No.	Name	Description	Size	U.S. $	Can. $	U.K. £
1	Mr. Frog	Dark green; bowler hat; cigar	40 x 58	250.	275.	150.
2	Mrs. Frog	Dark green; bonnet; umbrella	40 x 58	250.	275.	150.
3	Boy Frog	Dark green; football	28 x 38	250.	275.	150.
4	Girl Frog	Dark green; bunch of flowers	28 x 38	250.	275.	150.

Note: For Frog Family Style Two, see page 15.

PENGUIN FAMILY

Circa 1948-1955

The *Comic Penguin Family* was produced in pastels and in dark colours. Before the 1950s these models were stamped "Wade England" and afterwards were printed with a "Wade England" mark. "Mr. Penguin" and "Mrs. Penguin" are also found as salt and pepper pots. The original price of "Mr. Penguin" and "Mrs. Penguin" was 2/6d each. "Benny" and "Penny" each sold for 1/6d.

Mrs. Penguin, Benny and Mr. Penguin

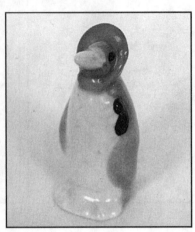

Penny

Backstamp: **A.** Black ink stamp "Wade England" (1b, 3)
B. Black transfer "Wade England" (1a, 4)
C. Unmarked (2, 5)

No.	Name	Description	Size	U.S. $	Can. $	U.K. £
1a	Mr. Penguin	White/grey; pale blue cap, scarf; black umbrella	90 x 40	200.	225.	110.
1b	Mr. Penguin	White; blue cap, scarf; black umbrella	90 x 40	200.	225.	110.
2	Mr. Penguin	Black/white; dark blue cap, scarf; yellow beak, hands, feet	65 x 40	200.	225.	110.
3	Mrs. Penguin	White/grey penguin, shawl; black bag	85 x 40	200.	225.	110.
4	Benny	White/grey; blue tam; black book	55 x 25	200.	225.	110.
5	Penny	White/grey; blue bonnet; black penguin doll	50 x 25	200.	225.	110.

Penguin Family Derivatives
Circa 1948

Backstamp: **A.** Black ink stamp "Wade England" (1, 2)
B. Black transfer "Wade England" (1, 2)
C. Unmarked (3, 4, 5)

No.	Name	Description	Size	U.S. $	Can. $	U.K. £
1	Mr. Penguin Pepper Pot	Black/white; maroon cap, scarf, umbrella	90 x 40	125.	135.	70.
2	Mr. Penguin Pepper Pot	Black/white; blue cap, scarf	65 x 40	125.	135.	70.
3	Mr. Penguin Pepper Pot	Pale green	75 x 40	125.	135.	70.
4	Mrs. Penguin Salt Pot	Black/white; maroon shawl, handbag	85 x 40	125.	135.	70.
5	Mrs. Penguin Salt Pot	Pale green	65 x 40	125.	135.	70.

PIG FAMILY

"Mr. Pig" and "Mrs. Pig" were produced in cream with dark coloured clothing. As no evidence of the "Boy Pig" and "Girl Pig" have been found, it is believed these models may be prototypes and never put into production.

Photograph not available
at press time

Backstamp: Black ink stamp "Wade England"

No.	Name	Description	Size	U.S. $	Can. $	U.K. £
1	Mr. Pig	Cream; maroon tie, jacket	90 x 32	150.	165.	80.
2	Mrs. Pig	Cream; dark yellow hat	80 x 30	150.	165.	80.
3	Boy Pig	Unknown	Unknown		Rare	
4	Girl Pig	Unknown	Unknown		Rare	

Pig Family Derivatives

Circa 1948

The "Mr. Pig Salt Pot" and "Mrs. Pig Pepper Pot" were issued as a cruet set, both standing on an oval tray. The ink stamp on these models is a type used before the 1950s.

Salt and Pepper Pots

Backstamp: Black ink stamp "Wade England"

No.	Name	Description	Size	U.S. $	Can. $	U.K. £
1	Mr. Pig Salt Pot	Cream; maroon tie, jacket	90 x 32	150.	165.	80.
2	Mrs. Pig Pepper Pot	Cream; dark yellow hat	90 x 32	150.	165.	80.
—	Set (2) with Tray		90 x 32	300.	325.	175.

Note: The model of Mr. Pig illustrated has damaged feet.

RABBIT FAMILY

Circa 1948-1955

Before the 1950s these models were produced in cream with dark coloured clothing; in the 1950s they were made in white with pastel markings. The original prices were 2/6d each for "Mr. Rabbit" and for "Mrs. Rabbit" and 1/6d each for "Fluff" and for "Puff."

Rabbit Family   Mr Rabbit

Backstamp: **A.** Black ink stamp "Wade England" (1a, 2a, 3a, 4a)
                B. Black transfer "Wade England" (1c, 2b, 3b, 4b)
                C. Unmarked (1b, 1d)

No.	Name	Description	Size	U.S. $	Can. $	U.K. £
1	Mr. Rabbit	Cream; dark green jacket	90 x 40	175.	200.	100.
1b	Mr. Rabbit	Cream; dark yellow jacket	90 x 40	175.	200.	100.
1c	Mr. Rabbit	Cream; black jacket	90 x 40	175.	200.	100.
1d	Mr. Rabbit	White; blue jacket	90 x 40	175.	200.	100.
1e	Mr. Rabbit	Bright yellow all over	90 x 40	175.	200.	100.
2a	Mrs. Rabbit	Cream; maroon bonnet; yellow basket	90 x 40	175.	200.	100.
2b	Mrs. Rabbit	Cream; yellow bonnet, basket; maroon ribbon	90 x 40	175.	200.	100.
2c	Mrs. Rabbit	White; grey ear tips; blue bonnet, basket	90 x 40	175.	200.	100.
3a	Fluff	Cream; dark blue shawl	40 x 30	160.	175.	90.
3b	Fluff	White; grey ear tips; blue/grey shawl	40 x 30	160.	175.	90.
4a	Puff	Cream; dark yellow jacket	40 x 30	160.	175.	90.
4b	Puff	White; grey ear tips; blue jacket	40 x 30	160.	175.	90.

Rabbit Family Derivatives

Circa 1948

The "Mr. Rabbit Salt Pot" and "Mrs. Rabbit Pepper Pot" were issued as a cruet set, both standing on an oval tray.

Backstamp: Black ink stamp "Wade England"

Salt and Pepper Pots

No.	Name	Description	Size	U.S. $	Can. $	U.K. £
1	Mr. Rabbit Salt Pot	Cream; black hat; yellow jacket	90 x 40	150.	165.	80.
2	Mrs. Rabbit Pepper Pot	Cream; maroon hat; yellow ribbon	90 x 40	150.	165.	80.
—	Set (2) with Tray		—	300.	325.	175.

RABBIT (LITTLE LAUGHING BUNNY)

Circa 1948-1952

This model is a miniature version of the *Laughing Rabbit* produced by Wade Heath, 1937-1939, in Flaxman ware glazes (see Novelty Animals). There are a number of variations in the size of the "Little Laughing Bunny," due to the die being retooled when worn. The colour of the grey models is also not consistent because the models were decorated in two different potteries. The original price was 1/-.

A poem by one of the Wade Heath figure casters in a spring 1954 *Jolly Potter* magazine refers to the "Comic Rabbit" as the "Little Laughing Bunny."

A "Comic Rabbit" with grey body, brown arms and feet has been found with a John Szeiler backstamp. Joseph Szeiler worked for the Wade pottery in the early 1950s. Before leaving to start his own pottery, 'Studio Szeiler,' he was given permission by Sir George and Anthony Wade to 'borrow' some of the discontinued Wade moulds to produce models for a limited time, providing these were clearly marked with a Szeiler backstamp. For other Wade/Szeiler models see "Cheerful Charlie and Doleful Dan," "Mr. and Ms. Duck," and the "Kissing Bunnies."

Little Laughing Bunnies

Backstamp: **A.** Black ink stamp "Wade England" (1a, 1b, 1c)
B. Black transfer print "Wade England" (1d)
C. Blue transfer print "Wade England" (1d)
D. Brown ink stamp (1e, 1f, 1g, 1h, 1i, 1j)

No.	Description	Size	U.S. $	Can. $	U.K. £
1a	Beige; red mouth; black eyes; white stomach	65 x 40	70.	80.	40.
1b	Dark grey; red mouth	63 x 40	70.	80.	40.
1c	Dark grey; red mouth; black eyes	63 x 40	70.	80.	40.
1d	Pale grey; brown ears, mouth; black eyes	63 x 38	70.	80.	40.
1e	Pale grey; brown ears, mouth; red eyes	63 x 38	70.	80.	40.
1f	Pale grey; brown striped ears; red mouth; black eyes	63 x 40	70.	80.	40.
1g	Pale grey; red mouth; black eyes	63 x 40	70.	80.	40.
1h	Pink; red mouth; black eyes	70 x 38	70.	80.	40.
1i	White; brown ears, toes	63 x 38	70.	80.	40.
1j	White; brown striped ears; red mouth; black eyes	65 x 40	70.	80.	40.

Rabbit Derivatives

Ashtrays, Circa 1948

This Art Deco shaped ashtray is similar in shape to a model produced by Sylvac in the late 1940s which would have an impressed "Sylvac" and a design No 1532 on the base. Although the illustrated model does not have a Wade mark, it has a registered design number 827631 on the base.

Art Deco Ashtray

S-Shaped Ashtray

Backstamp: **A.** Ink stamp "Regd 827631 Made in England"
B. Green-brown ink stamp "Wade England"

No.	Description	Size	U.S. $	Can. $	U.K. £
1a	Beige rabbit; grey Art Deco ashtray	92 x 92	150.	165.	90.
1b	Grey rabbit; speckled blue Art Deco ashtray	92 x 92	150.	165.	90.
2a	Dark grey rabbit; yellow S-shaped ashtray	110 x 110	150.	165.	90.
2b	Dark grey rabbit; marbled blue S-shaped ashtray	110 x 110	150.	165.	90.

Mustard Pot, Circa 1948

Rabbit Mustard Pot

Rabbit Mustard Pot (1d)

Backstamp: Green-brown ink stamp "Wade England"

No.	Description	Size	U.S. $	Can. $	U.K. £
1a	Blue; bramble-ware mustard pot	85 x 80	120.	135.	65.
1b	Green; bramble-ware mustard pot	85 x 80	120.	135.	65.
1c	Yellow; bramble-ware mustard pot	85 x 80	120.	135.	65.
1d	Grey/white rabbit; multicoloured mustard pot	85 x 80	120.	135.	65.

HAPPY FAMILIES

Cat Family	14
Dog Family	14
Elephant Family	15
Frog Family	15
Giraffe Family	16
Hippo Family	16
Mouse Family	17
Owl Family	18
Pig Family	18
Rabbit Family	19
Tiger Family	20

HAPPY FAMILIES
Circa 1961-1987

The *Happy Families* series was first issued from 1961 to 1965 and consisted of a mother animal and her two babies. The original five sets were sold in boxes with "Happy Families" printed in large letters in different colours on the front.

The first three *Happy Families* were the *Hippo Family* (3/11d), the *Tiger Family* (4/6d) and the *Giraffe Family* (4/11d). They were modelled by Leslie McKinnon and issued in the autumn and winter of 1961. They proved to be so popular that in spring 1962, Wade issued two more families, the *Rabbit Family* and the *Mouse Family*. In 1978 four sets were reissued using the original moulds. The *Tiger Family* (which is the most sought after set) was not considered suitable for reissue. The only way to distinguish the reissued models from the earlier models is by a slight variation in colour. By 1984 four more families had been added — the *Frog Family*, *Pig Family*, *Elephant Family* and *Owl Family*. In spring 1987, the last year of the series, the *Dog Family* and *Cat Family* joined the series, making a total of eleven sets issued from 1961 to 1987.

The firsts sets were issued in two-tone, end opening boxes of blue and green, and lilac and navy, with large lettering "Happy Families" in alternate colours. The second series were issued in white and blue, top opening boxes, with giraffes, rabbits, mice and hippos printed on them. The boxes were changed again in 1984 to white with pastel-coloured jungle scenes.

At some time during the late 1980s, Wade sold off its remaining stock of *Happy Families* to Tesco Stores, a British discount company. The Tesco Stores' box had a rigid cellophane top, front and sides; the base and back were cardboard. There is no reference to Wade on these boxes.

For "Mother" models in different colourways see "Pocket Pals" page 122. See also Cricket Design Incorporated, page 245.

Cat Family

Dog Family

CAT FAMILY
1987

Backstamp: Black transfer "Wade Made in England"

No.	Name	Description	Size	U.S. $	Can. $	U.K. £
1	Mother	Grey/white; blue eyes; pink ear tips	45 x 35	60.	65.	35.
2	Kitten, lying	Grey/white; blue eyes; pink ears	30 x 35	30.	35.	16.
3	Kitten, seated	Grey/white; blue eyes; pink ears	30 x 20	30.	35.	16.
—	3 pce set	Boxed	—	110.	120.	65.

DOG FAMILY
1987

Backstamp: **A.** Black transfer "Wade Made in England" (1-3)
　　　　　　　 B. Unmarked (1-3)

No.	Name	Description	Size	U.S. $	Can. $	U.K. £
1	Mother	Brown; white face, chest	55 x 35	45.	50.	25.
2	Puppy, lying	Brown; white face, chest	30 x 40	20.	23.	12.
3	Puppy, standing	Brown; white face, chest	30 x 35	20.	23.	12.
—	3 pce set	Boxed	—	85.	95.	50.

ELEPHANT FAMILY
1984-1987

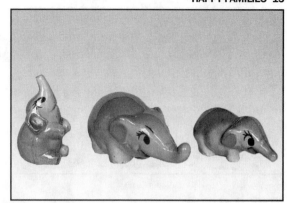

Backstamp: Black transfer "Wade Made in England"

No.	Name	Description	Size	U.S. $	Can. $	U.K. £
1a	Mother	Blue; pink ears, mouth	35 x 70	45.	50.	25.
1b	Mother	Grey; pink ears, mouth	35 x 70	45.	50.	25.
2a	Baby, trunk down	Blue; pink ears, mouth	25 x 55	20.	23.	12.
2b	Baby, trunk down	Grey; pink ears, mouth	25 x 55	20.	23.	12.
3a	Baby, trunk up	Blue; pink ears, mouth	45 x 22	20.	23.	12.
3b	Baby, trunk up	Grey; pink ears, mouth	45 x 22	20.	23.	12.
—	3 pce set	Boxed	—	85.	95.	50.

FROG FAMILY
STYLE TWO
1984-1987

Backstamp: **A.** Black transfer "Wade Made in England" (1-3)
B. Red transfer "Wade Made in England" (1-3)

No.	Name	Description	Size	U.S. $	Can. $	U.K. £
1a	Mother	Brown; red-brown spots	25 x 45	45.	50.	25.
1b	Mother	Dark brown	25 x 45	45.	50.	25.
2	Baby, singing	Brown; red-brown spots	25 x 25	20.	23.	12.
3	Baby, smiling	Brown; red-brown spot	20 x 30	20.	23.	12.
—	3 pce set	Boxed	—	85.	95.	50.

Note: For Frog Family, Style One, see page 5.

Giraffe Family

Hippo Family

GIRAFFE FAMILY

FIRST ISSUE, 1961-1965

Except for a slight variation in eyelid and horn colour, the original and reissued models are hard to distinguish from each other.

Backstamp: **A.** Brown ink stamp "Wade England" with cricket (1-3)
B. Black and gold label Genuine "Wade Porcelain Made in England" (1-3)
C. Unmarked (1-3)

No.	Name	Description	Size	U.S. $	Can. $	U.K. £
1	Mother	Beige; light blue eyelids; light grey horns	60 x 45	45.	50.	25.
2	Baby, awake	Beige; light blue eyelids; light grey horns	40 x 28	25.	28.	15.
3	Baby, sleeping	Beige; light blue eyelids; light grey horns	15 x 30	25.	28.	15.
—	3 pce set	Boxed	—	85.	95.	50.

SECOND ISSUE, 1978-1987

Backstamp: **A.** Black transfer "Wade Made in England" (1-3)
B. Brown transfer "Wade Made in England" (1-3)
C. Unmarked (1-3)

No.	Name	Description	Size	U.S. $	Can. $	U.K. £
1	Mother	Beige; turquoise eyelids; dark grey horns	60 x 45	45.	50.	25.
2	Baby, awake	Beige; turquoise eyelids; dark grey horns	40 x 28	20.	23.	12.
3	Baby, sleeping	Beige; turquoise eyelids; dark grey horns	15 x 30	20.	23.	12.
—	3 pce set	Boxed	—	85.	95.	50.

HIPPO FAMILY

FIRST ISSUE, 1961-1965

Backstamp: Unknown

No.	Name	Description	Size	U.S. $	Can. $	U.K. £
1	Mother	Dark blue/brown eyes	35 x 50	45.	50.	25.
2	Baby, asleep	Eyes shut	20 x 25	25.	28.	15.
3	Baby, awake	Dark blue/brown eyes	28 x 25	25.	28.	15.
—	3 pce set	Boxed	—	85.	95.	50.

SECOND ISSUE, 1978-1987

Backstamp: Black transfer "Wade Made in England"

No.	Name	Description	Size	U.S. $	Can. $	U.K. £
1	Mother	Smoky blue; blue tear; brown eyes	35 x 50	45.	50.	25.
2	Baby, asleep	Smoky blue; blue tear; brown eyes	20 x 25	25.	28.	15.
3	Baby, awake	Smoky blue; blue tear; brown eyes	28 x 25	25.	28.	15.
—	3 pce set	Boxed	—	85.	95.	50.

MOUSE FAMILY

FIRST ISSUE, 1962-1965

The *Mouse Family* was issued in spring 1962 and reissued from 1978 to 1984. The original models have yellow tails, compared with the pink tails of the later figures.

Backstamp: **A.** Brown ink stamp "Wade Made in England" (1-3)
B. Unmarked (1-3)

No.	Name	Description	Size	U.S. $	Can. $	U.K. £
1	Mother	White; pink ears; yellow tail	50 x 28	50.	55.	30.
2	Baby, eyes closed	White; pink ears, nose; yellow tail	28 x 28	35.	40.	20.
3	Baby, eyes open	White; blue eyes; pink ears, nose; yellow tail	25 x 30	35.	40.	20.
—	3 pce set	Boxed	—	100.	110.	60.

SECOND ISSUE, 1978-1987

Backstamp: **A.** Black transfer "Wade Made in England" (1-3)
B. Unmarked (1-3)

No.	Name	Description	Size	U.S. $	Can. $	U.K. £
1a	Mother	White; brown mouth; grey patch; pink ears, tail	50 x 28	45.	50.	25.
1b	Mother	White; pink mouth; grey patch; pink ears, tail	50 x 28	45.	50.	25.
2a	Baby, eyes closed	White; brown mouth, grey patch, pink ears, tail	28 x 28	20.	23.	12.
2b	Baby, eyes closed	White; pink mouth, grey patch; pink ears, tail	28 x 28	20.	23.	12.
3a	Baby, eyes open	White; brown mouth, grey patch; pink ears, tail	25 x 30	20.	23.	12.
3b	Baby, eyes open	White; pink mouth; grey patch; pink ears, tail	25 x 30	20.	23.	12.
—	3 pce set	Boxed	—	85.	95.	50.

OWL FAMILY
1984-1987

Backstamp: **A.** Black transfer "Wade Made in England" (1-3)
B. Red transfer "Wade Made in England" (1-3)

No.	Name	Description	Size	U.S. $	Can. $	U.K. £
1	Mother	Cream; beige head, back, wings	40 x 40	50.	55.	30.
2	Baby, wings closed	Cream; beige head, back, wings	25 x 20	35.	40.	20.
3	Baby, wings open	Cream; beige head, back, wings	25 x 32	35.	40.	20.
—	3 pce set	Boxed	—	85.	95.	50.

PIG FAMILY
1984-1987

Backstamp: **A.** Black transfer "Wade Made in England" (1-3)
B. Red transfer "Wade Made in England" (1-3)

No.	Name	Description	Size	U.S. $	Can. $	U.K. £
1a	Mother	Pink; black eyes; red mouth	28 x 65	50.	55.	30.
1b	Mother	Reddish pink; white face; black eyes; red mouth	28 x 65	50.	55.	30.
2	Baby, asleep	Pink; blue eyelids	15 x 45	35.	40.	20.
3a	Baby, awake	Pink; black eyes; red mouth	18 x 40	35.	40.	20.
3b	Baby, awake	Reddish pink; white face; black eyes; red mouth	18 x 40	35.	40.	20.
—	3 pce set	Boxed	—	85.	95.	50.

RABBIT FAMILY
FIRST ISSUE, 1963-1965

Backstamp: **A.** Black and gold label "Genuine Wade Porcelain Made in England" (1-3)
    B. Unmarked (1-3)

No.	Name	Description	Size	U.S. $	Can. $	U.K. £
1	Mother	White; turquoise patches	55 x 30	50.	55.	30.
2	Baby, seated	White; turquoise patches	34 x 28	35.	40.	20.
3	Baby, standing	White; turquoise patches	30 x 35	35.	40.	20.
—	3 pce set	Boxed	—	100.	110.	60.

SECOND ISSUE, 1978-1984

Backstamp: **A.** Black transfer "Wade made in England" (1-3)
    B. Unmarked (1-3)

No.	Name	Description	Size	U.S. $	Can. $	U.K. £
1	Mother	White; blue patches	55 x 30	45.	50.	25.
2	Baby, seated	White; blue patches	34 x 28	25.	28.	15.
3	Baby, standing	White; blue patches	30 x 35	25.	28.	15.
—	3 pce set	Boxed	—	85.	95.	50.

TIGER FAMILY

1961-1965

This set was not reissued, so it is rare and highly sought after.

Backstamp: Unmarked

No.	Name	Description	Size	U.S. $	Can. $	U.K. £
1	Mother	Beige; brown stripes; green eyes; red tongue	40 x 40	100.	110.	55.
2	Baby, asleep	Beige; brown stripes; green eyes; red tongue	10 x 30	70.	80.	40.
3	Baby, awake	Beige; brown stripes; green eyes; red tongue	10 x 30	70.	80.	40.
—	3 pce set	Boxed	—	200.	225.	120.

NOVELTY ANIMALS AND BIRDS

Baby Bird   22
Cheeky Duckling   22
Duckling, Head Back, Beak Closed   23
Duckling, Head Forward, Beak Open   23
Laughing Rabbit   24
Laughing Squirrel   24
Old Buck Rabbit   25
Pongo   26

NOVELTY ANIMALS AND BIRDS
Circa 1935-Circa 1949

BABY BIRD
Circa 1935

Backstamp: **A.** Black ink stamp "Flaxman Ware
Hand Made Pottery By
Wadeheath England" (1)
B. Black ink stamp "Wadeheath
Ware England" (2)

No.	Name	Description	Size	U.S. $	Can. $	U.K. £
1a	Baby Bird, large	Mottled green	200 x 165	155.	170.	90.
1b	Baby Bird, large	Pale orange	200 x 165	155.	170.	90.
1c	Baby Bird, large	Yellow	200 x 165	155.	170.	90.
2a	Baby Bird, small	Green	90 x 65	60.	70.	35.
2b	Baby Bird, small	Orange	90 x 65	60.	70.	35.
2c	Baby Bird, small	Yellow	90 x 65	60.	70.	35.

CHEEKY DUCKLING
Circa 1935

Backstamp: Black ink stamp "Flaxman Ware Hand Made
Pottery by Wadeheath England"

No.	Name	Description	Size	U.S. $	Can. $	U.K. £
1	Cheeky Duckling, large	Blue	180 x 115	175.	200.	150.
2a	Cheeky Duckling, small	Blue	150 x 85	210.	240.	125.
2b	Cheeky Duckling, small	Orange	150 x 85	210.	240.	125.

DUCKLING, HEAD BACK, BEAK CLOSED
Circa 1937-1939

Backstamp: None

No.	Name	Description	Size	U.S. $	Can. $	U.K. £
1a	Duckling, head back, beak closed	Green	95	160.	175.	90.
1b	Duckling, head back, beak closed	Pale green	100	200.	225.	115.

DUCKLING, HEAD FORWARD, BEAK OPEN
Circa 1937-1939

Backstamp: **A.** Ink stamp "Flaxman Wade Heath
England" (1937-1939) (1a)
B. None (1b)

No.	Name	Description	Size	U.S. $	Can. $	U.K. £
1a	Duckling, head forward, beak open	Beige brown	95	155.	170.	90.
1b	Duckling, head forward, beak open	Green	95	155.	170.	90.
1c	Duckling, head forward, beak open	Green	Miniature/60	130.	145.	75.

LAUGHING RABBIT

1937-1939

The shape number for the Laughing Rabbit is 335. This model was scaled-down and issued as Rabbit (Little Laughing Bunny), see page 11.

Backstamp: Black ink stamp "Flaxman Wade Heath England"

No.	Name	Description	Size	U.S. $	Can. $	U.K. £
1a	Laughing Rabbit, large	Bright green	175 x 75	130.	150.	75.
1b	Laughing Rabbit, large	Orange	175 x 75	130.	150.	75.
2a	Laughing Rabbit, medium	Blue	160 x 70	115.	125.	65.
2b	Laughing Rabbit, medium	Brown	160 x 70	115.	125.	65.
2c	Laughing Rabbit, medium	Green	160 x 70	115.	125.	65.
3a	Laughing Rabbit, small	Beige	140 x 65	100.	110.	60.
3b	Laughing Rabbit, small	Blue	140 x 65	100.	110.	60.
3c	Laughing Rabbit, small	Green	140 x 65	100.	110.	60.

LAUGHING SQUIRREL

c.1940

This miniature comical squirrel model is very similar in face decoration to one of the Little Laughing Bunny models. As this is the only example of this model seen to date, it may be a prototype that was not put into production.

Backstamp: Ink stamp "Wade England"

No.	Name	Description	Size	U.S. $	Can. $	U.K. £
1	Laughing Squirrel	Fawn; brown mouth, toes	45		Rare	

Note: As this is a unique or one-of-a-kind piece the price must be decided between the buyer and seller.

OLD BUCK, RABBIT

Late 1930s

Old Buck is a comical rabbit holding his head back and with a budging chest. He carries a walking cane under his left arm. He is shown advertised in a late 1930's Wadeheathe avdertisement.

Backstamp: Unknown

No.	Name	Description	Size	U.S. $	Can. $	U.K. £
1	Old Buck	Brown	165 x 128		Rare	

PONGO

1935-Circa 1949

Pongo was in production from 1935 to 1939 and was reissued for a short time in the late 1940s.

Backstamp: **A.** Black ink stamp "Flaxman Ware Hand Made Pottery By Wadeheath England"
B. Black ink stamp "Wadeheath Ware England"
C. Black ink stamp "Wade Heath England," 1938-1940s

No.	Name	Description	Size	U.S. $	Can. $	U.K. £
1a	Pongo, large	Blue; mauve nose	140 x 128	140.	155.	80.
1b	Pongo, large	Green	140 x 128	140.	155.	80.
1c	Pongo, large	Lilac; mauve nose	140 x 128	140.	155.	80.
1d	Pongo, large	Mottled blue/orange	140 x 128	140.	155.	80.
1e	Pongo, large	Orange	140 x 128	140.	155.	80.
1f	Pongo, large	Orange; mauve nose	140 x 128	140.	155.	80.
2a	Pongo, medium	Blue; mauve nose	128 x 115	140.	155.	80.
2b	Pongo, medium	Lilac; mauve nose	128 x 115	140.	155.	80.
2c	Pongo, medium	Mottled blue/orange	128 x 115	140.	155.	80.
2d	Pongo, medium	Orange; mauve nose	128 x 115	140.	155.	80.
2e	Pongo, medium	Turquoise; black eyes, nose	128 x 115	140.	155.	80.
3	Pongo, miniature	Blue	105 x 95	125.	135.	70.
4a	Pongo, small	Blue; mauve nose	115 x 100	85.	95.	50.
4b	Pongo, small	Green; blue eyes, nose	120 x 110	85.	95.	50.
4c	Pongo, small	Lilac; mauve nose	115 x 100	85.	95.	50.
4d	Pongo, small	Mauve	120 x 110	85.	95.	50.
4e	Pongo, small	Orange; mauve nose	115 x 100	85.	95.	50.
4f	Pongo, small	Pink; black nose	115 x 100	85.	95.	50.

STORYBOOK FIGURES

Alice and the Dodo   28
Bengo and His Puppy Friends, TV Pets   29
Butcher, The Baker and The Candlestick Maker   30
Dismal Desmond   31
Goldilocks and the Three Bears   32
Jumbo Jim   33
Noddy Set   33
Nursery Favourites   34
Nursery Miniatures   36
Nursery Rhymes   37
Nursery Rhyme Blow Ups   38
Sam and Sarah (Mabel Lucie Attwell Figures)   39
Thomas the Tank Engine   40
Tinker, Tailor, Soldier, Sailor   41
Tom and Jerry   42
Wynken, Blynken, Nod and I've a Bear Behind   43
Yogi Bear and Friends   44

STORYBOOK FIGURES

At the end of World War II the giftware restrictions on potteries were lifted. Although there was plenty of work available to replace war-damaged industrial wares, a few novelty figurines were produced by the Wade Heath Royal Victoria Pottery and by the George Wade Pottery.

Before 1953 these models were produced in the Royal Victoria Pottery and were marked with a green ink stamp. Models produced in 1953 and after, in either the Royal Victoria Pottery or in the George Wade Pottery, were marked with black transfers.

The first nursery rhyme and fairy tale models produced by Wade were coloured in delicate shades of pastel blues, whites and greys. Because they were produced in both potteries, and dies were replaced when worn, there are slight variations in size and in hair colour on the earlier models. Models are listed in alphabetical order for ease of reference.

Alice and the Dodo was produced with a 1930s experimental cellulose glaze, which cracked and flaked when exposed to heat, damp and sunlight. It is rare to find cellulose models in mint condition. Sylvac produced models in a cellulose glaze, these also suffered the same fate as the Wade models.

Some models are marked with a 1935-1937 mark ("Flaxman Ware Hand Made Pottery by Wadeheath England") or any of the 1937-1939 marks ("Flaxman Wade Heath England or Wadeheath Ware England"). Most have an all-over, one-colour matt glaze. All the following storybook models are slip cast, and therefore hollow.

ALICE AND THE DODO

Circa 1935-1938

Alice and the Dodo was produced in the cellulose glaze described above. It is rare to find these models in perfect condition.

Cellulose Glaze

High Gloss Glaze

Backstamp: **A.** Black hand-painted "Wade Alice 2" with black ink stamp "Made in England" (1)
B. Black hand-painted "Wade Alice" with red ink stamp of leaping deer (2a, 2b, 2c)

No.	Description	Glaze	Size	U.S. $	Can. $	U.K. £
1	Orange-yellow dress; black band; light brown bird; black beret	Cellulose	130 x 80	475.	525.	275.
2a	Green dress; red band; dark brown bird; blue beret	Cellulose	130 x 80	475.	525.	275.
2b	Pink dress; red band; dark brown bird; blue beret	Cellulose	130 x 80	475.	525.	275.
2c	Blue dress; red band; dark brown bird; blue beret	Cellulose	130 x 80	475.	525.	275.
3	Purple streaked dress, green blouse; mottled brown bird, green beret	Gloss	130 x 80		Rare	

BENGO AND HIS PUPPY FRIENDS, TV PETS

1959-1965

TV Pets was based on a popular British television cartoon series called "Bengo and his Puppy Friends." The cartoon series was created by Austrian cartoonist William Timym, a British resident, who signed his cartoons "Tim." William Timym designed the TV Pets and also the *British Character* models for Wade.

The issue date for "Bengo," "Simon," "Pepi" and "Fifi" was May 1959; "Mitzi" and "Chee-Chee" came into production in September 1959; and "Bruno" and "Droopy" were issued in February 1961. At the beginning of 1965, the last two puppies "Percy" and "Whisky" joined the series, the same year the series came to an end, making a total of ten models in the set. The last two models are difficult to find, as they were only in production for a few months at most. The original price was 3/11d each.

Backstamp: **A.** Black and gold label "Genuine Wade Porcelain Made in England" (1-10)
  B. Unmarked (1-10)

No.	Name	Description	Size	U.S. $	Can. $	U.K. £
1	Bengo (Boxer)	Light brown/white; grey muzzle	55 x 50	70.	80.	40.
2	Bruno Junior (Saint Bernard)	Brown rump, head, ears; red tongue	55 x 35	100.	110.	55.
3	Chee-Chee (Pekinese)	Beige; white face, chest, paws	60 x 35	70.	80.	40.
4	Droopy Junior (Basset Hound)	Light brown; white chest; grey ear tips	55 x 40	150.	165.	75.
5	Fifi (Poodle)	Grey-blue head, ears, legs; red bow	55 x 35	50.	55.	30.
6	Mitzi (kitten)	Blue-grey/white; pink mouth	50 x 50	70.	80.	40.
7	Pepi (Chihuahua)	Tan patches; large black eyes; red mouth	55 x 35	100.	110.	60.
8	Percy (Afghan)	Beige; orange patches; grey face	65 x 30	130.	145.	75.
9	Simon (Dalmatian)	White; black spots	60 x 40	80.	90.	45.
10	Whisky (Corgi)	Beige; white face, chest, paws; red tongue	55 x 65	200.	225.	110.

Note: For the Bengo Money Box see *Charlton Standard Catalogue of Wade Collectables*, 4th edition.

THE BUTCHER, THE BAKER AND THE CANDLESTICK MAKER

1953-Circa 1958

The Butcher, the Baker and the Candlestick Maker is a set of three characters, from a 1940s children's rhyme. It was modelled by Nancy Great-Rex.

Backstamp: **A.** Black transfer "Wade England [name of model]" (1, 2a, 2b, 3)
B. Blue transfer "Wade England [name of model]" (2a, 2b)

No.	Name	Description	Size	U.S. $	Can. $	U.K. £
1	The Butcher	Blue/white apron; grey trousers	95 x 40	350.	385.	200.
2a	The Baker	Blue/white shirt; blue trousers	95 x 30	350.	385.	200.
2b	The Baker	White shirt; blue trousers	95 x 30	350.	385.	200.
3a	The Candlestick Maker	Black coat; grey trousers; yellow candlestick	110 x 25	450.	500.	250.
3b	The Candlestick Maker	Black coat; grey trousers; beige candlestick	110 x 25	450.	500.	250.
3c	The Candlestick Maker	Green coat; grey trousers; beige candlestick	110 x 25	450.	500.	250.
3d	The Candlestick Maker	White coat; grey trousers; brown candlestick	110 x 25	450.	500.	250

DISMAL DESMOND

Circa 1935

This model of "Dismal Desmond," a weeping Dalmatian, is based on a British children's comic character who featured in *Deans Rag Books* during the mid 1930s.

The all-over colourways of "Dismal Desmond" are in Flaxman glazes. The shape number 525 is impressed into the base of the green model.

Dismal Desmond: White with black markings

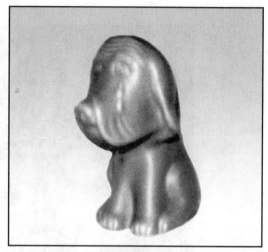

Dismal Desmond: All-over green

Backstamp: **A.** Ink stamp "Wadeheath England" with lion (1934-1935)
B. Black printed "Made in England" with impressed 525

No.	Name	Description	Size	U.S. $	Can. $	U.K. £
1a	Dismal Desmond	Green	165	400.	450.	225.
1b	Dismal Desmond	Pale blue	165	400.	450.	225.
1c	Dismal Desmond	White; black markings; brownish-red tears, collar	165	525.	575.	300.

GOLDILOCKS AND THE THREE BEARS

STYLE ONE

1953-Circa 1958

Goldilocks and the Three Bears is a set of four models based on the children's fairy tale. It is believed that these models were intended for export only, because they are named "Poppa Bear" and "Mama Bear," which are North American expressions, instead of "Father Bear" and "Mother Bear," as they would be called in Britain.

For *Goldilocks and the Three Bears,* Style Two, see Membership Exclusives, page 186.

Backstamp: Black transfer "Wade England [name of model]"

No.	Name	Description	Size	U.S. $	Can. $	U.K. £
1	Goldilocks	Blonde; blue/white skirt; pink petticoat, bonnet	100 x 60	300.	330.	175.
2	Poppa Bear	Light brown; blue jacket; grey waistcoat	95 x 30	300.	330.	175.
3	Mama Bear	Light brown; blue-grey dress	100 x 65	300.	330.	175.
4	Baby Bear	Brown; blue dungarees	50 x 30	300.	330.	175.

JUMBO JIM

Circa 1930s-1940s

The shape number for *Jumbo Jim* is 331. *Jumbo Jim* is believed to have appeared in a 1930s/40s children's book.

Backstamp: **A.** Black ink stamp "Flaxman Wade Heath England" (1a)

B. Ink stamp "Flaxman Wade Heath England" with impressed No 331 (1b)

No.	Name	Description	Size	U.S. $	Can. $	U.K. £
1a	Jumbo Jim	Light brown	180 x 105	475.	525.	275.
1b	Jumbo Jim	Turquoise blue	180 x 105	475.	525.	275.

THE NODDY SET

STYLE ONE

1958-1961

The *Noddy* set consists of four characters created by the English children's writer Enid Blyton. Only four models were issued, with an original price of 3/11d each. Production was discontinued in autumn 1961. The models were not marked but originally had black and gold paper labels.

For *Noddy*, Style Two, see page 339.

Backstamp: Unmarked

No.	Name	Description	Size	U.S. $	Can. $	U.K. £
1	Noddy	Red shirt, shoes; blue hat, trousers, bows	70 x 35	300.	330.	175.
2	Big Ears	Blue jacket; yellow trousers; red hat	70 x 35	250.	275.	150.
3	Mr. Plod	Blue uniform, helmet; yellow buttons	60 x 35	175.	290.	100.
4	Miss Fluffy Cat	Brown coat, collar; yellow hat; red bag	60 x 35	175.	290.	100.

Note: For the Toadstool Cottage Money Boxes with Noddy Figures attached see the *Charlton Standard Catalogue of Wade Collectables*, 4th edition.

NURSERY FAVOURITES

1972-1981

Nursery Favourites is a series of 20 large nursery rhyme and storybook characters. It was issued in four sets of five models, and each set was sold in a different coloured box. The original selling price for each figure was 7/6d. In 1990 and 1991, five *Nursery Favourites* were commissioned and reissued for Gold Star Gifthouse, see page 256.

SET ONE: DARK GREEN BOXES
1972

Backstamp: Embossed "Wade England"

No.	Name	Description	Size	U.S. $	Can. $	U.K. £
1	Jack	Brown hair, waistcoat; green trousers	75 x 30	45.	50.	25.
2	Jill	Green bonnet, dress	75 x 40	45.	50.	25.
3	Little Miss Muffett	Yellow hair; grey-green dress	60 x 50	45.	50.	25.
4	Little Jack Horner	Green jacket; yellow trousers; brown hair	70 x 40	45.	50.	25.
5	Humpty Dumpty	Honey brown; green suit; red tie	65 x 43	45.	50.	25.

SET TWO: BLUE BOXES
1973

Backstamp: Embossed "Wade England"

No.	Name	Description	Size	U.S. $	Can. $	U.K. £
6	Wee Willie Winkie	Yellow hair; grey nightshirt	75 x 35	45.	50.	25.
7	Mary Had a Little Lamb	Blue bonnet, skirt; grey-blue jacket	75 x 40	45.	50.	25.
8	Polly Put the Kettle On	Brown; pink cap, kettle	75 x 35	45.	50.	25.
9	Old King Cole	Yellow/grey hat; blue-grey cloak	75 x 35	45.	50.	25.
10	Tom Tom the Piper's Son	Grey hat, kilt; brown jacket	75 x 35	45.	50.	25.

SET THREE: YELLOW BOXES
1974

Backstamp: Embossed "Wade England"

No.	Name	Description	Size	U.S. $	Can. $	U.K. £
11	Little Boy Blue	Blue cap, jacket, trousers	75 x 30	50.	55.	30.
12	Mary Mary	Yellow hair; blue dress; pink shoes	75 x 45	50.	55.	30.
13	The Cat and the Fiddle	Brown/grey cat; yellow fiddle	70 x 50	50.	55.	30.
14	The Queen of Hearts	Pink crown, hearts; beige dress	75 x 48	50.	55.	30.
15	Little Tommy Tucker	Yellow hair; blue pantaloons	75 x 30	50.	55.	30.

SET FOUR: PURPLE BOXES
1976

Backstamp: Embossed "Wade England"

No.	Name	Description	Size	U.S. $	Can. $	U.K. £
16	The Three Bears	Grey; green base	70 x 60	70.	80.	40.
17	Little Bo-Peep	Beige bonnet, dress; pink ribbon	70 x 40	90.	100.	50.
18	Goosey Goosey Gander	Beige; pink beak; blue-brown steps	66 x 55	130.	150.	75.
19	Old Woman in a Shoe	Blue bonnet, dress; brown roof, door	60 x 55	90.	100.	50.
20	Puss in Boots	Beige; blue boots	70 x 30	90.	100.	50.

NURSERIES MINIATURES

Circa 1979-1980

The *Nurseries* is a boxed set of five models from the Canadian Red Rose Tea *Miniature Nurseries*. For some reason these figures did not sell well to British collectors, so Wade discontinued the intended series with only five models issued. When these figures are out of their boxes, they are hard to distinguish from the Red Rose Tea models. As the *Nurseries* were advertised after the Corgies and Yorkshire terriers from the *Whimsies Dogs and Puppies* series (issued in 1979), the issue date for this series is set during late 1979.

The value given is for a complete boxed set.

Backstamp: Embossed "Wade England"

No.	Name	Description	Size	U.S. $	Can. $	U.K. £
1	Little Jack Horner	Beige; blue plum; pink cushion	37 x 21			
2a	Old King Cole with Blue Hem	Beige; blue hat; pink sleeves; blue hem	37 x 32			
2b	Old King Cole without Blue Hem	Beige; blue hat; pink sleeves	37 x 32			
3	Old Woman in a Shoe	Honey; red-brown roof	35 x 40			
4	Little Bo-Peep	Light brown; blue apron; green base	44 x 24			
5	The Cat and the Fiddle	Beige; yellow fiddle	47 x 33			
—	5 pce set	Boxed	—	90.	100.	50.

NURSERY RHYMES

1953-Circa 1958

Although Wade may have intended to add to this series each year, only two *Nursery Rhymes* characters were produced.

Backstamp: Black transfer "Wade [name of model] England"

No.	Name	Description	Size	U.S. $	Can. $	U.K. £
1a	Little Jack Horner	Blue trousers; dark blue braces	70 x 42	475.	525.	275.
1b	Little Jack Horner	Grey trousers, braces	70 x 42	475.	525.	275.
1c	Little Jack Horner	White shirt, trousers	70 x 42	475.	525.	275.
2	Little Miss Muffett	Blonde hair; blue dress; pink petticoat	72 x 66	475.	525.	275.

NURSERY RHYME BLOW UPS

2004-2007

Beginning in March 2004, Wade introduced a set of blow up nursery rhyme characters based on the original Wade Red Rose Tea Canada models

Baa Baa Black Sheep

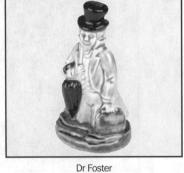

Dr Foster

House That Jack Built

Little Bo Peep

Queen of Hearts

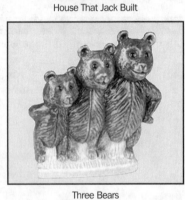

Three Bears

Backstamp: "Wade Made in England"

Date	Name	Description	Size	U.S. $	Can. $	U.K. £
2004	Cat and the Fiddle	Brown; dark brown fiddle	76 x 25	18.	20.	10.
2004	Gingerbread Man	Honey; green base	70 x 50	18.	20.	10.
2004	Hickory Dickory Dock	Honey; yellow pendulum; dark brown mice	73 x 57	18.	20.	10.
2004	Humpty Dumpty	Honey; black bow tie, shoes; grey wall	63 x 38	18.	20.	10.
2004	Little Bo Peep	Honey; brown crook; yellow bow	70 x 32	18.	20.	10.
2004	Old Woman Who Lived in a Shoe	Honey; yellow roof; green base	63 x 73	18.	20.	10.
2005	Dick Whittington's Cat	Grey; green eyes; black boots	76 x 38	18.	20.	10.
2005	Goosey Gander	White	57 x 73	18.	20.	10.
2005	Jack	Honey; green grass	60 x 63	18.	20.	10.
2005	Jill	Honey; green grass	50 x 60	18.	20.	10.
2005	Little Red Riding Hood	Honey; red cape	76 x 28	18.	20.	10.
2005	Queen of Hearts	Honey; red hearts; black trim on dress	76 x 38	18.	20.	10.
2006	Baa Baa Black Sheep	Black	44 x 67	18.	20.	10.
2006	Dr Foster	Beige; black umbrella, hat; blue water	70 x 38	18.	20.	10.
2006	House That Jack Built	Honey; red roof; green grass	60 x 73	18.	20.	10.
2006	Little Miss Muffet	Honey; blue dress; black spider	57 x 50	18.	20.	10.
2006	Mother Goose	Honey; red hat; green grass	63 x 50	18.	20.	10.
2006	Three Bears	Brown; honey base	70 x 63	18.	20.	10.

SAM AND SARAH (MABEL LUCIE ATTWELL FIGURES)
Style One
1959-1961

Manufactured under license to designs by Mabel Lucie Attwell, these two figures of "Sam" and "Sarah," with their pet dogs, were produced to test the public's reaction to a change of style. Apparently, they were not very popular at the time, perhaps due to the high retail price of 6/11d. Subsequently these models, which are sought after by Wade and by Mabel Lucie Attwell collectors, are in high demand.

The issue date for "Sam" and "Sarah" was October 1959, and they were discontinued in summer 1961. Their original price was 6/11d each.

Backstamp: Embossed Raised "Wade Porcelain-Mabel Lucie Attwell © Made in England"

No.	Name	Description	Size	U.S. $	Can. $	U.K. £
1	Sam	Ginger hair; yellow shirt; grey dog	78 x 85	225.	250.	130.
2a	Sarah	Blue shoes; blue/white dress; white/black dog	75 x 100	225.	250.	130.
2b	Sarah	Green shoes; blue/white dress; white/black dog	75 x 100	225.	250.	130.
2c	Sarah	Red shoes; blue/white dress; white/black dog	75 x 100	225.	250.	130.

THOMAS THE TANK ENGINE

STYLE ONE

1986

Thomas the Tank Engine, based on the storybooks by Reverend Wilbert Awdry and on the British television cartoon, was a very short-lived series due to complicated copyright laws. Only two models were produced, "Thomas" and "Percy." They came in two forms, a money box train and a miniature train. A prototype of "The Fat Controller" has been seen, but the model was not put into production. These models are very rare.

For *Thomas The Tank Engine,* Money Box, see the *Charlton Standard Catalogue of Wade Collectables.*

Backstamp: Black transfer "Wade Made in England"

No.	Name	Description	Size	U.S. $	Can. $	U.K. £
1	Thomas the Tank Engine	Blue; red markings	28 x 40	135.	150.	75.
2	Percy the Small Engine	Green; red markings	28 x 38	135.	150.	75.

Note: Prices listed are for models attached to original cards.

TINKER, TAILOR, SOLDIER, SAILOR

1953-Circa 1958

Tinker, Tailor, Soldier, Sailor is a series of eight little boys dressed in adult clothes, depicting the characters from a 1940s children's rhyme.

Backstamp: Black transfer "Wade [name of model] England"

No.	Name	Description	Size	U.S. $	Can. $	U.K. £
1a	Tinker	Blue suit; white/grey cap; grey base	55 x 45	225.	250.	125.
1b	Tinker	Pale blue suit; grey checkered cap; grey base	55 x 45	225.	250.	125.
2	Tailor	Blue suit; grey trousers, base	55 x 45	225.	250.	125.
3	Soldier	Blue suit, base; white/grey hat	80 x 45	225.	250.	125.
4a	Sailor	Blue suit, base; white/grey hat	90 x 45	300.	325.	170.
4b	Sailor	Pale blue suit; white/grey hat	90 x 45	300.	325.	170.
5	Rich Man	Blue coat; grey hat, trousers; blue-green base	90 x 45	250.	275.	150.
6a	Poor Man	Blue suit, base; grey hat	75 x 45	250.	275.	150.
6b	Poor Man	Pale blue suit; grey hat	75 x 45	250.	275.	150.
7	Beggar Man	Blue suit; white/blue scarf; blue-green base	65 x 45	250.	275.	150.
8a	Thief	Blue suit; grey mask; blue-green base	80 x 45	250.	275.	150.
8b	Thief	Pale blue suit; grey mask; blue-green base	80 x 45	250.	275.	150.

TOM AND JERRY
STYLE ONE
1973-1979

Only two models were issued in the Tom and Jerry series, courtesy of Metro-Goldwyn-Mayer. The original prices for the set of two cartoon character models was 95p.

For Tom and Jerry, Style Two, see page 339.

Backstamp: Embossed "Wade England © M.G.M."

No.	Name	Description	Size	U.S. $	Can. $	U.K. £
1	Tom	Blue; yellow/black eyes; pink ears	90 x 55	80.	90.	45.
2	Jerry	Beige; pink ears; green base	50 x 30	80.	90.	45.
—	Set (2)	Boxed	—	200.	225.	110.

WYNKEN, BLYNKEN, NOD AND I'VE A BEAR BEHIND

Circa 1948-1958

FIRST VERSION: FLOWER BASE

This set of four nursery rhyme characters was based on the poem "Wynken, Blynken and Nod," by American writer Eugene Field: "Wyken, Blyken and Nod one night; sailed off in a wooden shoe; Sailed on a river of crystal light into a sea of dew."

The poem does not include the character "I've a Bear Behind"; this was purely a whim of the Wade modeller. Green moss covers the feet of some models, so their slippers cannot be seen.

The "Wynken, Blynken and Nod " figures were first advertised in a 1948 *Pottery and Glass Trade Review* magazine as a set of three models. "I've a Bear Behind" added later, was based on a scene in the 1938 Walt Disney *Silly Symphony Wynken, Blynken and Nod*, in which when leaning over the side of the "Wooden Shoe" fishing for star, the buttons popped off the characters' pyjama bottoms exposing their bare behinds.

There are two versions of this set to be found: Version One has applied flowers around a green base, and Version Two has a plain green base. Many of these models, along with other Wade Heath and George Wade popular 'Novelties' were exported to Australia, Canada, New Zealand and South Africa during the late 1940s-late 1950s. The "Wynken, Blynken and Nod" models were advertised at $2.50 per set in a Canadian magazine.

There are many examples of Japanese copies of this set to be found. They were made as a genuine 'copy' to boost Japanese pottery sales, and were not made to deliberately deceive people. All were originally backstamped or labelled 'Made in Japan', unfortunately over time the ink stamp wears away and the labels are lost or disintergrate.

A number of English and foreign potteries when they saw that a particular product was getting 'rave' advertising reviews and collectors attention would copy the product idea. Hence you will see Wade and Sylvac models which are almost identical except for a small change in shape, colour and backstamp, or if it is still present the paper label.

It is almost impossible to differentiate the Japanese copies from the Wade models just by look or feel. The best way to be sure is to look through the hole in the base of the model; if you can see light shining through the head or body then it is Japanese egg shell or soft past porcelain (also known as bone china). Wade produced hard paste porcelain, which is much stronger and thicker, and light cannot shine through.

Backstamp: **A.** Green ink stamp "[Name of model] Wade England (1a, 1b, 2, 3, 4)
B. Black transfer print "Wade England" and green ink stamp " Wade England [model name]" (4)

No.	Name	Description	Size	U.S. $	Can. $	U.K. £
1a	Wynken	Blond hair; blue suit	75 x 40	200.	225.	115.
1b	Wynken	Brown hair; blue suit	75 x 40	200.	225.	115.
2a	Blynken	Blond hair; blue suit	58 x 40	200.	225.	115.
2b	Blynken	Brown hair; blue suit	58 x 40	200.	225.	115.
3	Nod	Blond hair; blue suit	70 x 40	200.	225.	115.
4	I've a Bear Behind	Blond hair; blue suit	70 x 40	200.	225.	115.

SECOND VERSION, GREEN BASE WITHOUT FLOWERS

Backstamp: Black transfer print: "Wade England [name of model]"

No.	Name	Description	Size	U.S. $	Can. $	U.K. £
1	Wynken	Blond hair; blue suit	75 x 40	175.	200.	100.
2a	Blynken	Blond hair; blue suit	58 x 40	175.	200.	100.
2b	Blynken	Light brown hair; blue suit	58 x 40	175.	200.	100.
3	Nod	Light brown hair; blue suit	70 x 40	175.	200.	100.
4	I've a Bear Behind	Light brown hair; blue suit	70 x 40	175.	200.	100.

YOGI BEAR AND FRIENDS

Yogi Bear and Firends is a set of three Hanna-Barbera cartoon characters that were popular on television in the late 1950s/early 1960s. Their original price was 3/6d each.

1962-1963

Backstamp: Unmarked

Yogi Bear, Mr. Jinks, Huckleberry Hound

No.	Name	Description	Size	U.S. $	Can. $	U.K. £
1	Yogi Bear	Beige; yellow/black hat; red tie	62 x 30	120.	135.	65.
2a	Mr. Jinks	Pink; white/yellow/black face; blue bow tie	63 x 30	120.	135.	65.
2b	Mr. Jinks	Yellow; white/yellow/black face; blue tie	63 x 30	120.	135.	65.
3	Huckleberry Hound	Blue; white face; yellow bow tie	60 x 28	120.	135.	65.

WHIMSIES
1954-2007

Christmas Crackers, Safari Whimsies	46
Collectable Limited Edition Crackers	47
Comical Whimsies	48
Cool Cats	48
Dinosaur Collection	49
Dogs and Puppies	50
English Whimsies	54
Family Pets	62
Farmyard Whimsies	62
First Whimsies	63
First Whimsies Blow Ups	77
Nativity Whimsies Set	78
New Colourway Whimsies	79
Pearl Lustre Whimsies	82
Polar Bear Blow Ups	83
Tetley Tea Folk Whimsies	84
Whimsie-land	85
Whimsey-in-the-Vale	89
Whimsey-on-Why	91
Whoppas	95

CHRISTMAS CRACKERS

SAFARI WHIMSIES 2003

Four of these models are from the 1984 *Whimsie-land* Wildlife series. The "Crocodile" is a new model, and the Giraffe is similar to the *English Whimsies* giraffe, but the front legs on this new model are bent upward. The retail price from Wade Ceramics was £20.00 per set.

Crocodile, Elephant (WL), Giraffe, Lion (WL), Panda (WL), Tiber (WL)

Backstamp: Embossed "Wade England"

No.	Name	Description	Size	U.S. $	Can. $	U.K. £
1	Crocodile	Light green; blue base	20 x 40	9.	10.	5.
2	Elephant (WL)	Grey; olive green base	35 x 40	9.	10.	5.
3	Giraffe	Beige	40 x 35	9.	10.	5.
4	Lion	Honey; dark brown mane; olive green base	35 x 45	7.	8.	4.
5	Panda (WL)	Black/white; blue-green base	22 x 50	5.	6.	3.
6	Tiger (WL)	Honey, brown stripes; mottled green base	22 x 50	7.	8.	4.
—	Set 6 pcs	Boxed	—	45.	50.	25.

COLLECTABLE LIMITED EDITION CRACKERS

MINIATURE NURSERY RHYMES

2001

As there were eight models in the set and only six crackers in a box, extra models could be purchased direct from Wade Ceramics at a cost of £2.99 each.

Ten complete sets were produced in an all-over gold glaze. As there were only six crackers to the box, two contained an extra model. A ticket allowing the finder to take four guests on a tour of the Wade Pottery was inserted into one of the boxes of crackers.

The cost direct from Wade was £19.99.

Backstamp: Embossed "Wade England"

No.	Name	Description	Size	U.S. $	Can. $	U.K. £
1a	Dr. Foster	Grey; black umbrella; brown bag	43 x 26	5.	6.	3.
1b	Dr. Foster	Gold	43 x 26		Rare	
2a	Goosey Gander	White; yellow beak, feet	33 x 36	5.	6.	3.
2b	Goosey Gander	Gold	33 x 36		Rare	
3a	Jack	Beige; brown hair; green base	34 x 33	5.	6.	3.
3b	Jack	Gold	34 x 33		Rare	
4a	Jill	Beige; yellow hair; green base	28 x 39	5.	6.	3.
4b	Jill	Gold	28 x 39		Rare	
5a	Little Jack Horner	Green; yellow hair; brown shoes	37 x 21	5.	6.	3.
5b	Little Jack Horner	Gold	37 x 21		Rare	
6a	Little Miss Muffett	Beige; yellow hair; black spider	39 x 35	5.	6.	3.
6b	Little Miss Muffett	Gold	39 x 35		Rare	
7a	Mother Goose	Pale honey; green hat; Goose: yellow beak, feet	41 x 31	5.	6.	3.
7b	Mother Goose	Gold	41 x 31		Rare	
8a	Wee Willie Winkie	Blue; dark brown hair	44 x 24	5.	6.	3.
8b	Wee Willie Winkie	Gold	44 x 24		Rare	
—	6 pce set	Boxed	—	30.	33.	17.
—	8 pce set	Boxed (gold)	—		Rare	

COMICAL WHIMSIES

2004

A completely new style of Whimsies was introduced in Feburary 2004. The issue price of this set, which includes cats, birds, a dog and a fox, was £17.50.

Backstamp: Unknown

No.	Name	Description	Size	U.S. $	Can. $	U.K. £
1	Cat, sitting	White and ginger	90	5.	6.	3.
2	Cat, standing	Beige with dark stripes	102	5.	6.	3.
3	Dog, sitting	Light grey, black eyes	75	5.	6.	3.
4	Duck	Blue and white, yellow beak and feet	90	5.	6.	3.
5	Fox	Red brown, black eyes	90	5.	6.	3.
6	Penguin	Black and white, yellow beak and feet	Unk.	5.	6.	3.
—	6 pce set	Boxed		30.	35.	18.

COOL CATS

2006

Backstamp: Unknown

No.	Name	Description	Size	U.S. $	Can. $	U.K. £
1	Cat	Black and white	—	7.	8.	4.
2	Cat	Brown and white	—	7.	8.	4.
3	Cat	Grey and white	—	7.	8.	4.
4	Cat	Honey and white	—	7.	8.	4.
5	Cat	White	—	7.	8.	4.
6	Cat and Kitten	White, black patches	—	7.	8.	4.
—	6 pce set	Boxed	—	35.	40.	20.

DINOSAUR COLLECTION

1993 and 2001

SET ONE,

1993

The *Dinosaur Collection* was issued in the wake of a series of documentary films about dinosaurs and the popular movie, *Jurassic Park*, released in early 1993. The subject stirred the imagination of the public, and it sparked the revival of dinosaur exhibits and a subsequent flood of dinosaur toys and models.

Backstamp: Embossed "Wade England"

No.	Name	Description	Size	U.S. $	Can. $	U.K. £
1	Camarasaurus	Brown/honey; green base	52 x 45	20.	23.	12.
2	Euoplocephalus	Red-brown/honey; green base	26 x 55	20.	23.	12.
3	Spinosaurus	Beige; grey spines; brown base	40 x 60	20.	23.	12.
4	Protoceratops	Brown; green base	25 x 58	20.	23.	12.
5a	Tyrannosaurus Rex	Dark brown/honey; green base	44 x 62	20.	23.	12.
5b	Tyrannosaurus Rex	Grey; greenish-brown base	44 x 62	20.	23.	12.

SET TWO

2001

The Protoceratops model in this second set is a reissued model from the 1993 set, but is much lighter in colour. The second set, which contained six models, was issued in 2001, and the original cost direct from Wade was £18.00 per set.

Backstamp: Embossed "Wade England"

No.	Name	Description	Size	U.S. $	Can. $	U.K. £
6	Corythosaurus	Apricot; blue-grey base	50 x 65	9.	10.	5.
7	Nodosaurus	Grey; grey-green base	27 x 58	9.	10.	5.
8	Protoceratops	Beige; green base	25 x 58	9.	10.	5.
9	Saurclephus	Green; brown base	45 x 52	9.	10.	5.
10	Scutellosaurus	Honey; brown base	32 x 62	9.	10.	5.
11	Vulcanodon	Blue; mottled brown-green base	50 x 67	9.	10.	5.

DOGS AND PUPPIES

1969-1982

This *Dogs and Puppies* series was advertised and labeled on the boxes as *Whimsies*. The models are of a mother dog and her two puppies, which were produced intermittently between 1969 and 1982. The mother dog was sold in one box and her two puppies in another. The boxes resemble books, and the inside of the lid has a description of the dog's breed printed on it. The first three sets were packaged in blue boxes, the last two sets in red. The original price was 7/6d per box.

SET ONE: ALSATIAN

1969-1982

Backstamp: Black and gold label "Genuine Wade Porcelain Made in England"

Puppy, lying; Mother; Puppy, seated

No.	Name	Description	Size	U.S. $	Can. $	U.K. £
1	Mother	Brown/honey brown	60 x 75	35.	40.	20.
2	Puppy, seated	Brown/honey brown	40 x 45	16.	18.	10.
3	Puppy, lying	Brown/honey brown	35 x 45	16.	18.	10.

SET TWO: CAIRN

1969-1982

Backstamp: Black and gold label "Genuine Wade Porcelain Made in England"

Puppy, lying; Mother; Puppy, standing

No.	Name	Description	Size	U.S. $	Can. $	U.K. £
1	Mother	Honey brown; brown ears, nose	65 x 70	35.	40.	20.
2	Puppy, standing	Honey brown; brown ears, nose	40 x 50	16.	18.	10.
3	Puppy, lying	Honey brown; brown ears, nose	35 x 50	16.	18.	10.

SET THREE: RED SETTER

1973-1982

Puppy, Lying, facing right; Mother; Puppy, lying, facing left

Backstamp: Black and gold label "Genuine Wade Porcelain Made in England"

No.	Name	Description	Size	U.S. $	Can. $	U.K. £
1	Mother	Red-brown	60 x 75	30.	35.	18.
2	Puppy, lying, facing left	Red-brown	40 x 45	15.	17.	8.
3	Puppy, lying, facing right	Red-brown	40 x 45	15.	17.	8.

SET FOUR: CORGI

1979-1982

Puppy, lying; Puppy, seated; Mother

Backstamp: Black and gold label "Genuine Wade Porcelain Made in England"

No.	Name	Description	Size	U.S. $	Can. $	U.K. £
1	Mother	Honey brown; brown ears, nose; green base	60 x 60	50.	55.	28.
2	Puppy, lying	Honey brown; brown ears, nose; green base	30 x 45	30.	35.	17.
3	Puppy, seated	Honey brown; brown ears, nose; green base	45 x 40	30.	35.	17.

SET FIVE: YORKSHIRE TERRIER

1979-1982

Backstamp: Black and gold label "Genuine Wade Porcelain Made in England"

Puppy, seated; Mother; Puppy, walking

No.	Name	Description	Size	U.S. $	Can. $	U.K. £
1	Mother	Black/brown; honey brown face, chest	55 x 70	70.	80.	40.
2	Puppy, seated	Black/brown; honey brown face, chest	40 x 40	50.	55.	30.
3	Puppy, walking	Black/brown; honey brown face, chest	35 x 45	50.	55.	30.

Dogs And Puppies Derivatives

Dog Pipe Stands

1973-1981

The *Dog Pipe Stands* have a mother dog from the 1969-1982 *Dogs and Puppies* series on the back rim of a stand. The original price was 72p each. A colour variation of the Alsatian, in an all-over honey glaze, has been found in the U.S.A.

Alsatian - Honey; Alsatian - Brown

Backstamp: Embossed "Wade England"

No.	Name	Description	Size	U.S. $	Can. $	U.K. £
1a	Alsatian	Brown/honey brown; green stand	60 x 115	25.	28.	15.
1b	Alsatian	Honey; green stand	60 x 115	35.	40.	20.
2	Cairn	Honey brown; green stand	60 x 115	60.	65.	35.
3	Corgi	Honey brown; green stand	60 x 115	50.	55.	30.
4	Red Setter	Red-brown; green stand	60 x 115	25.	28.	15.
5	Yorkshire Terrier	Black/brown; green stand	60 x 115	50.	55.	30.

Cat And Puppy Dishes

1974-1981

The *Cat and Puppy Dishes* is a series of 11 basket dishes with the puppies from the 1969-1982 *Dogs and Puppies* series sitting in them. The only change is the addition of a new model and the first in the series, the "Tabby Cat." With the exception of style 1b, the baskets are coloured in mottled greys and browns. The puppy dishes were packaged in pastel boxes marked "Pup-in-a-Basket" in North America.

Backstamp: Embossed "Wade England"

No.	Name	Description	Size	U.S. $	Can. $	U.K. £
1a	Tabby Cat	Brown stripes	50 x 75	25.	28.	15.
1b	Tabby Cat	Brown stripes; dark brown basket	50 x 75	25.	28.	15.
2	Alsatian puppy, seated	Brown/honey-brown	40 x 75	25.	28.	15.
3	Alsatian puppy, lying	Brown/honey brown	35 x 75	25.	28.	15.
4	Cairn puppy, standing	Honey brown	40 x 75	25.	28.	15.
5	Cairn puppy, lying	Honey brown	35 x 75	25.	28.	15.
6	Red Setter puppy, lying, facing left	Red brown	40 x 75	25.	28.	15.
7	Red Setter puppy, lying, facing right	Brown	40 x 75	25.	28.	15.
8	Corgi puppy, seated	Honey brown	45 x 75	60.	65.	35.
9	Corgi puppy, lying	Honey brown	30 x 75	60.	65.	35.
10	Yorkie puppy, sitting	Grey/brown	30 x 75	40.	45.	25.
11	Yorkie puppy, standing	Grey/brown	35 x 75	40.	45.	25.

ENGLISH WHIMSIES

1971-1984

In 1971, 25 of the original Red Rose Tea Canada models were individually boxed and sold by Wade as a retail line. Unlike their famous forerunners, *First Whimsies*, this series has five models per set, with each figure sold in its own numbered box. The boxes in each set were the same colour (for example, set one was dark blue, set two was red, etc.). An updated list of models was added to the back of the boxes each year.

A new set was usually issued annually, although on some occasions when demand was strong, two sets were issued per year. A further 35 new models were added to the 25 original Canadian models, making an English series of 60 models.

Note that the "Trout" when it was first issued was unmarked, and the back of the base differed slightly from the second issue, which is marked "Wade England" on the back rim. The "Hedgehog" has two pads on the base. The "Hippo," "Bison" and "Pig" come in more than one size, due to the replacement of broken dies. In fact, there can be slight size variations in all the models listed below.

The black "Zebra" was glazed dark grey with black stripes, but after the first production run through the kiln, it emerged looking black all over, with very few markings to show it was a zebra. The Wade management then decided to change the colour to beige. The black "Zebra" is rare. The "Bullfrog" is the same model as the Red Rose Tea "Frog," but has been changed from green-yellow to brown. The "Kitten" can be found with or without a backstamp.

English Whimsies was offered as a pocket-money line to children for a price of 2/2d each.

SET ONE: DARK BLUE BOX

1971

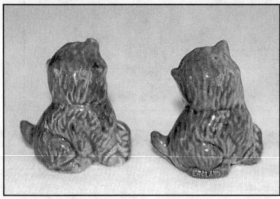

Without backstamp (left),
with backstamp (right)

Backstamp: **A.** Embossed "Wade England"
B. Embossed "England" (4)

No.	Name	Description	Size	U.S. $	Can. $	U.K. £
1	Fawn	Brown; blue ears	30 x 30	7.	8.	4.
2	Rabbit	Beige; ears open	30 x 30	7.	8.	4.
3	Mongrel	Dark brown back; light brown front	35 x 35	7.	8.	4.
4	Kitten	Dark/light brown; pink wool	30 x 30	7.	8.	4.
5	Spaniel	Honey; green base	35 x 35	7.	8.	4.

SET TWO: RED BOX
1972

Backstamp: Embossed "Wade England"

No.	Name	Description	Size	U.S. $	Can. $	U.K. £
6	Duck	Blue/brown, yellow beak	30 x 40	10.	11.	6.
7	Corgi	Honey brown	30 x 35	10.	11.	6.
8	Beaver	Grey-brown; honey-brown face	35 x 45	5.	6.	3.
9	Bushbaby, Type 1	Brown; blue ears; black nose	30 x 30	5.	6.	3.
10	Fox	Dark brown body, tail; fawn brown face, chest	30 x 30	9.	10.	5.

SET THREE: DARK GREEN BOX
1972

Backstamp: **A.** Embossed "Wade" between front feet and "England" on back of model (11)
B. Embossed "Wade England" (12-15)
C. Unmarked (15)

No.	Name	Description	Size	U.S. $	Can. $	U.K. £
11	Bear Cub	Grey; beige face	30 x 40	7.	8.	4.
12	Otter	Beige; blue base	30 x 35	7.	8.	4.
13	Setter	Brown; grey-green base	35 x 50	7.	8.	4.
14	Owl	Dark brown; light brown chest, face	35 x 20	7.	8.	4.
15	Trout	Brown; black patch; red tail; grey-green base	30 x 30	7.	8.	4.

SET FOUR: YELLOW BOX, 1973

Large Hippo (left),
Small Hippo (right)

Backstamp: Embossed "Wade England"

No.	Name	Description	Size	U.S. $	Can. $	U.K. £
16	Lion	Light brown; dark brown head, mane	35 x 45	9.	10.	5.
17	Elephant	Grey; some may have black eyes	35 x 28	14.	15.	8.
18	Giraffe	Beige	35 x 35	7.	8.	4.
19	Chimpanzee	Dark brown; light brown face, patches	35 x 35	7.	8.	4.
20a	Hippo	Large; honey brown	25 x 45	20.	22.	11.
20b	Hippo	Small; honey brown	20 x 40	7.	8.	4.

SET FIVE: DARK RED BOX , 1974

Backstamp: A. Embossed "Wade England" (21, 23, 25)
B. Embossed in recessed base "Wade England" (22)

No.	Name	Description	Size	U.S. $	Can. $	U.K. £
21	Squirrel	Grey; beige head, legs; yellow acorn	35 x 30	7.	8.	4.
22	Hedgehog, Type 2	Dark brown; light brown face; black nose	23 x 40	7.	8.	4.
23	Pine Marten	Honey	30 x30	7.	8.	4.
24	Fieldmouse	Honey; yellow corn; green on base	35 x 25	12.	13.	7.
25	Alsatian	Grey; tan face	30 x 40	7.	8.	4.

SET SIX: LIGHT BLUE BOX

1975

A colour variation of the "Horse" has been found. The original horse was issued in a dark grey colourway, however, the origin of the beige model is unknown. Due to the mould being renewed there are three sizes of the Pig. This model was used in the *English Whimsies* series, and both the Red Rose Tea (Canada) Ltd. and Red Rose Tea (U.S.A) Ltd. promotions.

Pigs in three sizes

Backstamp: Embossed "Wade England"

No.	Name	Description	Size	U.S. $	Can. $	U.K. £
26	Collie	Golden brown; green base	35 x 35	12.	13.	7.
27	Cow	Honey brown	35 x 35	12.	13.	7.
28a	Pig	Large; beige; green base	27 x 44	30.	33.	17.
28b	Pig	Medium; beige; green base	25 x 40	23.	25.	13.
28c	Pig	Small; beige; green base	25 x 35	23.	25.	13.
29a	Horse	Beige; dark brown/green base	38 x 30	23.	25.	13.
29b	Horse	Dark grey; green base	38 x 30	23.	25.	13.
30	Lamb	Fawn brown; green base	35 x 28	12.	13.	7.

SET SEVEN: ORANGE BOX, 1976

Black Zebra, faint stripes (left);
Zebra, beige (right)

Backstamp: Embossed "Wade England"

No.	Name	Description	Size	U.S. $	Can. $	U.K. £
31	Rhino	Grey; green base	25 x 35	9.	10.	5.
32	Leopard	Yellow/brown; green base	17 x 45	12.	13.	7.
33	Gorilla, standing	Grey; grey-green base	35 x 25	9.	10.	5.
34	Camel	Light grey; green base	35 x 35	12.	13.	7.
35a	Zebra	Black; faint stripes	40 x 35	60.	65.	35.
35b	Zebra	Beige; green base	40 x 35	12.	13.	7.

7

SET EIGHT: MAGENTA BOX, 1977

Backstamp: Embossed "Wade England"

No.	Name	Description	Size	U.S. $	Can. $	U.K. £
36	Donkey	Light brown; green base	30 x 30	20.	22.	11.
37	Barn Owl	Light brown; dark brown head, back; blue base	35 x 20	25.	27.	15.
38	Cat	Light brown/ginger; grey-green base	40 x 17	25.	27.	15.
39	Mouse, seated	Beige; grey-blue base	40 x 25	20.	22.	12.
40	Ram	White; grey face; green base	30 x 30	20.	22.	12.

SET NINE: MID BLUE BOX
1978

Backstamp: **A.** Embossed "Wade England" (41, 42, 43, 45)
B. Embossed "Wade England" in recessed base (44)

No.	Name	Description	Size	U.S. $	Can. $	U.K. £
41	Dolphin	Grey-brown; blue base	30 x 40	28.	30.	16.
42	Pelican	Honey; brown back; yellow beak; green base	45 x 40	25.	28.	15.
43	Angel Fish	Dark grey; blue base	35 x 30	14.	15.	8.
44	Turtle	Greenish-grey	15 x 50	14.	15.	8.
45	Seahorse	Honey yellow; grey-blue base	50 x 17	25.	28.	15.

SET TEN: LIGHT GREEN BOX
1979

Backstamp: Embossed "Wade England"

No.	Name	Description	Size	U.S. $	Can. $	U.K. £
46	Kangaroo	Dark brown; light brown base	45 x 25	20.	22.	11.
47	Orang-outan	Ginger	30 x 30	9.	10.	5.
48	Tiger	Honey; green base	35 x 25	20.	22.	11.
49a	Koala	Yellow-brown; black nose; green base	35 x 25	25.	28.	14.
49b	Koala	Yellow-brown; black nose; green leaves, base	35 x 25	25.	28.	14.
50	Langur, Type 1	Light brown; dark brown stump; green leaves	35 x 30	9.	10.	5.

SET ELEVEN: DARK BROWN BOX
1979

Large Bison (left), Small Bison (right)

Backstamp: **A.** Embossed "Wade England" (51a, 51b, 54, 55)
B. Embossed in recessed base "Wade England" (52, 53)

No.	Name	Description	Size	U.S. $	Can. $	U.K. £
51a	Bison	Large; honey brown; dark brown head, mane	32 x 45	17.	18.	10.
51b	Bison	Small; honey brown; dark brown head, mane	28 x 40	7.	8.	4.
52	Bluebird	Beige body, tail; blue wings, head	15 x 35	12.	13.	7.
53	Bullfrog	Brown	15 x 30	23.	25.	13.
54	Wild Boar	Light brown; green base	30 x 40	10.	11.	6.
55	Raccoon	Brown; grey-green base	25 x 35	17.	18.	10.

SET TWELVE: DEEP BLUE BOX
1980

Backstamp: Embossed "Wade England"

No.	Name	Description	Size	U.S. $	Can. $	U.K. £
56	Penguin	Grey; white face, chest; yellow beak, feet	38 x 19	25.	28.	15.
57	Seal Pup	Beige; blue base	25 x 37	25.	28.	15.
58	Husky	Grey; grey/green base	35 x 30	25.	28.	15.
59	Walrus	Light brown; grey base	30 x 30	10.	11.	6.
60	Polar Bear, head forward	White; black nose; blue base	30 x 30	25.	28.	15.

English Whimsies Derivatives
English Whimtrays
1971-1984

These *Whimtrays* were made with models from the *English Whimsies* series.

Photograph not available
at press time

Backstamp: Embossed "Whimtrays Wade Porcelain Made in England"

No.	Name	Description	Size	U.S. $	Can. $	U.K. £
1	Duck	Blue/brown; yellow beak; black tray	50 x 75	20.	22.	12.
2	Fawn	Brown; blue ears; black tray	50 x 75	20.	22.	12.
3	Trout	Brown; black patch; red tail; black tray	50 x 75	20.	22.	12.

FAMILY PETS
2005

Backstamp: Embossed "Wade England"

No.	Name	Description	Size	U.S. $	Can. $	U.K. £
1	Basset Hound	Tan and white; black nose	30	9.	10.	5.
2	Boxer	Brown and white; black nose	30	9.	10.	5.
3	English Bull Terrier	White, tan patch; black nose	30	9.	10.	5.
4	Great Dane	Honey; black nose; green-brown base	35	9.	10.	5.
5	Setter	Brown and white; black nose	30	9.	10.	5.
6	Spaniel	Tan and white; black nose	30	9.	10.	5.
—	6 pce set	Boxed	—	35.	40.	20.

FARMYARD WHIMSIES
2004

In 2004 this set was sold at the USA Wade Summer Fest, also Wade Collectors Fair, Dunstable. Ten sets were kept aside to be allocated on a draw basis for those not able to attend either of these shows.

Backstamp: Embossed "Wade England"

No.	Name	Description	Issued	Size	U.S. $	Can. $	U.K. £
1	Cockerel	Gold	100	50 x 35	9.	10.	5.
2	Cow	Gold	100	30 x 45	9.	10.	5.
3	Duck	Gold	100	45 x 35	9.	10.	5.
4	Goat	Gold	100	35 x 35	9.	10.	5.
5	Pig	Gold	100	30 x 35	9.	10.	5.
6	Pony	Gold	100	37 x 47	9.	10.	5.

Note: See page 81, New Colourway Whimsies, Set Five, for the coloured version of Farmyard Animals.

FIRST WHIMSIES

1954-1961

Following the end of World War II, the massive program to replace war-damaged houses and factories created a heavy demand for industrial ceramics. By the early 1950s, this demand had slackened, and new products had to be produced in order to avoid worker layoffs in the George Wade Potteries. With many years of experience making small pressed articles for industrial use, coupled with a unique ability in specialist tool-making, it was decided to manufacture a range of miniature animals.

The first set of five models was produced in 1954 and was designed for children to spend their pocket money on. When Mr. Wade's secretary referred to the models as whimsical, the series was named *Whimsies* (and later referred to as the *First Whimsies*).

The original models were packaged and sold in sets of five pieces for 5/9d. Only those models on bases wide enough for a Wade stamp were marked; free-standing models with open-cast legs generally had no room for marks. All boxes were marked "Wade Whimsies," but once the unmarked figures were removed from their boxes, there was no way to tell that they were Wade.

Whimsies models had their first showing at the British Industries Fair in 1954. At first, the reaction of dealers and wholesalers to the five tiny models was discouraging. But the following day, when the public was allowed into the show, they quickly changed their attitude when they saw the growing numbers of children and parents queuing to buy *Whimsies*.

For the next six years, Wade produced and sold nine sets of five and one set of four miniature animal models. Today these *First Whimsies* are highly sought after by collectors all over the world.

The "Spaniel with Ball" in the beige rump colourway is so rarely seen it is now believed to have been a prototype and not put into full production.

SET ONE: ENGLISH ANIMALS

1954-1958

Backstamp: **A.** Embossed "Wade" (1, 2)
             B. Unmarked (3, 4, 5)

No.	Name	Description	Size	U.S. $	Can. $	U.K. £
1	Leaping Fawn	White; green base	40 x 40	35.	40.	20.
2	Horse	Light brown; green/brown base	35 x 50	35.	40.	20.
3	Spaniel with ball	White; beige rump, tail	25 x 40	35.	40.	20.
4	Poodle	Light brown; white markings	35 x 35	35.	40.	20.
5	Squirrel	Light grey	25 x 50	35.	40.	20.

Note: Whimsies animals are arranged in issue order.

SET TWO: ENGLISH ANIMALS

1954-1958

Backstamp: **A.** Black and gold label "Genuine Wade Porcelain Made in England" (1, 3)
B. Unmarked (1, 2, 3, 4, 5)

No.	Name	Description	Size	U.S. $	Can. $	U.K. £
1	Bull	Brown legs; green base	45 x 55	90.	100.	50.
2	Lamb	Brown muzzle, front legs; green base	45 x 25	50.	55.	30.
3	Kitten	White; grey face, paws, tail; blue bow	15 x 40	80.	90.	45.
4	Hare	Light grey/white, white base	30 x 45	55.	60.	30.
5	Dachshund	Beige	35 x 45	90.	100.	50.

SET THREE: ENGLISH COUNTRY ANIMALS

1955-1958

Backstamp: **A.** Unmarked (1, 2, and 3)
B. Embossed "Wade" (4, 5)

No.	Name	Description	Size	U.S. $	Can. $	U.K. £
1	Badger	Grey; black/white face	30 x 40	35.	40.	20.
2	Fox Cub	Light brown	35 x 35	80.	90.	45.
3	Stoat	Grey tail; red eyes	20 x 35	60.	65.	35.
4	Shetland Pony	Grey mane; green base	35 x 40	45.	50.	25.
5	Retriever	Brown; white legs; green/white base	30 x 40	35.	40.	20.

Note: Whimsies animals are arranged in issue order.

SET FOUR: AFRICAN JUNGLE ANIMALS

1955-1958

Backstamp: **A.** Unmarked (1, 5)
B. Black ink stamp "Wade Made in England" (2, 3, 4)

No.	Name	Description	Size	U.S. $	Can. $	U.K. £
1	Lion	Light brown	30 x 35	60.	65.	35.
2	Crocodile	Green-brown	15 x 40	80.	90.	45.
3	Monkey and Baby	Brown; green stump	45 x 25	45.	50.	25.
4	Rhinoceros	Grey; green base	45 x 45	45.	50.	25.
5	Baby Elephant	Grey	40 x 40	60.	65.	35.

SET FIVE: HORSES

1956-1959

This is the only *First Whimsies* set of four figures and, despite its title, it includes a Beagle dog.

Backstamp: **A.** Embossed "Wade"
B. Unmarked (4)

No.	Name	Description	Size	U.S. $	Can. $	U.K. £
1a	Mare	Light brown; brown tail, mane; green base	45 x 40	45.	50.	25.
1b	Mare	White; brown mane, tail, hooves; green base	45 x 40	45.	50.	25.
2a	Foal	Light brown; brown mane, tail; green base	40 x 40	45.	50.	25.
2b	Foal	Dark brown; green base	40 x 40	45.	50.	25.
2c	Foal	White; brown mane, tail, hooves; green base	45 x 40	45.	50.	25.
3a	Colt	Light brown; brown mane, tail; green base	40 x 40	45.	50.	25.
3b	Colt	White; brown mane, tail, hooves; green base	40 x 40	45.	50.	25.
4	Beagle	Brown patches; green base	20 x 20	70.	80.	40.

SET SIX: POLAR ANIMALS

1956-1959

The original price was 6/6d for the set.

Backstamp: Unmarked

No.	Name	Description	Size	U.S. $	Can. $	U.K. £
1	King Penguin	Black back, head, flippers; yellow beak, feet	35 x 20	45.	50.	25.
2	Husky	Fawn/white; grey ears, muzzle	30 x 25	45.	50.	25.
3	Polar Bear	Grey muzzle; blue base	45 x 45	45.	50.	25.
4	Baby Seal	Light grey; white base	25 x 25	35.	40.	20.
5a	Polar Bear Cub	White; brown eyes, nose, claws	20 x 30	45.	50.	25.
5b	Polar Bear Cub	Pink; brown eyes, nose, claws	20 x 30	45.	50.	25.

Note: Whimsies animals are arranged in issue order.

SET SEVEN: PEDIGREE DOGS
1957-1961

The original price for Set Seven was 6/6d for a box of five models.

A variation in the St. Bernard dog has been found, in Type 1 the barrel has two vertical ridges, in Type 2, the barrel has one horizontal ridge. There are also slight variations in the brown glazes.

St. Bernard, Type 1 (left), Type 2 (right)

Backstamp: Unmarked

No.	Name	Description	Size	U.S. $	Can. $	U.K. £
1	Alsatian	Grey/brown, green-brown base	35 x 40	45.	50.	25.
2	West Highland Terrier	White	25 x 30	45.	50.	25.
3	Corgi	Beige/white	25 x 30	45.	50.	25.
4	Boxer	Brown; grey face; brown-green base	35 x 40	55.	60.	30.
5a	Saint Bernard, Type 1	Brown/white; beige barrel	40 x 45	55.	60.	30.
5b	Saint Bernard, Type 2	Dark brown/white; beige barrel	40 x 45	55.	60.	30.

Note: Whimsies animals are arranged in issue order.

SET EIGHT: ZOO ANIMALS

1957-1961

Two "Panda" figures were issued by Wade, one larger than the other. The smaller one, with a black band across its chest, is the right model for this set; the larger, 35 by 25 millimetre figure is out of proportion to the other models in the set. The larger model may have been produced first, then found to be too large and was set aside for possible use in special offers or premiums. Whether or not it was actually used in a premium set or simply sold off is not known. The original advertised retail price was 6/6d, but was later reduced to 5/9d per set

Backstamp: Unmarked

No.	Name	Description	Size	U.S. $	Can. $	U.K. £
1	Bactrian Camel	Light brown; dark brown humps; green base	40 x 40	45.	50.	25.
2	Cockatoo	Yellow crest; grey base	30 x 30	60.	65.	35.
3a	Giant Panda, large	Black/white	35 x 25	35.	40.	20.
3b	Giant Panda, small	Black/white; black band on chest	30 x 18	35.	40.	20.
4	Lion Cub	Brown; white chest	25 x 25	35.	40.	20.
5	Llama	Grey face; brown-green base	45 x 30	45.	50.	25.

SET NINE: NORTH AMERICAN ANIMALS, 1958-1961

The "Grizzly Cub" (model 4a), is the figure issued as part of this set. Models 4b and 4c were issued at a later time. The original issue price was 6/6d per set.

Backstamp: **A.** Unmarked (1, 2, 4a, 4b, 4c, 5)
B. Embossed "Wade" (3)
C. Embossed "Wade England" (3)

No.	Name	Description	Size	U.S. $	Can. $	U.K. £
1	Snowy Owl	Brown eyes, claws	28 x 30	55.	60.	30.
2	Raccoon	Grey/black, white base	30 x 30	45.	50.	25.
3	Grizzly Bear	Brown/white; green base	50 x 25	60.	65.	35.
4a	Grizzly Cub	Light brown, green base	25 x 25	45.	50.	25.
4b	Grizzly Cub	Brown; pink ears	25 x 30	45.	50.	25.
4c	Grizzly Cub	White; pink ears	25 x 25	45.	50.	25.
5	Cougar	Brown; white face, feet	20 x 45	60.	65.	35.

SET TEN: FARM ANIMALS

1959-1961

These are the hardest of all *First Whimsies* models to find. This was the last set made and was only in production for a short time.

The "Shire Horse" and "Swan" in this set have been unlawfully reproduced and sold as authentic *First Whimsies*. The "Shire Horse" fake is slightly larger, it leans backwards in an ungainly way (most will not stand) and its nose is longer. It does not have the appearance of a real horse, but looks more like a caricature. The counterfeit "Swan" has a thicker neck and shorter beak, and the detailing of the feathers is not as fine as on the original.

The original price was 5/9d per boxed set.

Backstamp: Unmarked

No.	Name	Description	Size	U.S. $	Can. $	U.K. £
1	Pig	Pink; green base	20 x 35	80.	90.	45.
2	Italian Goat	Grey; white face, chest; green base	30 x 30	80.	90.	45.
3a	Foxhound	Beige patches; green base	25 x 45	80.	90.	45.
3b	Foxhound	Light brown patches; green/white base	25 x 45	80.	90.	45.
4a	Shire Horse	Creamy beige; brown mane and tail	50 x 50	200.	225.	115.
4b	Shire Horse	White; grey mane; brown hooves	50 x 40	200.	225.	115.
4c	Shire Horse	Red brown; cream mane; cream/black hooves	50 x 50	275.	300.	150.
5	Swan	Yellow beak; black tip	25 x 35	180.	200	100.

First Whimsies Derivatives Disney Lights, Candleholder

Circa 1960

A "Panda" model has been found on a Disney Light candle holder base, which is much thicker and heavier than the Zoo light candle holder base.

Photograph not available
at press time

No.	Name	Description	Size	U.S. $	Can. $	U.K. £
1	Panda, large	Black/white; black base	55 x 50	35.	45.	20.

Note: For *English Whimsies* and *First Whimsies* Derivatives on Irish Whimtrays see the *Charlton Standard Catalolgue of Wade Collectables*, 4th edition.

First Whimsies Derivatives Mare And Foal Dish

1963

The *Mare and Foal Dish* has two models from the *First Whimsies Horses*, set 5, on the rim of a figure-eight shaped dish. The original price was 6/6d. This dish is rare.

Backstamp: Embossed "Wade Porcelain Made in England"

No.	Name	Description	Size	U.S. $	Can. $	U.K. £
1	Mare and foal dish	Light brown horses; black dish	110 x 20	115.	125.	65.

First Whimsies Derivatives Snack Tray

Mid 1960s

This snack tray is possibly part of a set of four or five sections that would make up a circular table centre decoration. Only one example, which has a *First Whimsies Racoon* on the back edge of the tray, has been found to date.

Backstamp: Unknown

No.	Name	Description	Size	U.S. $	Can. $	U.K. £
1	Snack tray	Grey, white, black raccoon; yellow tray	115		Rare	

First Whimsies Derivative Whimtrays

1958-1965

Whimtrays are small round dishes with a *First Whimsies* animal on the back edge of the tray. The issue date was January 1958 (except for the Bactrian Camel, Cockatoo, Giant Panda, Llama and Lion Cub *Whimtrays*, which were issued in August 1958), and they originally sold for 2/6d each. The trays come in black, blue, yellow and pink. The following *Whimtrays* are listed in alphabetical order.

Bactrian Camel (2)

Racoon (2)

Backstamp: Embossed "Whimtrays Wade Porcelain Made in England"

No.	Name	Description	Size	U.S. $	Can. $	U.K. £
1a	Alsatian	Grey/brown, black tray	55 x 75	35.	40.	20.
1b	Alsatian	Grey/brown, blue tray	55 x 75	35.	40.	20.
1c	Alsatian	Grey/brown, pink tray	55 x 75	35.	40.	20.
1d	Alsatian	Grey/brown, yellow tray	55 x 75	35.	40.	20.
2a	Bactrian Camel	Light brown; black tray	60 x 75	35.	40.	20.
2b	Bactrian Camel	Light brown; blue tray	60 x 75	35.	40.	20.
2c	Bactrian Camel	Light brown; pink tray	60 x 75	35.	40.	20.
2d	Bactrian Camel	Light brown; yellow tray	60 x 75	35.	40.	20.
3a	Baby Seal	Grey; black tray	40 x 75	35.	40.	20.
3b	Baby Seal	Grey; blue tray	40 x 75	35.	40.	20.
3c	Baby Seal	Grey; pink tray	40 x 75	35.	40.	20.
3d	Baby Seal	Grey; yellow tray	40 x 75	35.	40.	20.
4a	Boxer	Brown; black tray	45 x 75	35.	40.	20.
4b	Boxer	Brown; blue tray	45 x 75	35.	40.	20.
4c	Boxer	Brown; pink tray	45 x 75	35.	40.	20.
4d	Boxer	Brown; yellow tray	45 x 75	35.	40.	20.
5a	Cockatoo	Yellow crest; black tray	50 x 75	35.	40.	20.
5b	Cockatoo	Yellow crest; blue tray	50 x 75	35.	40.	20.
5c	Cockatoo	Yellow crest; pink tray	50 x 75	35.	40.	20.
5d	Cockatoo	Yellow crest; yellow tray	50 x 75	35.	40.	20.
6a	Corgi	Beige/white; black tray	45 x 75	35.	40.	20.
6b	Corgi	Beige/white; blue tray	45 x 75	35.	40.	20.
6c	Corgi	Beige/white; pink tray	45 x 75	35.	40.	20.
6d	Corgi	Beige/white; yellow tray	45 x 75	35.	40.	20.
7a	Giant Panda	Black/white; black tray	50 x 75	35.	40.	20.
7b	Giant Panda	Black/white; blue tray	50 x 75	35.	40.	20.
7c	Giant Panda	Black/white; pink tray	50 x 75	35.	40.	20.
7d	Giant Panda	Black/white; yellow tray	50 x 75	35.	40.	20.

First Whimsies Derivatives Whimtrays (cont.)

No.	Name	Description	Size	U.S. $	Can. $	U.K. £
8a	Giant Panda, small	Black/white; black tray	45 x 75	35.	40.	20.
8b	Giant Panda, small	Black/white; blue tray	45 x 75	35.	40.	20.
8c	Giant Panda, small	Black/white; pink tray	45 x 75	35.	40.	20.
8d	Giant Panda, small	Black/white; yellow tray	45 x 75	35.	40.	20.
9a	Grizzly Bear	Brown/white; black tray	65 x 75	35.	40.	20.
9b	Grizzly Bear	Brown/white; blue tray	65 x 75	35.	40.	20.
9c	Grizzly Bear	Brown/white; pink tray	65 x 75	35.	40.	20.
9d	Grizzly Bear	Brown/white; yellow tray	65 x 75	35.	40.	20.
10a	Grizzly Cub	Brown; black tray	45 x 75	35.	40.	20.
10b	Grizzly Cub	Brown; blue tray	45 x 75	35.	40.	20.
10c	Grizzly Cub	Brown; pink tray	45 x 75	35.	40.	20.
10d	Grizzly Cub	Brown; yellow tray	45 x 75	35.	40.	20.
11a	Hare	Light grey/white; black tray	50 x 75	35.	40.	20.
11b	Hare	Light grey/white; blue tray	50 x 75	35.	40.	20.
11c	Hare	Light grey/white; pink tray	50 x 75	35.	40.	20.
11d	Hare	Light grey/white; yellow tray	50 x 75	35.	40.	20.
12a	Husky	Fawn/white; black tray	50 x 75	35.	40.	20.
12b	Husky	Fawn/white; blue tray	50 x 75	35.	40.	20.
12c	Husky	Fawn/white; pink tray	50 x 75	35.	40.	20.
12d	Husky	Fawn/white; yellow tray	50 x 75	35.	40.	20.
13a	King Penguin	Black/white; black tray	50 x 75	35.	40.	20.
13b	King Penguin	Black/white; blue tray	50 x 75	35.	40.	20.
13c	King Penguin	Black/white; pink tray	50 x 75	35.	40.	20.
13d	King Penguin	Black/white; yellow tray	50 x 75	35.	40.	20.
14a	Lion Cub	Brown; black tray	45 x 75	35.	40.	20.
14b	Lion Cub	Brown; blue tray	45 x 75	35.	40.	20.
14c	Lion Cub	Brown; pink tray	45 x 75	35.	40.	20.
14d	Lion Cub	Brown; yellow tray	45 x 75	35.	40.	20.
15a	Llama	Grey face; black tray	65 x 75	35.	40.	20.
15b	Llama	Grey face; blue tray	65 x 75	35.	40.	20.
15c	Llama	Grey face; pink tray	65 x 75	35.	40.	20.
15d	Llama	Grey face; yellow tray	65 x 75	35.	40.	20.
16a	Mare	Light brown; black tray	55 x 75	35.	40.	20.
16b	Mare	Light brown; blue tray	55 x 75	35.	40.	20.
16c	Mare	Light brown; pink tray	55 x 75	35.	40.	20.
16d	Mare	Light brown; yellow tray	55 x 75	35.	40.	20.
17a	Monkey and Baby	Brown; black tray	65 x 75	35.	40.	20.
17b	Monkey and Baby	Brown; blue tray	65 x 75	35.	40.	20.
17c	Monkey and Baby	Brown; pink tray	65 x 75	35.	40.	20.
17d	Monkey and Baby	Brown; yellow tray	65 x 75	35.	40.	20.
18	Piglet	Pink/green; black tray	35 x 75	35.	40.	20.
19a	Polar Bear	White; black tray	65 x 75	35.	40.	20.
19b	Polar Bear	White; blue tray	65 x 75	35.	40.	20.
19c	Polar Bear	White; pink tray	65 x 75	35.	40.	20.
19d	Polar Bear	White; yellow tray	65 x 75	35.	40.	20.

First Whimsies Derivatives Whimtrays (cont.)

No.	Name	Description	Size	U.S. $	Can. $	U.K. £
20a	Polar Bear Cub	White; black tray	40 x 75	35.	40.	20.
20b	Polar Bear Cub	White; blue tray	40 x 75	35.	40.	20.
20c	Polar Bear Cub	White; pink tray	40 x 75	35.	40.	20.
20d	Polar Bear Cub	White; yellow tray	40 x 75	35.	40.	20.
21a	Raccoon	Grey/black; black tray	50 x 75	35.	40.	20.
21b	Raccoon	Grey/black; blue tray	50 x 75	35.	40.	20.
21c	Raccoon	Grey/black; pink tray	50 x 75	35.	40.	20.
21d	Raccoon	Grey/black; yellow tray	50 x 75	35.	40.	20.
22a	Snowy Owl	White; black tray	44 x 75	35.	40.	20.
22b	Snowy Owl	White; blue tray	44 x 75	35.	40.	20.
22c	Snowy Owl	White; pink tray	44 x 75	35.	40.	20.
22d	Snowy Owl	White; yellow tray	44 x 75	35.	40.	20.
23a	Spaniel	White; black tray	45 x 75	35.	40.	20.
23b	Spaniel	White; blue tray	45 x 75	35.	40.	20.
23c	Spaniel	White; pink tray	45 x 75	35.	40.	20.
23d	Spaniel	White; yellow tray	45 x 75	35.	40.	20.
24a	Squirrel	Light grey; black tray	45 x 75	35.	40.	20.
24b	Squirrel	Light grey; blue tray	45 x 75	35.	40.	20.
24c	Squirrel	Light grey; pink tray	45 x 75	35.	40.	20.
24d	Squirrel	Light grey; yellow tray	45 x 75	35.	40.	20.
25a	Swan	White; black tray	40 x 75	35.	40.	20.
25b	Swan	White; blue tray	40 x 75	35.	40.	20.
25c	Swan	White; pink tray	40 x 75	35.	40.	20.
25d	Swan	White; yellow tray	40 x 75	35.	40.	20.
26a	West Highland Terrier	White; black tray	40 x 75	35.	40.	20.
26b	West Highland Terrier	White; blue tray	40 x 75	35.	40.	20.
26c	West Highland Terrier	White; pink tray	40 x 75	35.	40.	20.
26d	West Highland Terrier	White; yellow tray	40 x 75	35.	40.	20.

First Whimsies Derivatives Zoo Lights, Candle Holders

1957-1960

George Wade's policy of using unsold models by adding them to new items produced many different "Stick-em-on-Somethings," such as *Zoo Lights*, *Whimtrays* and *Disney Lights*. Luckily for collectors, single models of *First Whimsies* animals, which were eluding capture in their original form, were attached to an oval base with a candle holder on the back to become *Zoo Lights*. Almost all the *First Whimsies* animals are on *Zoo Lights*. The candle holders come in black, yellow, blue and pink, and all the animals are in their original colour glazes.

The *Zoo Lights* were first issued prior to Christmas 1957 as *Animal Candlesticks* (with the exception of the Camel, Llama and Panda, which were issued in August 1958), and were discontinued in January 1960. They are listed in alphabetical order.

Backstamp: Embossed "Wade Porcelain Made in England"

No.	Name	Description	Size	U.S. $	Can. $	U.K. £
1a	Alsatian	Grey/brown; black holder	47 x 48	35.	40.	20.
1b	Alsatian	Grey/brown; blue holder	47 x 48	35.	40.	20.
1c	Alsatian	Grey/brown; pink holder	47 x 48	35.	40.	20.
1d	Alsatian	Grey/brown; yellow holder	47 x 48	35.	40.	20.
2a	Baby Seal	Light grey; black holder	35 x 48	35.	40.	20.
2b	Baby Seal	Light grey; blue holder	35 x 48	35.	40.	20.
2c	Baby Seal	Light grey; pink holder	35 x 48	35.	40.	20.
2d	Baby Seal	Light grey; yellow holder	35 x 48	35.	40.	20.
3a	Bactrian Camel	Light brown; black holder	52 x 48	35.	40.	20.
3b	Bactrian Camel	Light brown; blue holder	52 x 48	35.	40.	20.
3c	Bactrian Camel	Light brown; pink holder	52 x 48	35.	40.	20.
3d	Bactrian Camel	Light brown; yellow holder	52 x 48	35.	40.	20.
4a	Badger	Grey/black/white; black holder	40 x 48	35.	40.	20.
4b	Badger	Grey/black/white; blue holder	40 x 48	35.	40.	20.
4c	Badger	Grey/black/white; pink holder	40 x 48	35.	40.	20.
4d	Badger	Grey/black/white; yellow holder	40 x 48	35.	40.	20.
5a	Boxer	Brown; black holder	45 x 48	35.	40.	20.
5b	Boxer	Brown; blue holder	45 x 48	35.	40.	20.
5c	Boxer	Brown; pink holder	45 x 48	35.	40.	20.
5d	Boxer	Brown; yellow holder	45 x 48	35.	40.	20.

First Whimsies Derivatives Zoo Lights Candle holders, 1957-1960

No.	Name	Description	Size	U.S. $	Can. $	U.K. £
6a	Cockatoo	Yellow crest; black holder	44 x 48	35.	40.	20.
6b	Cockatoo	Yellow crest; blue holder	44 x 48	35.	40.	20.
6c	Cockatoo	Yellow crest; pink holder	44 x 48	35.	40.	20.
6d	Cockatoo	Yellow crest; yellow holder	44 x 48	35.	40.	20.
7a	Corgi	Beige/white; black holder	37 x 48	35.	40.	20.
7b	Corgi	Beige/white; blue holder	37 x 48	35.	40.	20.
7c	Corgi	Beige/white; pink holder	37 x 48	35.	40.	20.
7d	Corgi	Beige/white; yellow holder	37 x 48	35.	40.	20.
8a	Giant Panda, small	Black/white; black holder	40 x 48	35.	40.	20.
8b	Giant Panda, small	Black/white; blue holder	40 x 48	35.	40.	20.
8c	Giant Panda, small	Black/white; pink holder	40 x 48	35.	40.	20.
8d	Giant Panda, small	Black/white; yellow holder	40 x 48	35.	40.	20.
9a	Grizzly Bear	Brown/white; black holder	60 x 48	35.	40.	20.
9b	Grizzly Bear	Brown/white; blue holder	60 x 48	35.	40.	20.
9c	Grizzly Bear	Brown/white; pink holder	60 x 48	35.	40.	20.
9d	Grizzly Bear	Brown/white; yellow holder	60 x 48	35.	40.	20.
10a	Hare	Light grey/white; black holder	40 x 48	35.	40.	20.
10b	Hare	Light grey/white; blue holder	40 x 48	35.	40.	20.
10c	Hare	Light grey/white; pink holder	40 x 48	35.	40.	20.
10d	Hare	Light grey/white; yellow holder	40 x 48	35.	40.	20.
11a	Husky	Fawn/white; black holder	44 x 48	35.	40.	20.
11b	Husky	Fawn/white; blue holder	44 x 48	35.	40.	20.
11c	Husky	Fawn/white; pink holder	44 x 48	35.	40.	20.
11d	Husky	Fawn/white; yellow holder	44 x 48	35.	40.	20.
12a	King Penguin	Black/white; black holder	44 x 48	35.	40.	20.
12b	King Penguin	Black/white; blue holder	44 x 48	35.	40.	20.
12c	King Penguin	Black/white; pink holder	44 x 48	35.	40.	20.
12d	King Penguin	Black/white; yellow holder	44 x 48	35.	40.	20.
13a	Lion Cub	Brown; black holder	37 x 48	35.	40.	20.
13b	Lion Cub	Brown; blue holder	37 x 48	35.	40.	20.
13c	Lion Cub	Brown; pink holder	37 x 48	35.	40.	20.
13d	Lion Cub	Brown; yellow holder	37 x 48	35.	40.	20.
14a	Llama	Grey face; black holder	55 x 48	35.	40.	20.
14b	Llama	Grey face; blue holder	55 x 48	35.	40.	20.
14c	Llama	Grey face; pink holder	55 x 48	35.	40.	20.
14d	Llama	Grey face; yellow holder	55 x 48	35.	40.	20.
15a	Mare	Light brown; black holder	55 x 48	35.	40.	20.
15b	Mare	Light brown; blue holder	55 x 48	35.	40.	20.
15c	Mare	Light brown; pink holder	55 x 48	35.	40.	20.
15d	Mare	Light brown; yellow holder	55 x 48	35.	40.	20.
15e	Mare	White; royal blue holder	55 x 48	35.	40.	20.
16a	Polar Bear Cub	White; black holder	35 x 48	35.	40.	20.
16b	Polar Bear Cub	White; blue holder	35 x 48	35.	40.	20.
16c	Polar Bear Cub	White; pink holder	35 x 48	35.	40.	20.
16d	Polar Bear Cub	White; yellow holder	35 x 48	35.	40.	20.

First Whimsies Derivatives Zoo Lights Candle holders, 1957-1962

No.	Name	Description	Size	U.S. $	Can. $	U.K. £
17a	Poodle	Light brown; black holder	44 x 48	35.	40.	20.
17b	Poodle	Light brown; blue holder	44 x 48	35.	40.	20.
17c	Poodle	Light brown; pink holder	44 x 48	35.	40.	20.
17d	Poodle	Light brown; yellow holder	44 x 48	35.	40.	20.
18a	Retriever	Brown/white; black holder	40 x 48	35.	40.	20.
18b	Retriever	Brown/white; blue holder	40 x 48	35.	40.	20.
18c	Retriever	Brown/white; pink holder	40 x 48	35.	40.	20.
18d	Retriever	Brown/white; yellow holder	40 x 48	35.	40.	20.
19a	Spaniel	White; black holder	35 x 48	35.	40.	20.
19b	Spaniel	White; blue holder	35 x 48	35.	40.	20.
19c	Spaniel	White; pink holder	35 x 48	35.	40.	20.
19d	Spaniel	White; yellow holder	35 x 48	35.	40.	20.
20a	Squirrel	Light grey; black holder	35 x 48	35.	40.	20.
20b	Squirrel	Light grey; blue holder	35 x 48	35.	40.	20.
20c	Squirrel	Light grey; pink holder	35 x 48	35.	40.	20.
20d	Squirrel	Light grey; yellow holder	35 x 48	35.	40.	20.
21a	West Highland Terrier	White; black holder	35 x 48	35.	40.	20.
21b	West Highland Terrier	White; blue holder	35 x 48	35.	40.	20.
21c	West Highland Terrier	White; pink holder	35 x 48	35.	40.	20.
21d	West Highland Terrier	White; yellow holder	35 x 48	35.	40.	20.

FIRST WHIMSIES BLOW UPS

SPANIEL

50th ANNIVERSARY 2004

To celebrate fifty years of Whimsies, Wade produced a blow-up model of the first Whimsie "Spaniel with Ball" from Set One of the *First Whimsies*. Although the backstamp dates are 1953-2003, an *Evening Sentinel* newspaper article reveals that the models were actually exhibited for the first time at a Trade Fair in May 1954. William Harper was the modeller of the *First Whimsies*. Included with the blow up model was a reissue (using the original mould) of the miniature First Whimsie "Spaniel," but this time he holds a gold ball in his mouth. The edition size of the models is limited to orders received before March 31st, 2004. The issue price of the two models is £39.95, and the club members price was £35.00.

Backstamp: **A. Blow Up:** Printed "Celebrating 50 Years of the Whimsie 1953-2003 Made in England" with red "Wade" logo
B. Whimsie: Embossed "Wade"

Spaniel with Ball (left); Blow Up Spaniel with Ball (right)

No.	Name	Description	Size	U.S. $	Can. $	U.K. £
1	Blow Up Spaniel with Ball	White; grey ears, markings; bright blue ball	70 x 135	Price	Per	Pair
2	Spaniel with Ball	White; grey ears, markings; gold ball	25 x 40	60.	70.	35.

SWAN

2004

This blow up model of a swan is based on the original Whimsies Swan produced between 1959-1961. It has the same wing feathering as the original model. The issue price was £39.95. It is the third model in the 'Blow Up' series.

Backstamp: Unknown

No.	Name	Description	Size	U.S. $	Can. $	U.K. £
1	Swan	White; black eyes, beak edging; yellow beak	100	45.	50.	25.

Note: For the Shetland Pony Blow Up see page 184.

NATIVITY WHIMSIES SET

2005

This Nativity set is a scaled down version of the Nativity set produced by Wade in 2001. Each model was issued in a limited edition of 1,000, and each model was individually boxed.

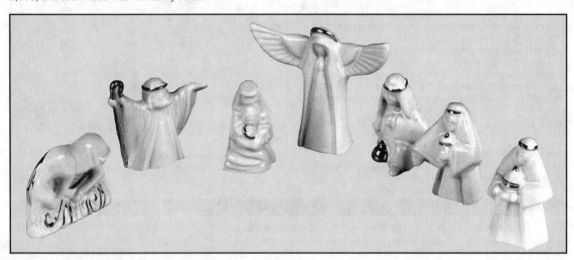

Backstamp: Printed gold "Wade" logo

Date	Name	Description	Issue	Price	Size	U.S. $	Can. $	U.K. £
2005	Angel	White, 22k gold highlights	1,000	£5.95	65 x 25	10.	12.	6.
2005	Donkey	White, 22k gold highlights	1,000	£5.95	30 x 40	10.	12.	6.
2005	Mary and Baby Jesus	White, 22k gold highlights	1,000	£5.95	40 x 30	10.	12.	6.
2005	Shepherd	White, 22k gold highlights	1,000	£5.95	43 x 51	10.	12.	6.
2005	Wiseman	White, 22k gold highlights	1,000	£5.95	45 x 30	10.	12.	6.
2005	Wiseman	White, 22k gold highlights	1,000	£5.95	45 x 30	10.	12.	6.
2005	Wiseman	White, 22k gold highlights	1,000	£5.95	40 x 40	10.	12.	6.
2005	7 pce set, Individually boxed		—	—	—	70.	75.	40.

NEW COLOURWAY WHIMSIES

SET ONE: ANIMALS

1998 and 2000

Wade reissued six *Whimsies* models in new colourways. Four models, the "Gorilla," "Hippo," "Leopard" and "Racoon" are from the Red Rose Tea Canada and *English Whimsies* series; and two, the "Mole" and the "Safari Park Lion," are Tom Smith models. The "Safari Park Lion" is identical in colour to the original model, except the base is a brighter green.

In 2000, Wade Ceramics sold these models singly or in boxed sets. Set one was reissued in a limited edition of 3,000 boxed sets of six models for £15.95. A label on the back of the box reads, "Introduced 2000 Limited Edition of 3000 No. ..." It goes on to list the models in the box, two of which are incorrectly named. The Seal is actually the *Tom Smith* 'Mole' and the Wolf is actually the *English Whimsies* / *Red Rose Tea* "Racoon." The *English Whimsies* 'Gorilla' model has been renamed Ape. Models are listed in correct name order.

Backstamp: Embossed "Wade England" on rim

No.	Name	Description	Size	U.S. $	Can. $	U.K. £
1	Gorilla, standing / Ape (RRC & EW)	Beige; grey-blue base	25 x 35	7.	8.	4.
2	Hippo (RRC & EW)	Light grey; blue base	23 x 35	7.	8.	4.
3	Leopard (RRC & EW)	Pale honey; bright green base	17 x 45	7.	8.	4.
4	Mole / Seal (TS)	Light grey; pale green base	25 x 40	7.	8.	4.
5	Racoon / Wolf (EW)	Light grey; black nose, striped tail	25 x 35	7.	8.	4.
6	Safari Park Lion (TS)	Honey; bright green base	30 x 45	7.	8.	4.
—	6 pce set	Boxed	—	28.	30.	16.

SET TWO: ANIMALS

2000-2001

During 2000-2001 Wade reissued more *Whimsie* models in new colourways. Five models, the "Beaver," "Elephant," "Kitten," "Polar Bear," and "Zebra" are from the *Red Rose Tea Canada* and *English Whimsies* series. The "Polar Bear" is in the same colourway as the original *English Whimsie* model except for a black nose. The "Puppy" was originally the "Spaniel Puppy" from the *Tom Smith Family Pets Set*. The models could be purchased in two ways direct from Wade Ceramics: as a boxed set of six models for £15.99, or individually boxed for £2.99 each. The second set was not issued in a limited edition.

Backstamp: Embossed "Wade England" on rim

No.	Name	Description	Size	U.S. $	Can. $	U.K. £
1	Beaver (RRC & EW)	Light grey, dark brown stump	35 x 45	7.	8.	4.
2	Elephant (RRC & EW)	Honey; bright green base	35 x 28	7.	8.	4.
3	Kitten, seated (RRC & EW)	Apricot; dark brown wool	30 x 30	7.	8.	4.
4	Polar Bear, head forward (EW)	White; blue base	30 x 30	7.	8.	4.
5	Spaniel Puppy (TS)	Honey; dark brown ears	25 x 30	7.	8.	4.
6	Zebra (EW)	White; black stripes	40 x 35	7.	8.	4.
—	6 pce set	Boxed	—	28.	30.	16.

NEW COLOURWAY WHIMSIES (cont.)

SET THREE: MINIATURE NURSERIES

2000

Wade reissued ten of the original *Red Rose Tea Canada Miniature Nurseries* and two of the *Tom Smith Miniature Nursery* models and reglazed them in new colourways. Each series was issued as a boxed set of six models for £15.95.

Backstamp: Embossed "Wade England" on rim

No.	Name	Description	Size	U.S. $	Can. $	U.K. £
1	Hickory Dickory Dock (RRC)	Apricot; dark brown mouse	44 x 20	5.	6.	3.
2	Humpty Dumpty (RRC)	Pale honey; black bow tie, shoes; grey wall	36 x 25	5.	6.	3.
3	Old Woman Who Lived in A Shoe (RRC)	Apricot; dark brown door; green base	35 x 40	5.	6.	3.
4	Puss in Boots (RRC)	Blue; black eyes, nose, boots	43 x 20	5.	6.	3.
5	Queen of Hearts (RRC)	Pale honey; dark red hearts	42 x 25	5.	6.	3.
6	Red Riding Hood (RRC)	Grey; yellow basket; black shoes	44 x 24	5.	6.	3.
—	6 pce set	Boxed	—	28.	30.	16.

SET FOUR: MINIATURE NURSERIES

2001

Backstamp: Embossed "Wade England" on rim

No.	Name	Description	Size	U.S. $	Can. $	U.K. £
1	Little Bo-Peep (RRC)	Blue; dark brown crook; pink bow	44 x 24	5.	6.	3.
2	Little Boy Blue (RRC)	Blue; green hat; dark brown shoes; yellow horn	41 x 25	5.	6.	3.
3	Cat and the Fiddle (RRC)	Apricot; dark brown fiddle; tan bow	47 x 33	5.	6.	3.
4	Gingerbread Man (RRC)	Honey; yellow hair; green base	43 x 30	5.	6.	3.
5	Ride-a-Cock Horse (RRC)	Apricot; orange hair; black shoes	45 x 55	5.	6.	3.
6	Tom, Tom the Piper's Son (RRC)	Honey; grey tam, kilt, socks; black shoes	39 x 33	5.	6.	3.
—	6 pce set	Boxed	—	28.	30.	16.

Note: The following initials indicate the origin of the models.
EW: *English Whimsies*
RRC: Red Rose Tea
TS: Tom Smith

NEW COLOURWAY WHIMSIES (cont.)

SET FIVE: FARMYARD ANIMALS

2003

In this set five models are from the original *Whimsieland*, Set Three, issued in 1985, and the sixth is the Pony from Set One: Pets. Although the same models, five of them are easily distinguished from the originals by the new colourways. The pig is in the original colours and therefore harder to distinguish, however the base is a brighter green than the model previously issued. The models could be purchased as a boxed set of six or as individual models. The issue price for the boxed set was £17.50, and the individual models were priced at £3.50.

Backstamp: Unknown

No.	Name	Description	Size	U.S. $	Can. $	U.K. £
1	Cockerel	White; red comb; blue wings, tail; grey base	50 x 35	5.	6.	3.
2	Cow	White; tan patches; green base	30 x 45	5.	6.	3.
3	Duck	White; yellow beak; blue wings; green base	45 x 35	5.	6.	3.
4	Goat	White; brown patch; green base	35 x 35	5.	6.	3.
5	Pig	Pink; bright green base	30 x 35	5.	6.	3.
6	Pony	White; brown patches; green base	37 x 47	5.	6.	3.
—	6 pce set	Boxed	—	30.	35.	18.

Note: For the Farmyard Animals Set in a gold colourway see page 62.

PEARL LUSTRE WHIMSIES

2004-2006

Each paying entrant to the venue received (while stocks lasted) one of the following models available at the venue.

2004 Dolphin

2004 Penguin

2005 Spaniel

2005 Giraffe

2005 English Bull Terrier

2006 Puppy

Backstamp: Embossed: Wade England
Puppy: Embossed: Wade Eng

Date	Name	Description	Venue	Price	Size	U.S. $	Can. $	U.K. £
2004	Dolphin	Pearl lustre	Wade Collectors Fair	Free	29 x 41	26.	30.	15.
2004	Penguin	Pearl lustre	Dunstable Coll. Fair	With	40 x 22	17.	18.	10.
2005	Spaniel	Pearl lustre	Wade Collectors Fair	Admission	29 x 38	17.	18.	10.
2005	Giraffe	Pearl lustre	Dunstable Coll. Fair	to	38 x 38	17.	18.	10.
2006	English Bull Terrier	Pearl lustre	Wade Collectors Fair	the	48 x 25	30.	33.	17.
2006	Puppy	Pearl lustre	Dunstable Coll. Fair	Venue	29 x 32	17.	18.	10.

Comic Animals and Birds

Cheerful Charlie - "Montreal" Pink
1948-1952 (P. 2)

**Cheerful Charlie
Colourway Coffee or Grey**
1948-1952 (P. 2)

Doleful Dan Posy Bowl
1948 (P. 3)

Mr. and Mrs. Duck with Dilly the Girl and Dack the Boy
1950s (P. 4)

Mr. Penguin
1948-1955 (P. 6)

**Mr. Penguin Pepper Pot
Mrs. Penguin Salt Pot**
1948 (P. 7)

Mr. and Mrs. Rabbit with Puff the Boy and Fluff the Girl
1948-1955 (P. 9)

Little Laughing Bunny in Brown, Pink and Grey
1948-1952 (P. 11)

Happy Families

Mouse Family
First issue with yellow tails
1962-1965 (P. 17)

Mouse Family
Second issue with pink tails
1978-1987 (P. 17)

Hippo Family
1978-1987 (P. 16)

Mother Hippo
Dark Blue, first issue, 1961-1965
Light Blue, second issue, 1978-1987 (P. 16)

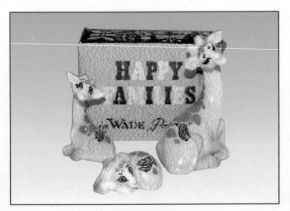

Giraffe Family
Boxed Set, 1961-1965 (P. 16)

Rabbit Family
1963-1965 (P. 19)

Novelty Animals and Birds

Baby Bird
Issued in two sizes and three colourways
c.1935 (P. 22)

Cheeky Duckling
Produced in two sizes and two colourways
c.1935 (P. 22)

Laughing Rabbit
Produced in three sizes and a variety
of colourways, 1937-1939 (P. 24)

**Duckling, head forward,
beak open**
1937-1939 (P. 23)

Duckling, head back, beak closed
1937-1939 (P. 23)

Pongo
Issued in four sizes and a variety of colurways
1935-c.1949 (P. 26)

Storybook Figures

Jumbo Jim
One of Wade's larger Storybook figures
c.1930s-1940s (P. 33)

Goldilocks and the Three Bears
Style One
1953-c.1958 (P. 32)

The Noddy Set
Noddy, Miss Fluffy Cat, Big Ears and Mr. Plod the Policeman are from the Enid
Blyton children's book *Noddy and His Adventures in Toytown*. 1958-1961 (P. 33)

Alice and The Dodo
Produced with a new experimental cellulose
glaze, c.1935-1938 (P. 28)

The Butcher, The Baker and The Candlestick Maker
Modelled by Nancy Great-Rex
1953-1958 (P. 30)

Storybook Figures

Little Miss Muffett and Little Jack Horner
1953-c.1958 (P. 37)

Yogi Bear and Friends
Three Hanna-Barbera cartoon characters
1962-1963 (P. 44)

Wynken, Blynken, Nod and I've a Bear Behind
Two versions are shown. The first two with a flower base and the second two with a plain base.
c.1948-1958 (P. 43 and 44)

Sam and Sarah, Style One
Mable Lucie Attwell designs were produced for a short period of time
1959-1961 (P. 39)

The British Character Set

Child Studies

Billingsgate Porter, Lawyer, Pearly King and Queen.
The hat colours differ in the Pearly Queen.
1959 (P. 103)

Child Studies is a set of four children in National Costume. The decorated bases reflect the country: **Daffodil (Wales)**, **Thistle (Scotland)**, **Shamrock (Ireland)**, and **Grass (England)**. 1962 (P.104)

Storybook Figures

Bengo and his Puppy Friends: Pepi, Fifi, Simon, and Chee Chee
1959-1965 (P. 29)

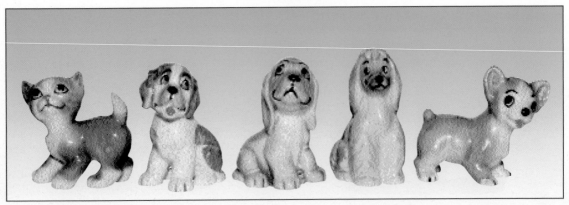

Mitzi the Kitten, Bruno Junior, Droopy Junior, Percy and Whisky. The last two models, **Percy the Afghan** and **Whisky the Corgi**, were only in production for a few months when the series came to an end.
1959-1965 (P. 29)

Dinosaur Collection

Set One: Camarasaurus, Euoplocephalus, Spinosaurus, Protoceratops, Tyrannosaurus Rex
The hugh success of "Jurassic Park" renewed interest in dinosaurs, Wade produced this set of Dinosaurs in 1993. (P. 49)

Drum Box Series

Drum Box Series: Clara, Dora, Harpy, Jem, and Trunky
This is a hard set to complete. 1957-1959 (P. 105)

Flying Birds Series

Fish Waiter

Set Two: Swifts
1958-1959 (P. 108)

The **Fish Waiter** was used as
an event piece. 1998 (P. 107)

Whimsey-On-Why

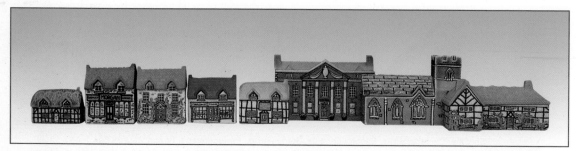

Set One: Pump Cottage, Morgan's the Chemist, Dr. Healer's House, Tobacconist's Shop, Why Knott Inn, Bloodshot Hall, St. Sebastian's Church, The Barley Mow, 1980-1981 (P. 91)

Set Two: The Greengrocer's Shop, The Antique Shop, Whimsey Service Station, The Post Office, Whimsey School, The Watermill, The Stag Hotel, The Windmill, 1981-1982 (P. 91)

Set Three: Tinker's Nook, Whimsey Station, Merryweather Farm, The Vicarage, Broomyshaw Cottage, The Sweet Shop, Briar Row, The Manor, 1982-1983 (P. 92)

Set Four: The District Bank, The Old Smithy, The Picture Palace, The Butcher Shop, The Barber Shop, Miss Prune's House, The Fire Station, The Market Hall, 1984-1985 (P. 93)

POLAR BLOW UPS

1962-1963

The *Polar Blow Ups* set is a series of slightly modified blow ups of three of the *First Whimsies Polar Animals*, set six. They are slip cast, hollow models, which because of high production costs, were never put into full production. Only a few hundred of these models are believed to exist. A blow up of the Polar set "Husky" has been seen and a description of colour and size has been reported; there are also unconfirmed reports of a "Dolphin," "Mermaid," and a "Penguin," but no written or visual evidence has been found.

For the previously listed *Walrus* see *The Charlton Standard Catalogue of Wade, Volume One, General Issues, Wade Ireland Animals*.

Backstamp: **A.** Black and gold label "Genuine Wade Porcelain Made in England" (1-7)
          B. Unmarked (1-7)

No.	Name	Description	Size	U.S. $	Can. $	U.K. £
1	Polar Bear Mother	White/beige; pink tongue; blue/beige/white fish	150 x 120	300.	325.	175.
2	Polar Bear Cub	White/beige; pink mouth	100 x 100	300.	325.	175.
3	Seal	Greenish black; pink tongue	120 x 105	300.	325.	175.
4	Husky	Beige/white	150 x 100		Rare	

TETLEY TEA FOLK WHIMSIES

2006-2007

Collectors who joined or renewed their membership in 2006 received two Tetley Tea Folk Whimsies, *Gaffer* and *Gordon*. To compliment these two figures, *Maurice* and *Sydney* were introduced at the Wade Collectors Fair, held April 9th, 2006, at the Kings Hall, Stoke-on-Trent.

Gaffer

Gordon

Maurice

Sydney

Backstamp: Printed "Wade England Tetley"

Date	Name	Description	Venue	Price	Size	U.S. $	Can. $	U.K. £
2006	Gaffer	White, blue, brown, red	Club Membership	Free	55	27.	30.	15.
2006	Gordon	White, blue, brown, grey	Club Membership	Free	55	27.	30.	15.
2006	Maurice	White overall, spotted bow tie	Wade Collectors Fair	—	55	27.	30.	15.
2006	Sydney	White overall, blue dungarees	Wade Collectors Fair	—	55	27.	30.	15.
2007	Maurice	White overall, gold bow tie/shoes	Wade Collectors Fair	—	55	—	—	—
2007	Sydney	White overall, gold dungarees	Wade Collectors Fair	—	55	—	—	—

WHIMSIE-LAND

1984-1988

Although the *English Whimsies* series was discontinued in 1984, George Wade and Son Ltd. continued to produce a range of inexpensive miniature animals, called the *Whimsie-land* series. Five sets of this series were issued between 1984 and 1988. There are five models per set, making a total of 25 figures.

All *Whimsie-land* models were issued in pastel coloured boxes with a complete numbered list of all the models in the series printed on the bottom. All these figures are marked on the back of the base. The original price was 49p each. A model of the *Whimsie-Land* 'Pony' has been found fixed on a small display card, this example was probably used for display purposes .

When the packaging department at the pottery ran out of a specific animal box in this series, a small paper label would be glued over the original printed name on surplus boxes: for example, the Whimsie-land Fox box can be found with an 'Owl' label.

The Elephant in this series is sometimes confused with the *English Whimsies* Elephant, as the pose is similar. However, the *Whimsie-land* Elephant has open-cast legs.

SET ONE: PETS

1984

Backstamp: Embossed "Wade England"

No.	Name	Description	Size	U.S. $	Can. $	U.K. £
1	Retriever	Beige; white face, underparts; green base	32 x 60	30.	35.	17.
2	Puppy	Beige; white face, chest; pink tongue	35 x 36	30.	35.	17.
3	Rabbit	Dark brown ears; honey; red-brown	50 x 25	30.	35.	17.
4a	Kitten, lying, facing left	Grey; white face; blue wool	20 x 42	30.	35.	17.
4b	Kitten, lying, facing left	Grey; white face; pink wool	20 x 42	30.	35.	17.
5	Pony	White; grey mane, tail; green base	37 x 47	* 30.	35.	17.

SET TWO: WILDLIFE
1984

Backstamp: Embossed "Wade England"

No.	Name	Description	Size	U.S. $	Can. $	U.K. £
6	Lion	Honey; brown mane; tail tip	30 x 50	15.	17.	8.
7	Tiger	Brown; dark stripes, base	22 x 50	15.	17.	8.
8	Elephant	Grey; grey-green base	35 x 40	25.	28.	15.
9	Panda	White; grey markings; green base	37 x 20	25.	28.	15.
10	Giraffe	Beige; black hooves; green base	50 x 35	25.	28.	15.

SET THREE: FARMYARD
1985

Backstamp: Embossed "Wade England"

No.	Name	Description	Size	U.S. $	Can. $	U.K. £
11	Cockerel	White; grey markings; pink tail, comb; grey/green base	50 x 35	25.	28.	15.
12	Duck	White; grey back, tail; yellow beak; green base	45 x 35	25.	28.	15.
13	Cow	White; black patches; green base	30 x 45	25.	28.	15.
14	Pig	Pink; green base	30 x 35	25.	28.	15.
15	Goat	White; grey patch; green base	35 x 35	25.	28.	15.

SET FOUR: HEDGEROW

1986

Backstamp: Embossed "Wade England"

No.	Name	Description	Size	U.S. $	Can. $	U.K. £
16	Fox	Red-brown; honey face, chest, feet	35 x 35	35.	38.	20.
17	Owl	White; yellow/black eyes	35 x 25	20.	22.	12.
18	Hedgehog	Grey-brown; beige	25 x 35	20.	22.	12.
19	Badger	Grey; white face; black markings	25 x 35	20.	22.	12.
20	Squirrel	White; grey	35 x 25	20.	22.	12.

SET FIVE: BRITISH WILDLIFE

1987

Backstamp: Embossed "Wade England"

No.	Name	Description	Size	U.S. $	Can. $	U.K. £
21	Pheasant	Honey; grey-blue head; red-brown tail	35 x 50	45.	50.	25.
22	Field Mouse	Brown; beige berry; green base	35 x 30	45.	50.	25.
23	Golden Eagle	Brown; dark brown base	35 x 40	45.	50.	25.
24	Otter	Brown; blue-grey base	40 x 40	45.	50.	25.
25	Partridge	White; black beak; green base	35 x 35	45.	50.	25.

Whimsie-Land Derivatives Whimtrays

1987

During the summer of 1987, Wade produced a set of kidney-shaped trays it called *New Whimtrays*. Because the new *Whimsie-land* animals were used on them, they are often referred to as *Whimsie-land trays*.

Backstamp: Embossed "Wade England"

No.	Name	Description	Size	U.S. $	Can. $	U.K. £
1a	Duck	Black tray	90 x 110	35.	40.	20.
1b	Duck	Blue tray	90 x 110	35.	40.	20.
1c	Duck	Green tray	90 x 110	35.	40.	20.
2a	Owl	Black tray	90 x 110	35.	40.	20.
2b	Owl	Blue tray	90 x 110	35.	40.	20.
2c	Owl	Green tray	90 x 110	35.	40.	20.
3a	Pony	Black tray	90 x 110	35.	40.	20.
3b	Pony	Blue tray	90 x 110	35.	40.	20.
3c	Pony	Green tray	90 x 110	35.	40.	20.
4a	Puppy	Black tray	90 x 110	35.	40.	20.
4b	Puppy	Blue tray	90 x 110	35.	40.	20.
4c	Puppy	Green tray	90 x 110	35.	40.	20.
5a	Squirrel	Black tray	90 x 110	35.	40.	20.
5b	Squirrel	Blue tray	90 x 110	35.	40.	20.
5c	Squirrel	Green tray	90 x 110	35.	40.	20.

Whimsie-land Derivatives Key Rings

1988

After the *Whimsie-land* series and the *New Whimtrays* were discontinued, surplus models were converted into key rings by adding a small chain and a ring. The *Whimsie-land* "Panda" was reglazed in black and white for this series.

Photograph not available
at press time

Backstamp: Embossed "Wade England"

No.	Name	Description	Size	U.S. $	Can. $	U.K. £
1	Badger	Grey; black markings	25 x 35	25.	28.	15.
2	Duck	White/grey; yellow beak	45 x 35	25.	28.	15.
3	Kitten, lying, facing left	Grey/white; pink wool	20 x 42	25.	28.	15.
4	Panda	Black/white	37 x 20	25.	28.	15.
5	Puppy	Beige/white	35 x 36	25.	28.	15.

WHIMSEY-IN-THE-VALE

1993

In 1993 two sets of houses were produced and named *Whimsey-in-the-Vale*. Each set consists of five models, and unlike the *Whimsey-on-Why models* were boxed individually and unnumbered.

The moulds from the 1980-1988 *Whimsey-on-Why* houses were used to make the following models in the *Whimsey-in-the-Vale* series:

Whimsey-on-Why Models became	Whimsey-in-the Vale Models
Why Knott Inn	Antique Shop
Whimsey Service Station	Florist Shop
Briar Row	Jubilee Terrace
The Fire Station	St. John's School
St. Sebastians Church	St. Lawrence Church
The Barley Mow	Boars Head Pub
The Antique Shop	Post Office
The Post Office	Rose Cottage
The Market Hall	Town Garage
The Stag Hotel	Vale Farm

SET ONE

Backstamp: Embossed "Wade England"

No.	Name	Description	Size	U.S. $	Can. $	U.K. £
1	Antique Shop	White; beige roof; green/yellow trim	33 x 39	35.	40.	20.
2	Florist Shop	White; light brown roof; green/yellow trim	40 x 38	30.	35.	18.
3	Jubilee Terrace	White; beige roof; yellow stonework	33 x 78	40.	45.	25.
4	St. John's School	White; dark brown roof; green windows, doors	33 x 30	40.	45.	25.
5	St. Lawrence Church	Grey; green doors	55 x 77	35.	40.	20.

SET TWO

Backstamp: A. Embossed "Wade England" (6, 7, 8, 10)
B. Unmarked (9)

No.	Name	Description	Size	U.S. $	Can. $	U.K. £
6	Boar's Head Pub	White; brown roof, windows; yellow doors	35 x 77	28.	30.	16.
7	Post Office	White; dark brown roof; blue doors	35 x 37	30.	33.	17.
8	Rose Cottage	White; beige roof; yellow windows, doors	40 x 38	30.	33.	17.
9	Town Garage	White; beige roof; blue doors, windows	35 x 50	28.	30.	16.
10	Vale Farm	Light brown; grey roof; dark brown beams	42 x 66	28.	30.	16.

WHIMSEY-ON-WHY

1980-1987

Whimsey-on-Why is a series of miniature porcelain houses based upon a mythical English village called Whimsey-on-Why. The highly accurate detail was achieved by the use of fired-on enamel transfers, which included the number of the model in an unobtrusive place. The original price for a set of eight models was £10, or the houses could be bought individually at prices ranging from 79p for a small model to £2.15 for a larger size.

SET ONE, 1980-1981

Set One was issued in spring 1980. All models are numbered.

Backstamp: Embossed "Wade England"

No.	Name	Description	Issue Price	Size	U.S. $	Can. $	U.K. £
1	Pump Cottage	Brown thatch, beams	.79p	28 x 39	18.	20.	10.
2	Morgan's the Chemist	Grey roof; yellow windows	.99p	40 x 39	26.	28.	15.
3	Dr. Healer's House	Brown roof, door	.99p	40 x 39	30.	33.	18.
4	Tobacconist's Shop	Brown roof; red doors	.99p	33 x 39	18.	20.	10.
5	Why Knott Inn	Beige thatch; black beams	.89p	33 x 39	26.	28.	15.
6	Bloodshott Hall	Red-brown; grey roof	£1.85	50 x 80	30.	33.	18.
7	St. Sebastian's Church	Grey; brown door	£2.15	55 x 77	50.	55.	30.
8	The Barley Mow	Beige roof; black wood	£1.85	35 x 77	45.	50.	25.

SET TWO, 1981-1982

This set was issued in spring 1981.

Backstamp:
A. Embossed "Wade England" (9-15)
B. Unmarked (16)

No.	Name	Description	Issue Price	Size	U.S. $	Can. $	U.K. £
9	The Greengrocer's Shop	Grey roof; green windows	.99p	35 x 35	9.	10.	5.
10	The Antique Shop	Purple-brown roof	.99p	35 x 37	30.	33.	18.
11	Whimsey Service Station	Beige roof; green pumps	£1.10	40 x 38	30.	33.	18.
12	The Post Office	Beige roof; yellow/blue windows	£1.10	40 x 38	18.	20.	10.
13	Whimsey School	Brown; grey roof; blue window	£1.50	38 x 51	60.	65.	35.
14	The Watermill	Red-brown; beige thatch	£1.85	42 x 66	30.	33.	18.
15	The Stag Hotel	Grey roof; black wood	£1.85	45 x 66	30.	33.	18.
16	The Windmill	White; copper pin	£2.15	60 x 30	120.	130.	70.

SET THREE

1982-1983

Set Three was issued in spring 1982. "The Tinker's Nook" originally sold for 89p, the "Whimsey Station" cost 99p, "Merryweather Farm" was £2.15, "The Vicarage" was £1.65, "The Manor" was £1.85, "Briar Row" was £1.95 and "Broomyshaw Cottage" and "The Sweet Shop" were each £1.10. "Tinker's Nook" has been found with a Wade Ireland Backstamp.

Backstamp: **A.** Embossed "Wade England" (18-24)
B. "Wade Ireland" (17)

No.	Name	Description	Size	U.S. $	Can. $	U.K. £
17	Tinker's Nook	Red-brown roof; yellow/white windows	38 x 22	9.	10.	5.
18	Whimsey Station	Red-brown; brown roof; yellow/blue windows	135 x 39	35.	40.	20.
19	Merryweather Farm	Cream; brown roof; blue/yellow windows	48 x 55	75.	85.	45.
20	The Vicarage	Pink; beige roof; blue/yellow windows	41 x 51	75.	85.	45.
21	Broomyshaw Cottage	Beige; brown roof; blue/yellow windows	40 x 40	18.	20.	10.
22	The Sweet Shop	Grey roof; black wood; blue windows	40 x 40	9.	10.	5.
23	Briar Row	Beige thatch; yellow/blue windows	33 x 78	60.	65.	35.
24	The Manor	Red-brown;brown roof; blue/yellow windows	42 x 66	30.	33.	18.

Note: For the Bally-Whim Irish Village (Wade Ireland) see the *Charlton Standard Catalogue of Wade Collectables*, 4th edition.

SET FOUR

1984-1985

Only three new *Whimsey-on-Why* models were released during 1984. "The District Bank," "The Old Smithy" and "The Picture Palace" were issued the same year Wade Ireland introduced its *Bally-Whim Irish Village* (marketed by George Wade & Son Ltd.). The remaining five models of this set were produced in early 1985.

A model of the *Bally-Whim Irish Village* "Undertaker's House" (#1), with a beige glaze, has been found with the transfer print of the *Whimsey-on-Why* "District Bank" (# 25) applied. This model is clearly marked with an embossed "Wade Ireland 1" on the base. The reason for this change of model shape has not been determined.

District Bank

Fire Station, brown roof (left), honey roof (right)

Backstamp: **A.** Embossed "Wade England" (25-31)
B. Embossed "Wade Ireland" (26)
C. Unmarked (32)

No.	Name	Description	Issue Price	Size	U.S. $	Can. $	U.K. £
25a	The District Bank	Red-brown; brown roof	£1.75	43 x 40	18.	20.	10.
25b	The District Bank	Beige walls; dark grey roof	£1.75	50 x 58	25.	27.	14.
26	The Old Smithy	Yellow thatch; black wood	£1.30	25 x 45	35.	40.	20.
27	The Picture Palace	Black wood; red lettering	£2.35	45 x 65	30.	35.	18.
28	The Butcher Shop	Brown roof; green/grey front	—	33 x 25	30.	35.	18.
29	The Barber Shop	Grey roof; green/yellow front	—	33 x 25	40.	45.	24.
30	Miss Prune's House	Grey roof; black wood; yellow door	—	38 x 38	9.	10.	5.
31a	The Fire Station	Brown roof; red fire engine	—	33 x 30	30.	35.	18.
31b	The Fire Station	Honey roof; red fire engine	—	33 x 30	25.	27.	14.
32	The Market Hall	Brown roof	—	35 x 50	30.	35.	18.

SET FIVE
1987-Circa 1988

The last *Whimsey-on-Why* set, issued in 1987, comprises four models. This brought the series to a close with a total of 36 models. The original prices of this set are unknown. For similar models, see the section on *Whimsey-in-the-Vale*.

Backstamp:
Embossed "Wade England"

No.	Name	Description	Size	U.S. $	Can. $	U.K. £
33	The School Teacher's House	Grey roof, walls	38 x 38	120.	130.	70.
34	The Fishmonger's Shop	Brown roof	43 x 27	100.	110.	60.
35	The Police Station	Blue; brown roof	43 x 27	150.	165.	90.
36	The Library	Brown; grey roof	50 x 38	90.	100.	50.

WHOPPAS

1976-1981

Whoppas are the big brothers of *Whimsies* and were in production from 1976 to 1981. They were issued in three sets of five models. The number of each model is embossed on the back of the base, and also appears on the model's box. The glaze on some of the models obscures the model number. The original price was 65p each.

SET ONE: RED BOX

1976-1981

Backstamp: Embossed "Wade England" with model number

No.	Name	Description	Size	U.S. $	Can. $	U.K. £
1a	Polar Bear, head forward	Beige brown; blue base	35 x 55	25.	28.	14.
1b	Polar Bear, head forward	White; grey-blue base	35 x 55	25.	28.	14.
2	Hippo	Grey; green base	35 x 50	25.	28.	14.
3	Brown Bear	Red-brown; brown base	35 x 45	25.	28.	14.
4	Tiger	Honey; green base	30 x 60	25.	28.	14.
5	Elephant	Grey; green base	55 x 50	25.	28.	14.

SET TWO: GREEN BOX

1977-1981

Backstamp: Embossed "Wade England"

No.	Name	Description	Size	U.S. $	Can. $	U.K. £
6	Bison	Brown; green base	40 x 50	25.	28.	14.
7	Wolf	Grey; green base	60 x 45	25.	28.	14.
8	Bobcat	Light brown; dark brown spots; green base	55 x 50	25.	28.	14.
9	Chipmunk	Brown; brown base	55 x 40	25.	28.	14.
10	Racoon	Brown; black stripes; eye patches; green base	40 x 50	25.	28.	14.

SET THREE: BROWN BOX

1978-1981

Backstamp: Embossed "Wade England"

No.	Name	Description	Size	U.S. $	Can. $	U.K. £
11	Fox	Red-brown; green base	30 x 60	25.	28.	14.
12	Badger	Brown; cream stripe; green base	35 x 45	25.	28.	14.
13	Otter	Brown; blue base	30 x 55	25.	28.	14.
14	Stoat	Brown; green base	35 x 55	25.	28.	14.
15	Hedgehog	Brown; green base	30 x 50	25.	28.	14.

MISCELLANEOUS SETS

Alphabet and London Trains	98
Angels	99
Bear Ambitions	102
Betty Boop "Top of the World"	102
British Character Set	103
Child Studies	104
Circus Set	105
Drum Box Set	105
Felix the Cat	106
Fish Waiter	107
Flying Birds	108
Goodie Boxes	109
Honey Bunch Bears	110
Horse Sets	111
Kissing Bunnies	112
Minikins	114
Mr Men and Little Miss	119
Mr Snowflake and His Family	120
My Pet	121
Pocket Pals	122
Pokemon	124
Rule Beartannia	125
Snippets	126
Tony the Tiger	128
Tortoise Family	129
Treasures Set	131
Various Novelty Models	132
Water Life Collection	133
Zoo Mazing	134

MISCELLANEOUS SETS

ALPHABET AND LONDON TRAINS

1958-1959

The *Alphabet Train* comprises a miniature engine pulling six carriages and was intended to be educational, as well as fun, for children to play with. The carriages have various numbers on their roofs and letters of the alphabet on both sides. The *London Train* has a single letter on the roof of each carriage (forming the name *London*), with scenes of Tower Bridge, St. Paul's Cathedral, Trafalgar Square, Piccadilly Circus, Big Ben or Westminster Abbey on each side.

The issue date for both sets was August 1958, and they originally sold for 6/11d. They were discontinued in January 1959. The trains are very rare. As they are only seen in complete sets, no individual prices are given below.

Alphabet Set

Backstamp: Unmarked

No.	Name	Description	Size	U.S. $	Can. $	U.K. £
1	Alphabet Set: engine, tender, 6 carriages	Blue engine	27 x 205	775.	850.	450.

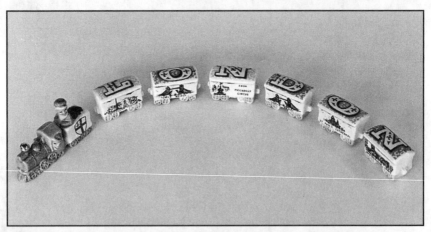

London Set

No.	Name	Description	Size	U.S. $	Can. $	U.K. £
1	London Set: engine, tender, 6 carriages	Grey engine	27 x 205	1,000.	1,100.	600.

ANGELS

1963

The *Angels* is a small series of models which were only produced for a short time. They were modelled in three different positions standing, sitting and kneeling and coloured in pastel shades of pink, green, yellow and blue. These figures are also found on angel dishes and on angel candle holders. The *Angels* originally sold for 1/11 each.

Angels Kneeling, Sitting and Standing

Backstamp: Unmarked

No.	Name	Description	Size	U.S. $	Can. $	U.K. £
1a	Kneeling Angel	Blue dress; brown hair	40 x 25	75.	85.	40.
1b	Kneeling Angel	Blue dress; yellow hair	40 x 25	75.	85.	40.
1c	Kneeling Angel	Green dress; brown hair	40 x 25	75.	85.	40.
1d	Kneeling Angel	Green dress; yellow hair	40 x 25	75.	85.	40.
1e	Kneeling Angel	Pink dress; brown hair	40 x 25	75.	85.	40.
1f	Kneeling Angel	Pink dress; yellow hair	40 x 25	75.	85.	40.
1g	Kneeling Angel	Yellow dress; brown hair	40 x 25	75.	85.	40.
1h	Kneeling Angel	Yellow dress; yellow hair	40 x 25	75.	85.	40.
2a	Sitting Angel	Blue dress; brown hair	40 x 30	75.	85.	40.
2b	Sitting Angel	Blue dress; yellow hair	40 x 30	75.	85.	40.
2c	Sitting Angel	Green dress; brown hair	40 x 30	75.	85.	40.
2d	Sitting Angel	Green dress; yellow hair	40 x 30	75.	85.	40.
2e	Sitting Angel	Pink dress; brown hair	40 x 30	75.	85.	40.
2f	Sitting Angel	Pink dress; yellow hair	40 x 30	75.	85.	40.
2g	Sitting Angel	Yellow dress; brown hair	40 x 30	75.	85.	40.
2h	Sitting Angel	Yellow dress; yellow hair	40 x 30	75.	85.	40.
3a	Standing Angel	Blue dress; brown hair	40 x 30	75.	85.	40.
3b	Standing Angel	Blue dress; yellow hair	40 x 30	75.	85.	40.
3c	Standing Angel	Green dress; brown hair	40 x 30	75.	85.	40.
3d	Standing Angel	Green dress; yellow hair	40 x 30	75.	85.	40.
3e	Standing Angel	Pink dress; brown hair	40 x 30	75.	85.	40.
3f	Standing Angel	Pink dress; yellow hair	40 x 30	75.	85.	40.
3g	Standing Angel	Yellow dress; brown hair	40 x 30	75.	85.	40.
3h	Standing Angel	Yellow dress; yellow hair	40 x 30	75.	85.	40.

Angel Derivatives

Angel Candle Holders

The angel models were mounted on the front of triangular-shaped candle holders (the same candle holders that were used for the 1960 *Disney Lights*). All the candle holders are black, and they were sold with a candy-twist candle for an original price of 2/11d each.

Kneeling Angel Candle Holder

Standing Angel Candle Holder

Backstamp: Embossed "Wade"

No.	Name	Description	Size	U.S. $	Can. $	U.K. £
1a	Angel Kneeling Candle Holder	Blue dress; brown hair	58 x 50	90.	100.	50.
1b	Angel Kneeling Candle Holder	Blue dress; yellow hair	58 x 50	90.	100.	50.
1c	Angel Kneeling Candle Holder	Green dress; brown hair	58 x 50	90.	100.	50.
1d	Angel Kneeling Candle Holder	Green dress; yellow hair	58 x 50	90.	100.	50.
1e	Angel Kneeling Candle Holder	Pink dress; brown hair	58 x 50	90.	100.	50.
1f	Angel Kneeling Candle Holder	Pink dress; yellow hair	58 x 50	90.	100.	50.
1g	Angel Kneeling Candle Holder	Yellow dress; brown hair	58 x 50	90.	100.	50.
1h	Angel Kneeling Candle Holder	Yellow dress; yellow hair	58 x 50	90.	100.	50.
2a	Sitting Angel Candle Holder	Blue dress; brown hair	58 x 50	90.	100.	50.
2b	Sitting Angel Candle Holder	Blue dress; yellow hair	58 x 50	90.	100.	50.
2c	Sitting Angel Candle Holder	Green dress; brown hair	58 x 50	90.	100.	50.
2d	Sitting Angel Candle Holder	Green dress; yellow hair	58 x 50	90.	100.	50.
2e	Sitting Angel Candle Holder	Pink dress; brown hair	58 x 50	90.	100.	50.
2f	Sitting Angel Candle Holder	Pink dress; yellow hair	58 x 50	90.	100.	50.
2g	Sitting Angel Candle Holder	Yellow dress; brown hair	58 x 50	90.	100.	50.
2h	Sitting Angel Candle Holder	Yellow dress; yellow hair	58 x 50	90.	100.	50.
3a	Standing Angel Candle Holder	Blue dress; brown hair	58 x 50	90.	100.	50.
3b	Standing Angel Candle Holder	Blue dress; yellow hair	58 x 50	90.	100.	50.
3c	Standing Angel Candle Holder	Green dress; brown hair	58 x 50	90.	100.	50.
3d	Standing Angel Candle Holder	Green dress; yellow hair	58 x 50	90.	100.	50.
3e	Standing Angel Candle Holder	Pink dress; brown hair	58 x 50	90.	100.	50.
3f	Standing Angel Candle Holder	Pink dress; yellow hair	58 x 50	90.	100.	50.
3g	Standing Angel Candle Holder	Yellow dress; brown hair	58 x 50	90.	100.	50.
3h	Standing Angel Candle Holder	Yellow dress; yellow hair	58 x 50	90.	100.	50.

Angel Derivatives Dishes

The dishes, similar to the *Whimtrays*, are black and the angel figure is positioned on the back rim. They originally sold for 2/11d each.

Angel Dishes - Kneeling, Standing and Sitting

Backstamp: Embossed Angel Dish, "Wade Porcelain, Made in England"

No.	Name	Description	Size	U.S. $	Can. $	U.K. £
1a	Kneeling Angel Dish	Blue dress; brown hair	40 x 75	90.	100.	50.
1b	Kneeling Angel Dish	Blue dress; yellow hair	40 x 75	90.	100.	50.
1c	Kneeling Angel Dish	Green dress; brown hair	40 x 75	90.	100.	50.
1d	Kneeling Angel Dish	Green dress; yellow hair	40 x 75	90.	100.	50.
1e	Kneeling Angel Dish	Pink dress; brown hair	40 x 75	90.	100.	50.
1f	Kneeling Angel Dish	Pink dress; yellow hair	40 x 75	90.	100.	50.
1g	Kneeling Angel Dish	Yellow dress; brown hair	40 x 75	90.	100.	50.
1h	Kneeling Angel Dish	Yellow dress; yellow hair	40 x 75	90.	100.	50.
2a	Standing Angel Dish	Blue dress; brown hair	40 x 75	90.	100.	50.
2b	Standing Angel Dish	Blue dress; yellow hair	40 x 75	90.	100.	50.
2c	Standing Angel Dish	Green dress; brown hair	40 x 75	90.	100.	50.
2d	Standing Angel Dish	Green dress; yellow hair	40 x 75	90.	100.	50.
2e	Standing Angel Dish	Pink dress; brown hair	40 x 75	90.	100.	50.
2f	Standing Angel Dish	Pink dress; yellow hair	40 x 75	90.	100.	50.
2g	Standing Angel Dish	Yellow dress; brown hair	40 x 75	90.	100.	50.
2h	Standing Angel Dish	Yellow dress; yellow hair	40 x 75	90.	100.	50.
3a	Sitting Angel Dish	Blue dress; brown hair	40 x 75	90.	100.	50.
3b	Sitting Angel Dish	Blue dress; yellow hair	40 x 75	90.	100.	50.
3c	Sitting Angel Dish	Green dress; brown hair	40 x 75	90.	100.	50.
3d	Sitting Angel Dish	Green dress; yellow hair	40 x 75	90.	100.	50.
3e	Sitting Angel Dish	Pink dress; brown hair	40 x 75	90.	100.	50.
3f	Sitting Angel Dish	Pink dress; yellow hair	40 x 75	90.	100.	50.
3g	Sitting Angel Dish	Yellow dress; brown hair	40 x 75	90.	100.	50.
3h	Sitting Angel Dish	Yellow dress; yellow hair	40 x 75	90.	100.	50.

BEAR AMBITIONS

1995

The *Bear Ambitions* set of six named Teddy Bears was reissued in 1996 for Tom Smith and Company (the British Christmas Cracker manufacturers) in three different glaze colours for their Christmas Time Crackers series, see page 318. See also Ripley Village Fete and Teddy Bears' Picnic for green colourways, page 154.

Backstamp: Embossed "Wade England"

No.	Name	Description	Size	U.S. $	Can. $	U.K. £
1	Admiral Sam	Honey	50	8.	9.	5.
2	Alex the Aviator	Honey	45	8.	9.	5.
3	Artistic Edward	Honey	40	8.	9.	5.
4	Beatrice Ballerina	Honey	50	8.	9.	5.
5	Locomotive Joe	Honey	50	8.	9.	5.
6	Musical Marco	Honey	45	8.	9.	5.

BETTY BOOP

Top of the World

2003

Produced as a Wade retail line in conjunction with C&S Collectables, who own the UK License for Betty Boop, this model is of Betty Boop seated on top of the world. Issued in a limited edition of 2000, the issue price was £55.00, with a 10% discount to Wade Club members.

A colourway version, with the countries in gold, was issued in a limited edition of twenty pieces. These models were available only as prizes in Bran Tub draws at various Wade events during the year.

Backstamp: Printed "Betty Boop Top of the World 2000 Limited edition" with "Wade" logo

No.	Name	Description	Size	U.S. $	Can. $	U.K. £
1a	Betty Boop, Top of the World	Red dress; black hair; blue globe; green countries	150	100.	110.	55.
1b	Betty Boop, Top of the World	Red dress; black hair; blue globe; gold countries	150	—	—	—

THE BRITISH CHARACTER SET

1959

The *British Character* set, also known to collectors as *London Characters*, includes four models: the "Pearly King," "Pearly Queen," "Lawyer" and the "Billingsgate Porter," who in the famous Billingsgate Fish Market tradition, is carrying a basket of fish on his head. They were produced for only one year and are rarely seen and highly sought after. This set was designed by William Timym, who also designed the series "Bengo and his Puppy Friends, TV Pets" (see page 29).

Backstamp:

A. Black and gold label "Genuine Wade Porcelain" (1-4)

B. Unmarked (1-4)

No.	Name	Description	Size	U.S. $	Can. $	U.K. £
1	Pearly King	White pearlised suit, cap: yellow brim	68 x 28	175.	200.	100.
2a	Pearly Queen	White pearlised dress, jacket; yellow ribbon; lower hat brim black	68 x 38	175.	200.	100.
2b	Pearly Queen	Blue/pink pearlised dress; lower hat brim grey	68 x 38	175.	200.	100.
2c	Pearly Queen	Blue/pink pearlised dress; lower hat brim pink	68 x 38	175.	200.	100.
2d	Pearly Queen	Blue/pink pearlised dress; lower hat brim white	68 x 38	175.	200.	100.
3	Lawyer	White wig; black gown, shoes; brown base	68 x 28	175.	200.	100.
4a	Billingsgate Porter	Pearlised fish; black hat, badge and shoes; green tie; blue trousers; and base	75 x 28	175.	200.	100.
4b	Billingsgate Porter	Pearlised fish; black hat, green tie; blue badge, trousers and base; brown shoes	75 x 28	175.	200.	100.

CHILD STUDIES

1962

Child Studies was a short-lived set of four children in national costumes, representing England, Ireland, Scotland and Wales. Each model stands on a circular base, which has an embossed flower design on it.

Their issue date was spring 1962, and they sold for an original price of 21/- each.

Backstamp: **A.** Blue transfer "Wade England" (1-4)
B. Unmarked (1-4)

No.	Name	Description	Size	U.S. $	Can. $	U.K. £
1	English Boy	Yellow hair; black hat; red jacket; blue waistcoat; grassy base	120 x 40	650.	725.	375.
2	Irish Girl	Green kilt; shamrock base	115 x 40	900.	1,000.	525.
3	Scots Boy	Blue kilt; black tam, jacket; thistle base	120 x 40	650.	725.	375.
4	Welsh Girl	Striped skirt; checkered shawl; daffodil base	135 x 40	650.	725.	375.

Note: Models have been found without the facial feathers. They may have been rejected during the quality control inspection process.

CIRCUS SET

2003

The Circus Set was produced as a retail line by Wade and was available from the Wade Shop and through retail outlets. The set consists of seven figures, all of which were individually boxed. A Circus Ring display base was produced for this set. Models would be purchased individually at £15.00 each, and £10.00 for the display stand. In September 2003, the cost for the complete set is advertised at $115.00. The words WADES CIRCUS are embossed on the base edge.

Backstamp: Red "Wade" logo

No.	Name	Description	Size	U.S. $	Can. $	U.K. £
1	Bear	Brown, red hat; yellow waistcoat; multicoloured base	74	25.	28.	15.
2	Clown	Green suit, hat; blue car	60	25.	28.	15.
3	Elephant	Grey; yellow, green blanket; multicoloured base	60	25.	28.	15.
4	Lion	Honey; brown mane; multicoloured base	58	25.	28.	15.
5	Pony	White; brown mane; blue saddle; multicoloured base	58	25.	28.	15.
6	Ringmaster	Black coat, top hat, boots; red waistcoat; white pants; yellow bow tie; multicoloured base	70	25.	28.	15.
7	Strongman	Brown hair; white/brown spotted leotard; tan shoes; multicoloured base	70	25.	28.	15.
8	Display stand	White; multicoloured design around edge; red lettering "Wades Circus"	180	18.	20.	10.

DRUM BOX SERIES

1957-1959

In the advertising literature of the time, Wade called this set the *Animal Band*, later changing it to the *Drum Box* series. The set consists of five comical animals, four playing a musical instrument and the fifth, "Dora" the donkey, is the soprano. They were sold in round cardboard drum-design boxes, from which the series got its name. The original price for each model was 3/11d. They were issued in May 1957 and discontinued in spring 1959.

Backstamp: Unmarked

No.	Name	Description	Size	U.S. $	Can. $	U.K. £
1	Jem	Red collar; grey trousers; black tie, eye patch	45 x 25	90.	100.	50.
2	Clara	White dress; yellow stripes; brown cello	50 x 25	90.	100.	50.
3	Harpy	Blue dress; mauve/white harp	45 x 28	90.	100.	50.
4	Trunky	White shirt, trousers; black tie	50 x 35	90.	100.	50.
5	Dora	White dress; red hem; yellow base	55 x 25	135.	150.	75.

FELIX THE CAT

Felix the Cat, Carpet Bag

Felix the Cat, Halloween

Felix's Seasonal Greetings

Cocktail Felix

Felix, right arm raised (Membership 2007)

Felix, Heart in His Hand

Date	Name	Description	Issue	Price	Size	U.S. $	Can. $	U.K. £
2006	Felix the Cat, Carpet Bag	Black, white cat; yellow carpet bag	100	—	110	150.	165.	90.
2006	Felix the Cat, Carpet Bag	Black, white cat, silver carpet bag	1	—	110		Unique	
2006	Felix the Cat, Carpet Bag	Black, white cat, gold carpet bag	1	—	110		Unique	
2006	Felix (left arm raised)	Black, white cat, red tongue	1,000	—	100	70.	75.	40.
2006	Felix Whimsie, solid model	Black, white cat, red tongue	—	—	—	25.	30.	15.
2006	Felix the Cat, Halloween	Black, white cat, Dracula costume	100	—	110	75.	85.	50.
2006	Felix's Seasonal Greetings	Black, white, red, yellow, blue	500	£45.00	100	80.	90.	45.
2007	Cocktail Felix	Black, white cat, blue jacket, red bow tie	100	—	100	125.	140.	70.
2007	Felix (Membership)	Black, white cat, red tongue	—	£28.00	100	55.	60.	28.
2007	Felix, Heart in his Hands	Black, white cat; red heart	—	£45.00	90	80.	90.	45.
2007	Felix, Heart in his Hands	Black, white cat; gold heart (members only)	100	£39.95	90	70.	75.	40.
2007	Felix Whimsie (left arm raised), cast figure	Black, white cat, red tongue	—	£15.00	—	25.	28.	15.

Note: See also Felix Christmas Surprise page 241 and Felix the Cat page 338.

THE FISH WAITER

June 1998

This model of a fish dressed as a waiter and holding a plate in his left fin was first available from the Wade shop. It was later sold at the Arundel and Buffalo shows.

The Fish Waiter was produced in a limited edition of 1,500, and the original cost direct from Wade was £15.00.

Backstamp: Black Printed "Genuine Wade Porcelain"

No.	Name	Description	Size	U.S. $	Can. $	U.K. £
1	Fish Waiter	Grey fish; green eyes; black coat, bow tie; white vest;brown trousers; tan feet; orange base	140	35.	40.	20.

FLYING BIRDS

1956-1960

Wade produced two sets in the *Flying Birds* series, "Swallows" and "Swifts." These models were first produced in England, then their production was moved to Wade (Ulster) Ltd. The *Flying Birds* series was sold in boxed sets of three models of the same colour. The "Swifts" models were the last production run and are harder to find. The original price for a set of three "Swallows" was 5/9d, which was later increased to 5/11d. The original price for three "Swifts" was 6/11d. For the Flying Birds produced by Wade Ireland see the *Charlton Standard Catalogue of Wade Collectables*, 4th edition.

SET ONE: SWALLOWS, 1956-1960

Set One: Swallow

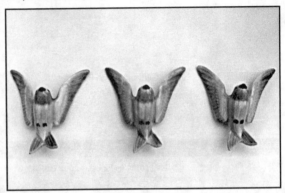

Set Two: Swifts

Backstamp: Unmarked

No.	Description	Size	U.S. $	Can. $	U.K. £
1a	Beige wings, tail; beige head, body	65 x 68	18.	20.	10.
1b	Beige wings, tail; salmon head, body	65 x 68	18.	20.	10.
1c	Beige wings, tail; white head, body	65 x 68	18.	20.	10.
2a	Blue wings, tail; beige head, body	65 x 68	18.	20.	10.
2b	Blue wings, tail; salmon head, body	65 x 68	18.	20.	10.
2c	Blue wings, tail; white head, body	65 x 68	18.	20.	10.
3a	Green wings, tail; beige head, body	65 x 68	18.	20.	10.
3b	Green wings, tail; salmon head, body	65 x 68	18.	20.	10.
3c	Green wings, tail; white head, body	65 x 68	18.	20.	10.
4a	Grey wings, tail; beige head, body	65 x 68	18.	20.	10.
4b	Grey wings, tail; salmon head, body	65 x 68	18.	20.	10.
4c	Grey wings, tail; white head, body	65 x 68	18.	20.	10.
5a	Salmon pink wings, tail; beige head, body	65 x 68	18.	20.	10.
5b	Salmon pink wings, tail; white head, body	65 x 68	18.	20.	10.
6a	Yellow wings, tail; beige head, body	65 x 68	20.	22.	12.
6b	Yellow wings, tail; salmon head, body	65 x 68	20.	22.	12.
6c	Yellow wings, tail; white head, body	65 x 68	20.	22.	12.
—	Boxed set (3)	—	60.	65.	35.
—	Boxed set (3—yellow)	—	80.	90.	45.

SET TWO: SWIFTS, 1958-1959

Backstamp: Unmarked

No.	Description	Size	U.S. $	Can. $	U.K. £
1	Blue wings, tail	86 x 76	35.	40.	20.
—	Boxed set (3)	—	115.	130.	65.

GOODIE BOXES
1998-2006

Rosie the Kitten (1998)

Fizzy the Fawn (1999)

Crunchie the Foal (2000)

Stilton the Mouse (2001)

Toots the Owl (2002)

Digger the Mole (2003)

Spaniel (2005)

Squeak the Guinea Pig (2006)

Backstamp: Embossed "Wade England"

Date	Model	Description	Edition	Size	U.S. $	Can. $	U.K. £
1998	Rosie the Kitten	Honey; black eyes	400	115	50.	55.	30.
1998	Rosie the Kitten	White; black eyes	100	115	140.	155.	80.
1999	Fizzy the Fawn	Honey; black eyes, nose	450	95	45.	50.	25.
1999	Fizzy the Fawn	White; black eyes, nose	75	95	140.	155.	80.
2000	Crunchie the Foal	Honey; black eyes, nose	450	70 x 73	50.	55.	30.
2000	Crunchie the Foal	White; black eyes, nose	75	70 x 73	110.	120.	65.
2001	Stilton the Mouse	Honey; black eyes, nose	425	60	50.	55.	30.
2001	Stilton the Mouse	White; black eyes, nose	75	60	110.	120.	65.
2002	Toots the Owl	Honey; black eyes, beak; yellow feet	425	68	50.	55.	30.
2002	Toots the Owl	White; black eyes, beak; yellow feet	75	68	120.	130.	70.
2003	Digger the Mole	Light grey; black eyes	500	Unk.	50.	55.	30.
2003	Digger the Mole	Mottled black	75	Unk.	70.	75.	40.
2004	Rabbit	Honey	425	95	35.	40.	20.
2004	Rabbit	White	75	95	70.	75.	40.
2005	Spaniel	Honey	425	88 x 46	35.	40.	20.
2005	Spaniel	White	75	88 x 46	85.	95.	50.
2005	Spaniel	Gold	25	88 x 46	100.	110.	60.
2006	Squeak the Guinea Pig	Brown	425	55 x 115	35.	40.	20.
2006	Squeak the Guinea Pig	White	75	Unk	85.	95.	50.

THE HONEY BUNCH BEARS

1998-2004

A set of three teddy bears named the *Honey Bunch* was introduced at the Trentham Gardens show on March 22nd 1998, and were added to the Wade Retailer's list. In October 2004, when the current retailer's list was distributed, each bear had been given a name. The original cost was £18.00 for the set, or individually for £6. See also *Collect It!* Fairs, page 149.

Golly Gosh Bear, Cross-eyed Bear, Honey Bear   Sunny Bear, Clever Bear, Sleepy Bear

Backstamp: Embossed "Wade"

No.	Name	Description	Size	U.S. $	Can. $	U.K. £
1	Clever Bear	Honey; black/white bee	57	10.	11.	6.
2	Cross-eyed Bear	Honey; black/white bee	57	10.	11.	6.
3	Golly Gosh Bear	Honey; black/white bee	55	10.	11.	6.
4	Honey Bear	Honey; black/white bee	57	10.	11.	6.
5	Sleepy Bear	Honey; black/white bee	38	10.	11.	6.
6	Sunny Bear	Honey; black sunglasses	45	10.	11.	6.

Colourways, 1998-1999

A small number of Honey Bunch Bears with the 'bee' decal omitted were hand decorated and sold by Wade at the 1998 Collect It! Fair and the C&S Collectables Christmas Bonanza. They were also available at the show held in San Antonio, Texas, in July 1999, hosted by Wade and the Internationall Association of Jim Beam Bottles & Specialties Club.

Backstamp: Embossed "Wade"

No.	Name	Description	Size	U.S. $	Can. $	U.K. £
1a	Cross-eyed Bear	Dark brown, maroon shirt, white collar, cuffs; black trousers	57	25.	28.	15.
1b	Cross-eyed Bear	Honey; red collar with red and yellow medallion	57	25.	28.	15.
1c	Cross-eyed Bear	Honey; white shirt, black bow tie, waistcoat	57	25.	28.	15.
2a	Golly Gosh Bear	Brown; yellow dungarees	55	25.	28.	15.
2b	Golly Gosh Bear	Honey; blue dungarees	55	25.	28.	15.
2c	Golly Gosh Bear	Honey; white dungarees with red dots	55	25.	28.	15.
3a	Honey Bear	Honey; gold collar, cuffs	57	25.	28.	15.
3b	Honey Bear	Honey; red collar, cuffs	57	25.	28.	15.
3c	Honey Bear	Honey; red collar, cuffs; gold honey pot	57	25.	28.	15.
3d	Honey Bear	Honey; yellow honey on paw and left leg	57	25.	28.	15.
4a	Sleepy Bear	Dark brown; green, dark green striped hat; dark green suit	38	25.	28.	15.
4b	Sleepy Bear	Honey; dark green hat, white bobble, suit	38	25.	28.	15.
4c	Sleepy Bear	Honey, pink hat, white bobble	38	25.	28.	15.

HORSE SETS

1974-1981

Two sets of horses were produced intermittently between 1974 and 1981. Each set comprised a "Mare" and her two foals. Although the models were sold with black and gold "Wade England" labels stuck on the bases, most of them either peeled off or wore off. But even without labels, the distinctive Wade glaze and their ribbed bases make these models easily recognizable. A variation in the glaze colour of the "Standing Foal" from Set One has been found, it is in an all-over honey glaze.

SET ONE,

1974-1981

Backstamp:
A. Black and gold label "Wade England" (1-3)
B. Unmarked (1-3)

No.	Name	Description	Size	U.S. $	Can. $	U.K. £
1	Mare	Dark brown; light brown face	75 x 76	25.	28.	15.
2	Foal, lying	Dark brown; light brown face	32 x 55	20.	23.	12.
3a	Foal, standing	Dark brown; light brown face	48 x 48	20.	23.	12.
3b	Foal, standing	Honey	48 x 48	35.	40.	20.
—	3 pce set	Boxed	—	70.	80.	40.

SET TWO

1978-1981

Backstamp:
A. Black and gold label "Wade England" (1-3)
B. Embossed "Wade England" on rim (1-3)
C. Unmarked (1-3)

No.	Name	Description	Size	U.S. $	Can. $	U.K. £
1	Mare	Honey; light brown mane	65 x 70	40.	45.	25.
2	Foal, lying	Honey; light brown mane	30 x 46	40.	45.	25.
3	Foal, sitting	Honey; light brown mane	38 x 38	40.	45.	25.
—	3 pce set	Boxed	—	95.	105.	55.

KISSING BUNNIES

Circa 1948-1950s

Care has to be taken when purchasing unmarked *Kissing Bunnies* models, as they were also produced by Joseph Szeiler and Sylvac as well as being copied by other ceramic manufacturers including those in Japan.

Kissing Bunnies, large eyes   Kissing Bunnies, small eyes

Backstamp: Black transfer print "Wade England"

No.	Description	Size	U.S. $	Can. $	U.K. £
1a	White bunny; beige bunny; large eyes	64 x 80	100.	110.	65.
1b	White bunny; grey bunny; large eyes	64 x 80	100.	110.	65.
1c	White bunny; grey bunny; white tail; large eyes	64 x 80	100.	110.	65.
1d	White bunny; grey ears, tail; brown bunny; white tail; small eyes	64 x 80	100.	110.	65.
1e	White bunny; grey tail; grey bunny; large eyes	64 x 80	100.	110.	65.

Kissing Bunnies Derivatives

Circa 1948

This Art Deco ashtray is similar in design to a model produced by Sylvac in the late 1940s known as an "Angular ashtray with Kissing Rabbits," and carrying an impressed design No. of 1532.

Although this Kissing Bunnies ashtray is unmarked, a similar ashtray has been seen which has an ink stamped "Wade Made in England" backstamp.

Backstamp: **A.** Ink stamp "Made in England Reg No 824" [the rest of the numbers are missing] (1)
B. Ink stamp "Wade Made in England"

No.	Name	Description	Size	U.S. $	Can. $	U.K. £
1	Art deco ashtray	White and brown bunnies; light green tray	85	100.	110.	60.
2	S-shaped ashtray	White and brown bunnies; mottled blue and cream tray	86 x 105	100.	110.	60.

Kissing Bunnies Mustard Pot

Backstamp: Green-brown ink stamp "Wade England"

No.	Name	Description	Size	U.S. $	Can. $	U.K. £
1a	Kissing Bunnies Mustard Pot	Blue; bramble-ware mustard pot	70 x 87	100.	110.	60.
1b	Kissing Bunnies Mustard Pot	Cream; bramble-ware mustard pot	70 x 87	100.	110.	60.
1c	Kissing Bunnies Mustard Pot	Green; bramble-ware mustard pot	70 x 87	100.	110.	60.
1d	Kissing Bunnies Mustard Pot	White; multicoloured bramble-ware mustard pot, flower, base	70 x 87	100.	110.	60.

MINIKINS

1955-1958

Minikins were issued in three separate series, with four different-shaped *Minikins* in each. They were sold to the retailer in boxes of 48 models (12 of each shape). *Minikins* were modelled by William Harper

The models are completely covered in white glaze, with decorative motifs on their bodies, different coloured ears and six eye styles. The combinations of eye expression, ear colour and body decoration could produce a total of 48 styles of *Minikins* in each set.

None of the *Minikins* was marked. Advertisements show that series B was offered for sale for Christmas 1956, and the demise of series C is mentioned in Wade's August 1958 "Wholesalers Newsletter." The original price was 1/- each.

MINIKINS SHOP COUNTER PLAQUE

1955-1958

These small half-circular plaques would have been used by the retailer in his shop display for *Minikins,* as they were not made for general sale. The wording on one plaque is "Porcelain Wade Minikins made in England." On the other 1/- (One Shilling) each has been added to the plaque.

No price shown

Price shown

Backstamp: None

No.	Description	Size	U.S. $	Can. $	U.K. £
1a	White; black lettering	28	200.	225.	125.
1b	White; black lettering 1/- each	28	200.	225.	125.

SERIES A: CATS AND RABBITS

1955-1958

Cat Walking (left), Cat Standing (right)

Rabbit Sitting (left), Narrow-Eared Rabbit (right)

Backstamp: Unmarked

No.	Name	Description	Size	U.S. $	Can. $	U.K. £
1a	Cat Walking	White; blue ears, tail; black/brown eyes	20 x 38	35.	40.	20.
1b	Cat Walking	White; blue ears, tail; green/black eyes; red nose	20 x 38	35.	40.	20.
1c	Cat Walking	White; yellow ears, tail; black/brown eyes	20 x 38	35.	40.	20.
1d	Cat Walking	White; yellow ears, tail; black/green eyes	20 x 38	35.	40.	20.
2a	Cat Standing	Brown; black eyes, nose	30 x 17	35.	40.	20.
2b	Cat Standing	White; green ears; black eyes, nose; blue patches	30 x 17	35.	40.	20.
2c	Cat Standing	White; green ears; black eyes; blue patches	30 x 17	35.	40.	20.
2d	Cat Standing	White; green ears; black/green eyes; blue patches	30 x 17	35.	40.	20.
2e	Cat Standing	White; yellow ears; black eyes; green starburst	30 x 17	35.	40.	20.
2f	Cat Standing	White; yellow ears; black eyes; red starburst	30 x 17	35.	40.	20.
2g	Cat Standing	White; yellow ears; black/green eyes; blue starburst	30 x 17	35.	40.	20.
2h	Cat Standing	White; yellow ears; black/green eyes; green daisy	30 x 17	35.	40.	20.
3a	Rabbit Sitting	Brown; turquoise ears; black eyes, nose	30 x 18	35.	40.	20.
3b	Rabbit Sitting	White; blue ears, nose; small black eyes	30 x 18	35.	40.	20.
3c	Rabbit Sitting	White; green ears; eyes open; red nose; blue patch	30 x 18	35.	40.	20.
3d	Rabbit Sitting	White; green ears; winking eyes; red nose; blue patch	30 x 18	35.	40.	20.
3e	Rabbit Sitting	White; green/yellow ears; eyes open; red nose	30 x 18	35.	40.	20.
3f	Rabbit Sitting	White; green/yellow ears; winking eyes; red nose	30 x 18	35.	40.	20.
3g	Rabbit Sitting	White; red ears/nose; winking eyes; blue patch	30 x 18	35.	40.	20.
3h	Rabbit Sitting	White; turquoise ears, nose; small black eyes	30 x 18	35.	40.	20.
4a	Narrow-eared Rabbit	White; green ears; large black/brown eyes; black nose; blue patch	30 x 18	35.	40.	20.
4b	Narrow-eared Rabbit	White; yellow ears; large black eyes; red nose; blue patch	30 x 18	35.	40.	20.
4c	Narrow-eared Rabbit	White; yellow ears; large black/brown eyes; black nose; blue patch	30 x 18	35.	40.	20.
4d	Narrow-eared Rabbit	White; yellow ears; large black eyes; red nose; blue OXO design	30 x 18	35.	40.	20.
4e	Narrow-eared Rabbit	White; yellow ears; large black eyes; red nose; green OXO design	30 x 18	35.	40.	20.
4f	Narrow-eared Rabbit	White; yellow ears; large black/brown eyes; red nose; green/red OXO design	30 x 18	35.	40.	20.

SERIES B: BULL, COW, MOUSE AND RABBIT

1956-1958

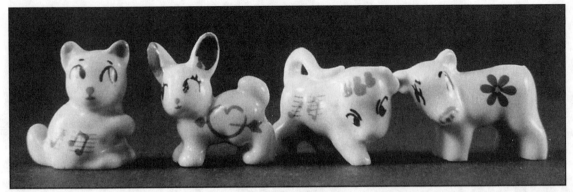

Mouse, Rabbit, Bull, Cow

Backstamp: Unmarked

No.	Name	Description	Size	U.S. $	Can. $	U.K. £
1a	Bull	Brown; small black eyes, nose; black spot (front and back)	20 x 25	35.	40.	20.
1b	Bull	Brown; small black eyes, nose; black spot/yellow X (back and front)	20 x 25	35.	40.	20.
1c	Bull	White; small black eyes, nose; black spot (front and back)	20 x 25	35.	40.	20.
1d	Bull	White; large black/blue eyes; black nose; black spot/yellow X (front and back)	20 x 25	35.	40.	20.
1e	Bull	White; green hair; large black eyes, nose; green daisy (front); red/green L-plate (back)	20 x 25	35.	40.	20.
1f	Bull	White; green hair; black eyes, nose; green heart/blue arrow (front); orange heart/green arrow (back)	20 x 25	35.	40.	20.
1g	Bull	White; green hair; large black eyes, nose; orange daisy (front); black daisy (back)	20 x 25	35.	40.	20.
1h	Bull	White; green hair; black eyes, nose; red/blue notes (front); orange heart/ blue arrow (back)	20 x 25	35.	40.	20.
1i	Bull	White; green hair; large black eyes, nose; red/blue notes (front); red/green L-plate (back)	20 x 25	35.	40.	20.
1j	Bull	White; green hair; large black eyes, nose; red/blue notes (front); red/blue L-plate (back)	20 x 25	35.	40.	20.
1k	Bull	White; green hair; large black eyes, nose; red/blue notes (front); red L-plate (back)	20 x 25	35.	40.	20.
1l	Bull	White; yellow hair; black eyes, nose; blue/green notes (front); blue heart/ yellow arrow (back)	20 x 25	35.	40.	20.
1m	Bull	White; yellow hair; black eyes, nose; blue/green notes (front); red/green L-plate (back)	20 x 25	35.	40.	20.
1n	Bull	White; yellow hair; large black eyes; red heart / blue arrow front; red L (back)	20 x 25	35.	40.	20.
1o	Bull	White; yellow hair; large brown eyes; blue and yellow flower (front); red musical notes with green lines (back)	20 x 25	35.	40.	20.
2a	Cow	White; green ears; black eyes; blue nose; orange daisy (front); blue daisy (back)	22 x 20	35.	40.	20.
2b	Cow	White; green ears; black eyes; blue nose; orange/green notes (front) orange heart/blue arrow (back)	22 x 20	35.	40.	20.
2c	Cow	White; pink ears; black eyes; red nose; red daisy (front); red heart/ green arrow (back)	22 x 20	35.	40.	20.
2d	Cow	White; yellow ears; black eyes; blue nose; orange/blue notes (front); orange heart/green arrow (back)	22 x 20	35.	40.	20.
2e	Cow	White; yellow ears; black eyes; blue nose; red heart/arrow (front); yellow daisy (back)	22 x 20	35.	40.	20.
2f	Cow	White; yellow ears; black eyes; red nose; blue daisy (front); orange L (back)	22 x 20	35.	40.	20.
2g	Cow	White; yellow ears; black eyes; red nose; blue daisy (front); red/ blue notes (back)	22 x 20	35.	40.	20.
2h	Cow	White; yellow ears; black eyes; red nose; green daisy (front); red daisy (back)	22 x 20	35.	40.	20.
2i	Cow	White; yellow ears; black eyes; red nose; blue heart/green arrow (front); blue daisy (back)	22 x 20	35.	40.	20.
2j	Cow	White; yellow ears; black eyes; blue nose; red heart and green arrow (front); red/blue notes (back)	22 x 20	35.	40.	20.

SERIES B: BULL, COW, MOUSE AND RABBIT (cont.)

Narrow-Eared Rabbit, Series A (left), Wide-Eared Rabbit, Series B, (right)

Backstamp: Unmarked

No.	Name	Description	Size	U.S. $	Can. $	U.K. £
3a	Mouse	Brown; small black eyes, nose	25 x 23	35.	40.	20.
3b	Mouse	Brown; small black eyes, nose; dark blue patch	25 x 23	35.	40.	20.
3c	Mouse	White all over	25 x 23	35.	40.	20.
3d	Mouse	White; small black eyes, nose; blue patch	25 x 23	35.	40.	20.
3e	Mouse	White; green ears, nose; large black eyes; orange daisy (front); green daisy (back)	25 x 23	35.	40.	20.
3f	Mouse	White; green ears, nose; large black eyes; orange/green notes (front); orange daisy (back)	25 x 23	35.	40.	20.
3g	Mouse	White; green ears, nose; large black eyes; red/green L-plate (back and front)	25 x 23	35.	40.	20.
3h	Mouse	White; pink ears; large black eyes; green nose; blue/red notes (front); blue daisy (back)	25 x 23	35.	40.	20.
3i	Mouse	White; pink ears; large black eyes; green nose; blue heart/green arrow (front); blue daisy (back)	25 x 23	35.	40.	20.
3j	Mouse	White; yellow ears; large black eyes; orange nose; blue/green notes (front) red/blue notes (back)	25 x 23	35.	40.	20.
3k	Mouse	White; yellow ears; large black eyes; orange nose; green daisy front; green heart/blue arrow back	25 x 23	35.	40.	20.
3l	Mouse	White; yellow ears; large black eyes; blue nose; red L (front); orange L (back)	25 x 23	35.	40.	20.
3m	Mouse	White; yellow ears; large black eyes; orange nose; orange daisy (front); orange/blue notes (back)	25 x 23	35.	40.	20.
3n	Mouse	White; yellow ears; large black eyes; red nose; red/yellow daisy (front); red/green daisy (back)	25 x 23	35.	40.	20.
4a	Rabbit	White; green ears; blue nose; red/green flower (front); red heart/blue arrow (back)	25 x 20	35.	40.	20.
4b	Rabbit	White; green ears; red nose; red heart/green arrow (front); blue heart/ green arrow (back)	25 x 20	35.	40.	20.
4c	Rabbit	White; pink ears; black nose; orange daisy (front); orange L (back)	25 x 20	35.	40.	20.
4d	Rabbit	White; pink ears; black nose; red L-plate (front and back)	25 x 20	35.	40.	20.
4e	Rabbit	White; pink ears; green nose; blue daisy (front); red notes (back)	25 x 20	35.	40.	20.
4f	Rabbit	White; yellow ears; blue/green notes (front); green heart/blue arrow (back)	25 x 20	35.	40.	20.
4g	Rabbit	White; yellow ears; red heart/blue arrow (front and back)	25 x 20	35.	40.	20.
4h	Rabbit	White; yellow ears; blue heart/red arrow (front); red daisy (back)	25 x 20	35.	40.	20.

SERIES C: DOG, DONKEY, FAWN AND PELICAN

1957-1958

| Pelican | Fawn | Dog | Donkey |

Backstamp: Unmarked

No.	Name	Description	Size	U.S. $	Can. $	U.K. £
1a	Dog	White; blue ears; small black/blue eyes; blue collar	28 x 15	35.	40.	20.
1b	Dog	White; blue/green ears; small black/blue eyes; orange flowers; blue collar	28 x 15	35.	40.	20.
1c	Dog	White; green ears; large black/blue eyes; red/green collar	28 x 15	35.	40.	20.
1d	Dog	White; green ears; small black/blue eyes; orange/red flowers; no collar	28 x 15	35.	40.	20.
1e	Dog	White; green ears; small black/blue eyes; red/green collar	28 x 15	35.	40.	20.
1f	Dog	White; pink ears; small black/blue eyes; orange/pink collar	28 x 15	35.	40.	20.
1g	Dog	White; yellow ears; small black/blue eyes; orange/yellow collar	28 x 15	35.	40.	20.
2a	Donkey	White; green ears; large black/blue eyes; pink/blue garland	35 x 20	35.	40.	20.
2b	Donkey	White; green ears; large black/blue eyes; red flower (front)	35 x 20	35.	40.	20.
2c	Donkey	White; pink ears; large black/blue eyes; red flower (front)	35 x 20	35.	40.	20.
2d	Donkey	White; pink ears; large black/blue eyes; red/yellow flower garland	35 x 20	35.	40.	20.
2e	Donkey	White; pink ears; large black/yellow eyes; red/yellow garland	35 x 20	35.	40.	20.
2f	Donkey	White; yellow ears; large black/blue eyes; red flower (front)	35 x 20	35.	40.	20.
2g	Donkey	White; yellow ears; large black/blue eyes; pink/blue garland	35 x 20	35.	40.	20.
2h	Donkey	White; yellow ears; large black/yellow eyes; red/yellow garland	35 x 20	35.	40.	20.
3a	Fawn	White; green ears, tail; black/blue eyes; yellow flower	28 x 20	35.	40.	20.
3b	Fawn	White; green ears, tail; black/yellow eyes; yellow heart; red arrow	28 x 20	35.	40.	20.
3c	Fawn	White; pink ears, tail; black/blue eyes; blue flowers/heart/notes	28 x 20	35.	40.	20.
3d	Fawn	White; pink ears; black/blue eyes; yellow flower	28 x 20	35.	40.	20.
3e	Fawn	White; pink ears; black/yellow eyes; yellow flower	28 x 20	35.	40.	20.
3f	Fawn	White; yellow ears, tail; black/blue eyes; blue flowers/heart/notes	28 x 20	35.	40.	20.
3g	Fawn	White; yellow ears, tail; black/yellow eyes; red flower	28 x 20	35.	40.	20.
4a	Pelican	White; black/blue eyes; blue wings, feet, anchor	30 x 15	35.	40.	20.
4b	Pelican	White; black/blue eyes; green wings, feet; blue anchor	30 x 15	35.	40.	20.
4c	Pelican	White; black/blue eyes; pink wings, feet; blue anchor	30 x 15	35.	40.	20.
4d	Pelican	White; black/blue eyes; yellow wings, feet; blue anchor	30 x 15	35.	40.	20.
4e	Pelican	White; black/blue eyes; green wings, feet; black waistcoat; red bowtie	30 x 15	35.	40.	20.
4f	Pelican	White; black/blue eyes; pink wings, feet; black waistcoat; red bowtie	30 x 15	35.	40.	20.
4g	Pelican	White; black/blue eyes; yellow wings, feet; black waistcoat; red bowtie	30 x 15	35.	40.	20.
4h	Pelican	White; black/blue eyes; yellow wings, feet; blue waistcoat; red bowtie	30 x 15	35.	40.	20.

MR. MEN AND LITTLE MISS
2004-2007

Little Miss Giggles

Mr Noisy

Miss Fun

Miss Bossy

Mr. Grumpy

Mr Noisy All Aboard

Backstamp: Wade Made in England Mr Men and Miss Little ™ & © The Hargreaves Organisastions

Date	Name	Description	Issue	Price	Size	U.S. $	Can. $	U.K. £
2004	Little Miss Giggles	Blue; red hair; yellow nose	—	£15.50	62	27.	30.	15.
2004	Little Miss Sunshine	Yellow; red hair ribbon	—	£15.50	76	27.	30.	15.
2004	Mr Bump	Blue; white bandage	—	£15.50	62	27.	30.	15.
2004	Mr Noisy	Red; black eyes, mouth	—	£15.50	76	27.	30.	15.
2005	Miss Bossy	Dark blue; red hat	—	£15.50	89	27.	30.	15.
2005	Miss Fun	Yellow; blue hair bow	—	£15.50	76	27.	30.	15.
2005	Mr Lazy	Pink; blue hat	—	£15.50	62	27.	30.	15.
2006	Mr Grumpy	Turquoise; blue nose; green hat	200	£35.00	144	65.	70.	35.
2006	Mr Noisy All Aboard	Red; yellow train	250	£35.00	85 x 130	65.	70.	35.

Note: For the Mr. Bump Money Box see *Wade Collectables*, 4th edition.

MR SNOW FLAKE AND HIS FAMILY
2004

Mr. Chill Flake

Mr. Christmas Flake

Mr. Cold Flake

Mr. Frost Flake

Mr. Snow Flake

Mr. Winter Flake

Backstamp: Unknown

Date	Name	Description	Issue	Price	Size	U.S. $	Can. $	U.K. £
2004	Mr. Chill Flake	White, blue, black	—	£16.50	75	18.	20.	10.
2004	Mr. Christmas Flake	White, blue, black	—	£16.50	75	18.	20.	10.
2004	Mr. Cold Flake	White, blue, black	—	£16.50	75	18.	20.	10.
2004	Mr. Frost Flake	White, blue, black	—	£16.50	75	18.	20.	10.
2004	Mr. Snow Flake	White, blue, black	—	£16.50	75	18.	20.	10.
2004	Mr. Winter Flake	White, blue, black	—	£16.50	75	18.	20.	10.

MY PET
2006

Beagle

Border Collie

Jack Russsell

Golden Retriever

Puppy Play, No. 1

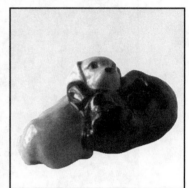

Puppy Play, No. 2

Backstamp: Unknown

Date	Name	Description	Issue	Price	Size	U.S. $	Can. $	U.K. £
2006	Beagle	Brown, black	—	£19.99	114 x 82	39.	40.	20.
2006	Border Collie	Black, white	—	£19.99	140 x 63	39.	40.	20.
2006	Border Collie	Blue merle	—	£19.99	140 x 63	39.	40.	20.
2006	Golden Retreiver	Golden	—	£19.99	150 x 76	39.	40.	20.
2006	Jack Russel Terrier	Black, white	—	£19.99	127 x 76	39.	40.	20.
2006	Jack Russell Terrier	Tan, white	—	£19.99	127 x 76	39.	40.	20.
2006	Puppy Play, No. 1	Chocolate, yellow	—	£19.99	63 x 63	39.	40.	20.
2006	Puppy Play, No. 2	Black, yellow	—	£19.99	63 x 76	39.	40.	20.

POCKET PALS

SERIES ONE: ANIMALS

October 1999

Pocket Pals, which were introduced in October 1999, are produced from the same moulds as the 1960s/1980s "Happy Families." The models used are the "Mother" animals from the Cat, Dog, Elephant, Frog, Giraffe, Hippo, Mouse, Owl, Pig, and Rabbit Happy Families. The models were sold attached by double-sided tape to a card base at a cost of £5.50. For Cat model named "Tango" please see C&S Collectables page 231; for Frog model "Hopper" and Dog model "Woofit" please see *Collect It!* Magazine page 240.

Backstamp: Gold transfer print "Wade Pp" in shield

No.	Name	Description	Size	U.S. $	Can. $	U.K. £
1	Cat Slinky	Dark brown body; honey face/chest; blue eyes	45 x 35	10.	11.	6.
2	Dog Waggs	White; black patches; brown eyes	55 x 35	10.	11.	6.
3	Elephant Tusker	Pale pink; pink ears; blue eyes	35 x 70	10.	11.	6.
4	Frog Hip Hop	Dark green; green spots; blue eyes	25 x 45	10.	11.	6.
5	Giraffe Stretch	Apricot; blue eyes	60 x 45	10.	11.	6.
6	Hippo Paddles	Pink; blue eyes	35 x 50	10.	11.	6.
7	Mouse Cheesy	Khaki; pink ears; blue eyes; brown tail	50 x 28	10.	11.	6.
8	Owl Specs	Brown; off white; yellow eyes	40 x 40	10.	11.	6.
9	Pig Truffle	White; tan brown patches; blue eyes	28 x 65	10.	11.	6.
10	Rabbit Bounce	White; black patches; pink ears; brown eyes	55 x 30	10.	11.	6.

SERIES TWO: POCKET HORRORS

October 2001

The second set of *Pocket Pals* was introduced in 2001, and is loosely based on fictional horror characters: Jekyll and Hyde (who has two faces), Wolfy (Wolfman) and Frankie (Frankenstein). The models were sold individually at a cost of £5.95 each.

Baby Bodzilla, Frankie, Igor Jr., Jekyll, Lizzie

Hyde

Lugsi, Spooky, Where's my Mummy, Witch Hazel, Wolfy

Jekyll

Backstamp: Gold label "Wade Pp"

No.	Name	Description	Size	U.S. $	Can. $	U.K. £
1	Baby Bodzilla	Green	54	18.	20.	10.
2	Frankie	Blue	65	18.	20.	10.
3	Igor Jr.	Royal blue	50	18.	20.	10.
4	Jekyll and Hyde	Blue-grey	56	18.	20.	10.
5	Lizzie	Turquoise	50	18.	20.	10.
6	Lugsi	Orange	58	18.	20.	10.
7	Spooky	White	50	18.	20.	10.
8	Where's my Mummy	White	50	18.	20.	10.
9	Witch Hazel	Purple	60.	18.	20.	10.
10	Wolfy	Orange	55.	18.	20.	10.

POKEMON

2001

This set of *Pokemon* characters was introduced in summer 2001, and is based on characters in a children's computer game. The models were sold individually at a cost of £8.99 each.

Gengar, Jigglypuff, Pikachu, Poliwhirl, Psyduck

Backstamp: Gold transfer print "Wade" and printed "Nintendo TM © 2001"

No.	Name	Description	Size	U.S. $	Can. $	U.K. £
1	Gengar	Purple; red eyes; blue mouth	55	20.	22.	12.
2	Jigglypuff	Pink; green eyes; red mouth	55	20.	22.	12.
3	Pikachu	Yellow; black eyes; red cheek spots	55	20.	22.	12.
4	Poliwhirl	Blue; black swirls; white hands	55	20.	22.	12.
5	Psyduck	Orange; white beak, feet	55	25.	28.	15.

RULE BEARTANNIA

1999-2002

This nine-piece set of "Royal Teddy Bears" was produced by Wade and issued in the United States in early 1999. They were modelled by a well-known American artist Jerome Walker. The models were later sold by Wade in the U.K. The series ended in 2002.

Queen Beatrice,　Queen Mum,　King Velveteen

Royal Guard

Nanny Fluffins and Baby Velveteena, Prince Tedward,
Princess Elizabeth Tedwina, Princess Plushette

Rule Beartannia Plaque

Backstamp: Printed "©Jerome Walker 1998 Wade Made in England"

No.	Name	Description	Size	U.S. $	Can. $	U.K. £
1	Princess Elizabeth Tedwina	Pale blue bonnet, dark red, pink/blue flowers; pale blue dress; pearl ribbon bow; white base	127	50.	55.	30.
2	King Velveteen	Red/gold crown; red cloak; pale blue/white edged robe; gold sceptre	165	75.	65.	45.
3	Queen Beatrice	Green/gold crown; pearl earrings, necklace; green/white cloak; pale blue dress; gold sceptre; gold/white orb	150	75.	65.	45.
4	Queen Mum	Pink hat, handbag, dress; dark blue/white cloak; gold spectacles	120	75.	65.	45.
5	Prince George Tedward	White sailor hat; dark blue/white sailor suit; gold telescope; white base	97	50.	55.	30.
6	Princess Plushette	White bonnet, dark red/pink flowers; yellow dress; dark red/pink flower posy; white base	97	50.	55.	30.
7	Nanny Fluffins and Baby Velveteena	Yellow hat, dark blue band; white dress, dark blue band; pale blue shawl, baby's pram, base	130	70.	75.	40.
8	Royal Guard	Black helmet, shoulder epaulettes, gold trim; dark red jacket; gold trim; gold trumpet; dark blue trousers; black shoes; white base	115	70.	75.	40.
9	Rule Beartannia Plaque	White; multicoloured bears; bee/honey pot print; red/black lettering	125	17.	18.	10.

SNIPPETS

1956-1957

Snippets models are thin, flat outlines of a figure with a rectangular porcelain box on the back, which enables the model to stand. It was a new idea by Wade, one which was not very successful at the time. Only two sets of three models were produced. Because of this and the fact that they are easily broken, these models are rare.

Set One was a set of three 15th, 16th and 17th century sailing ships, modelled as an outline of the ships and enameled in bright colours. The three ships are in graduated sizes.

SET ONE: SAILING SHIPS

1956

Backstamp: **A.** Black transfer "Wade Snippet No. 1 Mayflower Carried 102 Pilgrims to North America 1620 Real Porcelain Made In England" (1)
   B. Black transfer "Wade Snippet No. 2 Santa Maria Flag ship of Columbus 1492 Real Porcelain Made In England" (2)
   C. Black transfer "Wade Snippet No. 3 Revenge Flag ship of Sir Richard Grenville 1591 Real Porcelain Made in England" (3)

No.	Name	Description	Size	U.S. $	Can. $	U.K. £
1	The Mayflower	Brown; yellow sails; red flags; blue/white waves	58 x 60	85.	95.	50.
2	The Santa Maria	Brown; green sails; red/yellow flags; blue/white waves	45 x 50	85.	95.	50.
3	The Revenge	Brown; red sails; yellow flags; blue/white waves	35 x 45	85.	95.	50.
—	3 pce set	Boxed	—	250.	275.	150.

SET TWO: HANSEL AND GRETEL

1957

Set Two comprises three characters from the fairy tale, *Hansel and Gretel*.

Backstamp: **A.** Black transfer "Wade Snippet No. 4 Hansel Real Porcelain Made in England" (4a, 4b)
B. Black transfer "Wade Snippet No. 5 Gretel Real Porcelain Made in England" (5)
C. Black transfer "Wade Snippet No. 6 Gingy Real Porcelain Made in England" (6)

No.	Name	Description	Size	U.S. $	Can. $	U.K. £
1a	Hansel	Yellow stockings; grey-blue trousers, jacket; red shirt, toadstools	64 x 42	225.	250.	125.
1b	Hansel	Green stockings; grey-blue trousers, jacket; red shirt, toadstools	64 x 42	225.	250.	125.
2	Gretel	Yellow pigtail, apron; blue shoe; green grass; red toadstools	56 x 42	225.	250.	125.
3	Gingy the Bear	Brown/beige; red toadstools	32 x 20	225.	250.	125.
—	3 pce set	Boxed	—	575.	625.	325.

TONY THE TIGER

2005

Star Player

Football Crazy

Backstamp: Unknown

Date	Name	Description	Issue	Price	Size	U.S. $	Can. $	U.K. £
2005	Football Crazy	Orange/black/white/blue	2,000	£39.95	100	50.	55.	25.
2005	Star Player	Orang/black/white/red	2,000	£39.95	110	50.	55.	25.

Note: 1. For Tony the Tiger Surfing, see Membership Series, page 128.
    2. For the Tony the Tiger Money Box see *Wade Collectables*, 4th edition.

THE TORTOISE FAMILY

1958-1988

Wade's first tortoise, the "Large (Father)," was issued in January 1958, and it proved so popular that the following January Wade introduced two more, the "Medium (Mother)" and "Small (Baby)," which were sold as a boxed pair and named "Baby Tortoises.". These three models were so successful that they were produced almost continuously for the next thirty years. Considered by Wade as their best-selling line, this family of tortoises is in plentiful supply. The original price for the "Large (Father)" was 4/6d the pair of "Medium (Mother)" and "Small (Baby)" cost 4/9d.

In 1973 the "Jumbo" tortoise was added to the family. It was modelled differently from the other tortoises, however, and resembles a turtle. Because it was not in production for as long as the rest of the *Tortoise Family*, it is harder to find. The "Large (Father)" and the "Jumbo" tortoises are the only ones in this series to have lift-off shells. The numbers 1 through 8 were embossed on the bases of model 3, which refer to the production tool used to press the model. Production tools usually lasted for one to three years before having to be replaced; therefore, the models with the lowest numbers should be the oldest.

Baby, Mother and Father

Jumbo Tortoise

Version One: Recessed Back   Version Two: Full Back

Backstamp: **A.** Embossed "Wade Porcelain Made in England No. 3" (1, 2, 3)
              B. Embossed "Wade Made in England" (4)

No.	Name	Description	Size	U.S. $	Can. $	U.K. £
1a	Small (Baby)	Brown/blue	25 x 45	12.	14.	7.
1b	Small (Baby)	Green/blue	25 x 45	35.	40.	20.
1c	Small (Baby)	Green	25 x 45	35.	40.	20.
2a	Medium (Mother)	Brown/blue	35 x 75	15.	16.	9.
2b	Medium (Mother)	Green/blue	35 x 75	50.	55.	30.
2c	Medium (Mother)	Green	35 x 75	50.	55.	30.
3a	Large (Father, Type 1)	Beige/blue	50 x 105	50.	55.	30.
3b	Large (Father, Type 2)	Brown/blue	50 x 105	50.	55.	30.
3c	Large (Father)	Green/blue	50 x 105	50.	55.	30.
3d	Large (Father)	Green	50 x 105	50.	55.	30.
4	Jumbo	Beige/blue	65 x 150	85.	95.	50.

The Tortoise Family Derivatives

1958-1984

The *Tortoise Ash Bowls* are large and round, with a scintillite, high-gloss finish. An embossed reptile-skin design covers the inside, and a model from the *Tortoise Family* set is fixed to the inside curve of the bowl. The ash bowl with the "Medium (Mother)" tortoise was issued in January 1958 for 12/6d. The ash bowl with the "Small (Baby)" tortoise was produced from 1975 to 1984.

The round tortoise ash bowls were such a successful line that Wade introduced a new oblong bowl in 1976. This bowl had small rounded feet and was embossed with a reptile-skin design and finished with a high-gloss finish. A second version with a flat base has been found. The "Medium (Mother)" tortoise figure was used on this bowl.

Wade retooled the "Medium (Mother)" tortoise from the *Tortoise Family* series by cutting a recess in the back of the model and inserting the name of a British colony resort in embossed letters in the top shell.

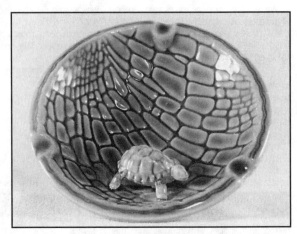

Ash Bowl

Souvenir Tortoise "Devil's Hole, Bermuda"

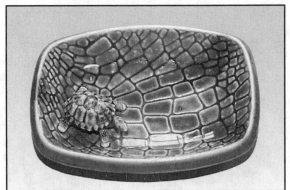

Footed Oblong Bowl

Backstamp: **A.** Impressed "Wade Porcelain Made in England" (1a, 1b, 4)
B. Large embossed "Wade Made in England" (2a, 2b, 3)

No.	Name	Description	Size	U.S. $	Can. $	U.K. £
1a	Ash bowl	Medium (Mother) tortoise; brown/blue	55 x 183	60.	65.	35.
1b	Ash bowl	Medium (Mother) tortoise; green/blue	55 x 183	60.	65.	35.
2a	Ash bowl	Small (Baby) tortoise; brown/blue	45 x 145	45.	50.	25.
2b	Ash bowl	Small (Baby) tortoise; green/blue	45 x 145	45.	50.	25.
3	Footed Oblong Bowl	Medium (Mother) tortoise; beige/blue	150 x 100	70.	75.	40.
4a	Souvenir Tortoise	**Bahamas** on shell; brown; blue markings	35 x 75	85.	95.	50.
4b	Souvenir Tortoise	**Bermuda** on shell; brown; blue markings	35 x 75	85.	95.	50.
4c	Souvenir Tortoise	**Bermuda Triangle** on shell; brown; blue markings	35 x 75	85.	95.	50.
4d	Souvenir Tortoise	**Devil's Hole, Bermuda** on shell; brown; blue markings	35 x 75	85.	95.	50.

Note: See page 238 for a commissioned set of tortoises for *Ciba Geigy* that is another derivative of the *Tortoise Family*.

TREASURES SET

1957-1959

The *Treasures* set was the first in an intended series, but unfortunately for collectors, no more sets were put into production. It consists of a set of five white elephants in varying sizes, with bright pink blankets decorated with orange, yellow, blue and green flowers. Early advertising material calls the set *Elephant Chains* and *Elephant Train*. The original price for a box of five elephants was 10/6d.

Backstamp: Blue transfer "Wade England"

No.	Name	Description	Size	U.S. $	Can. $	U.K. £
1	Elephant, large	White; pink blanket; howdah and mahout; blue turban	47 x 63	150.	165.	85.
2	Elephant, medium	White; pink blanket; gold tassel	35 x 57	130.	145.	75.
3	Elephant, small	White; pink blanket; gold tassel	28 x 54	100.	110.	60.
4	Elephant, tiny	White; pink blanket; gold tassel	24 x 45	100.	110.	60.
5	Elephant, miniature	White; pink blanket; gold tassel	20 x 39	100.	110.	60.
—	5 pce set	Boxed	—	625.	675.	350.

Treasures Elephant Derivative Whimtray

1957-1959

This unusual model of the *Treasure Set* miniature elephant attached to a Whimtray is the only example known to date.

Backstamp: Embossed "Whimtrays Wade Porcelain Made in England"

No.	Name	Description	Size	U.S. $	Can. $	U.K. £
1	Elephant, miniature	Blue-grey; pink/blue blanket; yellow tray	40 x 75	125.	150.	75.

VARIOUS NOVELTY MODELS

1955-1960

This set of five models was advertised as "Various Novelty Models" in late 1955. Although Wade advertisements suggest that they were in production for five years, they are hard to find and are considered rare.

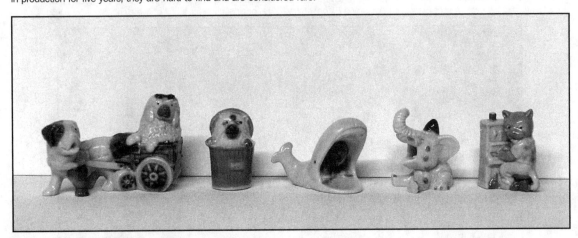

Backstamp: **A.** Embossed "Wade" (1, 2)
B. Embossed "Wade Ireland" (on 2b Dustbin Cat)
C. Black and gold label "Wade England" (3, 4, 5)
D. Unmarked (3, 4, 5)

No.	Name	Description	Size	U.S. $	Can. $	U.K. £
1	Bernie and Poo	One white/brown; one white/blue	55 x 75	175.	200.	100.
2a	Dustbin Cat	White cat; beige dustbin	45 x 25	175.	200.	100.
2b	Dustbin Cat	White cat; grey dustbin	45 x 25	175.	200.	100.
3	Jonah in the Whale	Blue jacket; white whale	40 x 40	1,400.	1,550.	800.
4	Jumbo Jim	Blue hat, tears	45 x 25	175.	200.	100.
5a	Kitten on the Keys	Grey cat; white, blue spotted shirt; white trousers	30 x 35	225.	250.	130.
5b	Kitten on the Keys	White cat	30 x 35	225.	250.	130.

Jumbo Jim Derivative Calendar

A model of *Jumbo Jim* has been found attached to a Bakelite perpetual calendar.

Backstamp: Unknown

No.	Name	Description	Size	U.S. $	Can. $	U.K. £
1	Jumbo Jim Calendar	White; blue hat, tears; brown Bakelite calendar	50 x 100	225.	250.	125.

WATER LIFE COLLECTION

1997

Alligator, Goldfish, Whale

Backstamp: Black printed (on Whale) and red printed (on goldfish and alligator) "Wade Made in England"

No.	Name	Description	Size	U.S. $	Can. $	U.K. £
1	Alligator	Green	25 x 65	14.	16.	8.
2	Goldfish	Orange fish; blue-grey, orange streaked water	50 x 40	14.	16.	8.
3	Whale	Light blue whale; blue waves	47 x 70	14.	16.	8.

Hermit Crab, Octopus, Seahorse

Backstamp: Gold "Wade England" between two gold lines

No.	Name	Description	Size	U.S. $	Can. $	U.K. £
4	Hermit Crab	Orange crab; grey-blue waves	30	14.	16.	8.
5	Octopus	Grey octopus; sea green-blue waves	50	14.	16.	8.
6	Seahorse	Beige seahorse; dark blue waves	30	14.	16.	8.

ZOO MAZING

Hip-Hippos

2002

Hip-Hippos were produced as a retail line of five models, plus four being produced as show specials, for a total of nine pieces. The hippos were produced in various poses and have names such as "Born to be Cool" and "Born to be Loved." The first five models, "Big Brother," "Cool," "Friends," "Loved" and "Wild," were launched at the Birmingham Trade Show in February 2002, and were available from retailers from March 2002.

The four show specials, "Sleepy," "Naughty," "Slide" and "Daydreamer," were available in April, July and September at various U.K. and U.S.A. Wade Shows. They were also available on-line and from the Wade Retail Shop in September 2003, at the U.K. and U.S.A. prices listed below (which included postage).

First row: "Naughty," "Cool," "Slide," "Wild"; Second row: "Daydreamer," "Loved"; Third row: "Friends," "Sleepy, " "Big Brother"

Backstamp: Printed "Hip Hippos Wade" [with name of model]

No.	Name	Description	Size	U.S. $	Can. $	U.K. £
1	Born to be a Big Brother	Grey; white toenails	70 x 50	30.	35.	18.
2	Born to be Cool	Grey; red cap; black sunglasses	70 x 50	30.	35.	18.
3	Born to be a Daydreamer	Grey; white toenails	55 x 80	30.	35.	18.
4	Born to be Friends	Grey; black bird	55 x 90	30.	35.	18.
5	Born to be Loved	Grey; red heart; white toenails	70 x 45	30.	35.	18.
6	Born to be Naughty	Grey; white toenails	65 x 50	30.	35.	18.
7	Born to be Sleepy	Grey; white toenails	70 x 55	30.	35.	18.
8	Born to Slide	Grey; white toenails	35 x 90	30.	35.	18.
9	Born to be Wild	Grey; white toe nails; red/black number "1"; brown wheels	80 x 70	30.	35.	18.

FAIRS AND EVENTS

U.K. Fairs
    Alexandra Palace, 1998 136
    Alton Towers Fair, 1998 137
    Arundel
        Christmas Bonanza, 1999-2006 138
        Collectors /Swap Meets, 2001-2006 143
    Birmingham Fairs, 1994-1996 148
    Collect It! Fairs
        Newark, 1998 149
        Stoneleigh, 1998 149
    Dunstable Fairs, 1996-2006 150
    Olympia Incentive Exhibition, 1998 153
    Ripley Village Fete and Teddy Bears' Picnic, 1998 154
    Stoke Fairs
        1997, Trentham Gardens 155
        1998, Trentham Gardens 155
        1999, Trentham Gardens 156
        2000, Trentham Gardens 156
        2000, Stratford Show Grounds 157
        2001, Trentham Gardens 158
        2002, Kings Hall Civic Centre 159
        2003, North Staffordshire Hotel 160
        2004, North Staffordshire Hotel 161
        2005, Kings Hall Civic Centre 161
        2006, Kings Hall Civic Centre 162
        2007, Discover Trentham 162
    Wade Christmas Extravaganza, 2000 163
U.S.A. Wade Collectors Shows
    Seattle, WA, 1996 164
    Oconomowoc, WI, 1997 164
    Buffalo, NY, 1998 164
    San Antonio, TX, 1999 164
    Kansas Wade Show, 2000-2001 165
    Red Rose Tea Fair, CT, 2006 166
    Rosemont Trade Show, Rosemont, IL, 1999 167
    Mini Wade Fair, York, PA, 1999 167
    Summer Wade Fest, Harrisburg, PA, 2000-2006 168
    West Coast Wade Collectors Fair, WA, 2002-2003 175
One-of-a-Kind Models 177

ALEXANDRA PALACE

THE TEDDY BEAR SHOW

1998

Wade Ceramics attended the Teddy Scene Event at Alexandra Palace held on October 31st - November 1st, 1998.

Backstamp: Gold printed "The Library Bear Limited edition of 500 Wade England"

Date	Name	Description	Issue	Price	Size	U.S. $	Can. $	U.K. £
1998	Library Bear	Amber; black/yellow hat; gold bow tie	500	£30	165	100.	110.	60.

ALTON TOWERS FAIR

1998

Wade held their Extravaganza in a marquee at Alton Towers, a theme park in Staffordshire, England, on November 22nd, 1998. A special limited edition of 100 each of the Tom Smith's Circus Poodle, with a pink or gold skirt, or an all-over white glaze, were given as prizes in the Wade Bran Tub draw at the show. Please note that models with red and green skirts exist, but these were not produced by Wade.

Bears Just Want to Have Fun (1998)

Panda Bear Plaque (1998)

Circus Poodle (1998)

Backstamp: **Bears Just Want to Have Fun:** "Bears Just Want To Have Fun Limited Edition of 500 Wade" with Alton Towers logo
Circus Poodle: Embossed "Wade England"
Panda Bear Plaque: "Wade England Extravaganza 1998"

Comm.	Name	Description	Issue	Price	Size	U.S. $	Can. $	U.K. £
Wade	Bears Just Want to Have Fun	Amber; dark blue dungarees; yellow shirt; pale blue shoes	500	£25	145	70.	75.	40.
Wade	Panda Bear Plaque	Black /white panda; white plaque; red lettering	—	£20	195	50.	55.	30.
Wade	Circus Poodle	White	100	Draw	43	35.	40.	20.
Wade	Circus Poodle	White; gold skirt	100	Draw	43	35.	40.	20.
Wade	Circus Poodle	White; pink skirt	100	Draw	43	35.	40.	20.

ARUNDEL

CHRISTMAS BONANZA

1999-2006

The Arundel Christmas Bonanza is organised jointly by Wade Ceramics and C&S Collectables. The Bonanza is held at the C&S Collectables shop (The Wade Collectors Centre, Arundel, West Sussex).

1999

Backstamp: "Oops! The Bear Ltd Edition of 250 Wade England"

Comm.	Name	Description	Issue	Price	Size	U.S. $	Can. $	U.K. £
Wade	Oops! The Bear, Style Two	Amber; creamy pink bandage on leg; brown crutch	300	£15	95	50.	55.	30.

2000

Oops! the Bear, Style Three (2000)

Santa's Flight (2000)

Backstamp: Oops! the Bear: "Oops! The Bear Ltd Edition of 300 Wade England"
            Santa's Flight: Printed "© 2000 C&S Collectables : with certificate of authenticity, Santa's Flight ™ Wade Christmas Bonanza 2000 250 Limited edition Wade England"

Comm.	Name	Description	Issue	Price	Size	U.S. $	Can. $	U.K. £
Wade	Oops! The Bear, Style Three	Beige bear; blue blanket	250	£15	70	50.	55.	30.
C&S	Santa's Flight	Green body, red wings, engine	250	£35	75 x 95	70.	75.	40.
C&S	Santa's Flight	Green body; gold wings; engine	10	Prizes	75 x 95	175.	200.	100.

CHRISTMAS BONANZA (cont.)

2001

Christmas Robin "Holly" (2001)　　　　Quackers on Ice (2001)

Backstamp: **Christmas Robin:** Printed "Wade C&S 8th December 2001"
Quackers on Ice: Printed "Wade Bonanza Arundel 2001"

Comm.	Name	Description	Issue	Price	Size	U.S. $	Can. $	U.K. £
C&S	Christmas Robin "Holly"	White; green holly leaves	100	£18	50	40.	45.	25.
C&S	Christmas Robin "Ivy"	Cream; green ivy leaves	100	£18	50	40.	45.	25.
C&S	Christmas Robin	Gold	15	Prizes	50	175.	200.	100.
Wade	Quackers on Ice	White duck; red hat	150	£15	75	40.	45.	25.

2002

Christmas Puppy (2002)　　　　Polar Bear Cub [white] (2002)　　　　Quackers on his Sleigh (2002)

Backstamp: **Christmas Puppy:** Printed "Wade" logo
Polar Bear Cub: Printed "Wade" logo
Quackers on his Sleigh: Printed "Christmas Bonanza Arundel 2002" and red "Wade" logo

Comm.	Name	Description	Issue	Price	Size	U.S. $	Can. $	U.K. £
Wade	Christmas Puppy	White/black dog, gold heart medallion	75	£20	60	100.	110.	60.
C&S	Polar Bear Cub	See Winter WonderLand Series, page 233	—	—	—	—	—	—
Wade	Quackers on his Sleigh	Red/white hat; blue/ white scarf; brown/silver sleigh	150	£20	80	40.	45.	25.

CHRISTMAS BONANZA (cont.)
2003

Lucky the Bear (2003)

Polar Bear Cub [seated] (2003)

Polar Bear Cub [standing] (2003)

Mama Seal and Pup (2003)

Papa Seal (2003)

Comm.	Name	Description	Issue	Price	Size	U.S. $	Can. $	U.K. £
C&S	Lucky the Bear	Blue	100	Prizes	—	45.	50.	25.
C&S	Lucky the Bear	Pink	100	Prizes	—	40.	45.	22.
C&S	Lucky the Bear	White	100	Prizes	—	40.	45.	22.
Club	Mama Seal and Pup	See Winter WonderLand Series, page 233	—	—	—	—	—	—
C&S	Mother and Baby Bear	See Winter WonderLand Series, page 233	—	—	—	—	—	—
C&S	Papa Seal	See Winter WonderLand Series, page 233	—	—	—	—	—	—
C&S	Partridge Whimsie	Burgundy	300	Unk.	35 x 35	18.	20.	10.
C&S	Partridge Whimsie	Bright blue	300	£6.50	35 x 35	18.	20.	10.
C&S	Partridge Whimsie	Dark blue	300	Unk.	35 x 35	18.	20.	10.
C&S	Partridge Whimsie	Pink	300	£6.50	35 x 35	18.	20.	10.
C&S	Partridge Whimsie	Salmon pink	300	Unk.	35 x 35	18.	20.	10.
C&S	Partridge Whimsie	Gold	20	Prizes	35 x 35	125.	140.	70.
C&S	Partridge Whimsie	Silver	20	Prizes	35 x 35	125.	140.	70.
C&S	Polar Bear Cub, seated	See Winter WonderLand Series, page 233	—	—	—	—	—	—
C&S	Polar Bear Cub, standing	See Winter WonderLand Series, page 233	—	—	—	—	—	—

Note: **1.** A dash in any of the technical data columns of the table indicates that we do not have the required information, if you do, we would be pleased to hear from you.

2. Dashes in the pricing columns indicate one of two things: firstly, there was insufficient market pricing available, and secondly, pieces issued in small quantities of 10 or 20 pieces will be subject to wide pricing swings.

CHRISTMAS BONANZA (cont.)
2004

Eskimo and Igloo (2004)

Hugging Bear Cubs (2004)

Standing Bear Cub (2004)

Comm.	Name	Description	Issue	Price	Size	U.S. $	Can. $	U.K. £
C&S	Betty Boop Whimsie	Green; See Betty Boop, page 223	—	—	—	—	—	—
C&S	Betty Boop Whimsie	Red; See Betty Boop, page 223	—	—	—	—	—	—
C&S	Eskimo and Igloo	See Winter WonderLand Series, page 233	—	—	—	—	—	—
Wade	Hugging Bear Cubs	See Winter WonderLand Series, page 233	—	—	—	—	—	—
C&S	Standing Bear Cub	See Winter WonderLand Series, page 233	—	—	—	—	—	—

2005

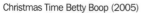
Christmas Time Betty Boop (2005)

Christmas Rabbit and Mouse (2005)

Kitten Whimsie (2005)

Comm.	Name	Description	Issue	Price	Size	U.S. $	Can. $	U.K. £
C&S	Betty Boop Whimsie	Apricot; See Betty Boop, page 223	—	—	—	—	—	—
C&S	Christmas Time Betty Boop	See Betty Boop, page 219	—	—	—	—	—	—
Wade	Christmas Rabbit / Mouse	Grey, green, tan, black, gold	100	£35	110 x 50	125.	135.	65.
Wade	Kitten Whimsie	Black; green eyes, pink ears	—	Bran Tub	25 x 30	15.	16.	8.

CHRISTMAS BONANZA (cont.)
2006

Floppy the Penguin (2006)

Betty Boop Christmas Present (2006)

Robin Whimsie (2006)

Comm.	Name	Description	Issue	Price	Size	U.S. $	Can. $	U.K. £
C&S	Betty Boop Christmas Present	Red, white; green base; gold trim	—	—	—	—	—	—
Wade	Floppy the Penguin	Black, white, red, brown, yellow	80	—	—	—	—	—
Wade	Floppy the Penguin	Black, white; gold hat	20	—	—	150.	165.	75.
C&S	Christmas Gingie Bear	See Gingie Bear Series, page 229	—	—	—	—	—	—
C&S	Christmas Snoopy	See Characters from Charlie Brown, page 225	—	—	—	—	—	—
Wade	Robin Whimsie	Burgundy	100	Free	15x35	28.	30.	15.
Wade	Robin Whimsie	Green	100	Free	15x35	28.	30.	15.

Note: 1. A dash in any of the technical data columns of the table indicates that we do not have the required information, if you do, we would be pleased to hear from you.

2. Dashes in the pricing columns indicate one of two things: firstly, there was insufficient market pricing available, and secondly, pieces issued in small quantities of 10 or 20 pieces will be subject to wide pricing swings.

ARUNDEL

COLLECTORS / SWAP MEETS

1997

Comm.	Name	Description	Issue	Price	Size	U.S. $	Can. $	U.K. £
OIWCC	Arundel Duck	Creamy white; blue base	100	£20	95	300.	325.	175.
OWICC	Arundel Duck	Dull yellow; green base	1,400	£15	95	85.	95.	50.

1998

Arundel Bunny (1998)

Teddy Bear Plaque (1998)

Comm.	Name	Description	Issue	Price	Size	U.S. $	Can. $	U.K. £
OWICC	Arundel Bunny	Honey; green ears; brown eyes	1,400	£25	110	50.	55.	30.
OWICC	Arundel Bunny	White; blue ears; black eyes	100	£25	110	250.	275.	150.
Wade	Teddy Bear Plaque	Caramel bear, plaque	1,500	£20	195	35.	40.	20.

COLLECTORS / SWAP MEETS (cont.)
1999

Arundel Chick (1999)

Puppy Love "Steino" (1999)

Comm.	Name	Description	Issue	Price	Size	U.S. $	Can. $	U.K. £
OWICC	Arundel Chick	Honey	900	£15	78	90.	100.	50.
OWICC	Arundel Chick	White	100	£15	78	250.	275.	150.
Wade	Puppy Love "Steino"	White, brown; blue ball	500	£20	70	50.	55.	28.

2000

Arundel Cat (2000)

Comm.	Name	Description	Issue	Price	Size	U.S. $	Can. $	U.K. £
Wade	Arundel Cat	Honey	900	£15	108	55.	60.	30.
Wade	Arundel Cat	White	100	£15	108	150.	165.	85.
Wade	Arundel Salmon, (EW) (RRC)	Pink	1,500	Free	30 x 30	14.	15.	8.
Wade	Clown, singing	Pearlised; black hat, shoes	250	£35 Pr	120	30.	33.	18.
Wade	Clown, banjo	Pearlised; black hat, shoes	250	£35 Pr	120	30.	33.	18.

COLLECTORS / SWAP MEETS (cont.)

2001

The Arundel Swap Meet was renamed Arundel Collectors Meet in 2001.

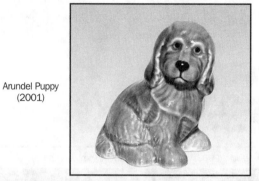

Arundel Puppy
(2001)

Clarence the Cow
Gold edition
(2001)

Comm.	Name	Description	Issue	Price	Size	U.S. $	Can. $	U.K. £
Wade	Arundel Puppy	Honey	900	£20	75 x 60	45.	50.	25.
Wade	Arundel Puppy	White	100	£20	75 x 60	150.	165.	80.
Wade	Clarence the Cow	White; black patches; blue flower	250	£20	50 x 75	45.	50.	25.
Wade	Clarence the Cow	White; gold patches; white flower	25	Goody	50 x 75	90.	100.	50.
Wade	Otter (WL)	Grey	2,000	Free	40 x 40	14.	15.	8.
Wade	Sumo the Elephant	Grey; blue balloon	250	£20	50 x 75	45.	50.	25.
Wade	Sumo the Elephant	Grey; gold balloon	25	Goody	50 x 75	90.	100.	50.

2002

The "Pony Whimsie" was formerly the Tom Smith Cracker "Family Pets" Shetland Pony.

Arundel Pony (honey and white) (2002)

Arundel Town Mouse [black hat /gold hat]

Sumo the Elephant - gold edition (2001)

Comm.	Name	Description	Issue	Price	Size	U.S. $	Can. $	U.K. £
Wade	Arundel Pony	Honey; brown hooves	900	£20	80 x 125	45.	50.	25.
Wade	Arundel Pony	White; brown hooves	100	£20	80 x 125	130.	145.	75.
OWICC/C&S	Arundel Town Mouse	White; black hat, tail, umbrella	200	£25	90	70.	80.	40.
OWICC/C&S	Arundel Town Mouse	White; gold hat, umbrella; black tail	20	Prizes	90	150.	165.	85.
Wade	Pony Whimsie (TS)	Honey	—	Free	25 x 30	9.	10.	5.
C&S	Swan	Black; orange beak	150	£20	70 x 95	30.	33.	18.
C&S	Swan	Pearl lustre	20	Prizes	70 x 95	80.	90.	45.
C&S	Swan	White; orange beak	150	£20	70 x 90	30.	33.	18.

COLLECTORS / SWAP MEETS (cont.)

2003

Badger Whimsie (2003)

Arundel Lamb (white and black) (2003)

Lady Townmouse (2003)

Comm.	Name	Description	Issue	Price	Size	U.S. $	Can. $	U.K. £
Wade	Arundel Lamb	Black	100	Prizes	60 x 90	20.	22.	12.
Wade	Arundel Lamb	White; black eyes, feet	900	£20	60 x 90	35.	40.	20.
C&S	Badger Baby	Black; white markings	150	£40 Pr	50 x 115	35.	40.	20.
C&S	Badger Mother	Black; white markings	150	£40 Pr	90 x 130	35.	40.	20.
C&S	Badger Mother	Gold	20	Prizes	90 x 130	—	—	—
Wade	Badger Whimsie	Grey	—	Free	25 x 30	17.	18.	10.
Wade	Bulldog Key chain	White; honey patches; black nose	—	£5	35	25.	28.	15.
C&S	Lady Town Mouse	White; blue bonnet, cloak, yellow ribbon	200	£26	80	45.	50.	25.

2004

Arundel Fox (2004)

Master Howard Town Mouse (2004)

Fox Whimsie (2004)

Comm.	Name	Description	Issue	Price	Size	U.S. $	Can. $	U.K. £
Wade	Arundel Fox	Ginger	900	£25	90 x 45	35.	40.	20.
Wade	Arundel Fox	White	100	£25	90 x 45	—	—	—
Wade	Blue Tit (on milk churn)	Blue, yellow, white, silver	Unk.	£25	Unk.	45.	50.	25.
C&S	Master Howard Town Mouse	White; blue, yellow tie; brown bag	200	£26	60 x 40	35.	40.	20.
C&S	Mother Hedgehog	Brown	150	£40 Pr	50 x 110	70.	75.	40.
C&S	Baby Hedgehog	Brown	150	£40 Pr	40 x 80	Price	Per	Pair
Wade	Spotty's Feeding Time	Black, white; gold bowl	25	£25	Unk.	—	—	—
Wade	Spotty's Feeding Time	Black, white; red bowl	Unk.	Unk.	Unk.	45.	50.	25.
Wade	Whimslieland Fox	Gold	10	Free	35 x 35	—	—	—
Wade	Whimslieland Fox	Honey	—	Free	35 x 35	20.	22.	12.

COLLECTORS / SWAP MEETS (cont.)

2005

Arundel Pig

Maise the Puppy

Spot the Dalmatian

Comm.	Name	Description	Issue	Price	Size	U.S. $	Can. $	U.K. £
Wade	Arundel Pig	Pink	400	£25	80 x 110	35.	40.	20.
Wade	Arundel Pig	White	100	£25	80 x 110	125.	135.	65.
C&S	Betty Boop Cheers	See Betty Boop Series, page 219	—	—	—	—	—	—
Wade	Maisie	Grey; brown basket; red cover	—	£25	65	45.	50.	25.
C&S	Miss Georgina Town Mouse	White mouse; honey bear	200	£26	60 x 40	45.	50.	25.
Wade	Spot the Dalmatian	White, black markings	—	£50	—	45.	50.	25.
Wade	WhimsieLand Pig	Black	100	Free	30 x 30	28.	30.	15.
Wade	WhimsieLand Pig	Silver	20	—	30 x 30	75.	80.	40.

2006

Arundel Bear

Bear Whimsie

Edward Town Mouse

Comm.	Name	Description	Issue	Price	Size	U.S. $	Can. $	U.K. £
Wade	Arundel Bear	Honey	450	—	60 x100	50.	55.	25.
Wade	Arundel Bear	Gold	25	Prizes	60 x 100	225.	250.	125.
Wade	Arundel Bear	White	50	—	60 x 100	100.	110.	55.
Wade	Bear Whimsie	Brown	—	Free	37	—	—	—
C&S	Betty Boop Cool Breeze	See Betty Boop Series, page 219	250	—	—	—	—	—
C&S	Edward Town Mouse	White mouse; blue bib; silver pin	150	—	57	50.	55.	25.

Note: 1. A dash in any of the technical data columns of the table indicates that we do not have the required information, if you do, we would be pleased to hear from you.

2. Dashes in the pricing columns indicate one of two things: firstly, there was insufficient market pricing available, and secondly, pieces issued in small quantities of 10 or 20 pieces will be subject to wide pricing swings.

BIRMINGHAM FAIRS

1994-1996

Spaniel (1994)   Grey-haired Rabbit (1995)   Smiling Frog (1996)

Backstamp: All: Embossed "Wade"

Date	Name	Description	Issue	Price	Size	U.S. $	Can. $	U.K. £
1994	Spaniel	Honey	1,000	£12.50	75 x 60	175.	200.	100.
1995	Grey-haired Rabbit	Grey-brown	1,250	£12.50	87 x 60	150.	165.	85.
1996	Smiling Frog	Green	1,250	£12.50	60 x 80	70.	80.	40.

COLLECT IT! FAIRS

NEWARK, 1998, STONELEIGH, 1998

Baby Bear in Pyjamas (1998)	Oops! the Bear, Style One (1998)	Travelling Frog (1998)

Date	Name	Description	Issue	Price	Size	U.S. $	Can. $	U.K. £
1998	Baby Bear in Pyjamas	Blue/white striped pyjamas	1,000	£25.00	153	60.	65.	35.
1998	Oops! the Bear, Style One	Amber; pink plaster on knee	500	£12.50	60	50.	55.	30.
1998	Travelling Frog	Green jacket; red cravat, bag	2,500	£20.00	135	45.	50.	25.

Honey Bunch Bears

Approximately 40 of each of the six Honey Bunch Bears, with the bee transfer omitted, were randomly decorated by freehand and sold at the Collect It! Fair wrapped in Christmas paper and shaped as a cracker. See also page 110.

Cross-eyed Bear	Honey Bear	Golly Gosh Bear; Sleepy Bear

Date	Name	Description	Issue	Price	Size	U.S. $	Can. $	U.K. £
1998	Cross-eyed Bear	Honey; gold collar, cuffs	40		57	35.	40.	20.
1998	Cross-eyed Bear	Honey; red/blue spots	40	Set	57	35.	40.	20.
1998	Golly Gosh Bear	Honey, blue dungarees	40	of six	55	35.	40.	20.
1998	Honey Bear	Honey; gold collar, cuffs	40	£25	57	35.	40.	20.
1998	Honey Bear	Honey; red vest; gold honey pot	40		57	35.	40.	20.
1998	Sleepy Bear	Honey; pink night cap, collar	40		55	35.	40.	20.

DUNSTABLE FAIRS — 1996-2006

Timid Mouse (1996)

Koala Bear (1997)

Cook Catkins (1998)

British Lion (1999)

Puppy Love "Ella" (1999)

Shoal of Fish (1999)

Lil' Witch (2002)

Polar Bear (2002)

Union Bear (2002)

Buttercup (2003)

Lil' Cricketer (2003)

Pearl Snail (2003)

1996

Backstamp: Timid Mouse: Embossed "Wade," black printed "Limited Edition of 1,750 Exclusively Dunstable Wade Fair 1996"

Comm.	Name	Description	Issue	Price	Size	U.S. $	Can. $	U.K. £
Wade	Timid Mouse	Light brown; green/brown base	1,750	£16	60	65.	70.	35.

1997

Backstamp: A. Black printed "The Koala Bear 1 of 1,500 Exclusive Edition for Dunstable Wade Fair 1997 ©UK Fairs Ltd and Wade Ceramics Ltd"
B. Black printed "The Koala Bear 1 of 150 Exclusive Edition of Dunstable Wade Fair Special Produced Soley for Over-seas Wade Collectors ©UK Fairs Ltd & Wade Ceramics Ltd"

Comm.	Name	Description	Issue	Price	Size	U.S. $	Can. $	U.K. £
Wade/UKI	Koala Bear	Beige; brown tree; green leaves	1,650	£20	127	65.	70.	35

1998

Backstamp: Cook Catkins: Printed "Cook Catkins 1 of 1,500 Exclusive Edition for the Dunstable Wade Fair 1998 UKWC02 ©UK Fairs Ltd and Wade ®Ceramics Ltd""
Printed "Wade Limited Edition of 350 ©Wade Ceramics LTD ©UKI Ceramics LTD Produced Exclusively for UKI

Comm.	Name	Description	Issue	Price	Size	U.S. $	Can. $	U.K. £
UKI	Cook Catkins	White apron	1,500	£25	140	65.	70.	35.
UKI	Cook Catkins	White/green apron	500	£25	140	65.	70.	35.

1999

Backstamp: British Lion: Printed "Wade Limited Edition of 350 ©Wade Ceramics LTD ©UKI Ceramics Limited Produced in an exclusive World-wide Edition" [name of model and UKI Ceramics tel no.]
Puppy Love "Ella": Black paw print with black and red lettering "Puppy L♥ve By Wade Puppy L♥ve Limited Edition 500 1999 Ella
Seals: Printed "Wade England"
Shoal of Fish: Printed "Wade Limited Edition of 350 ©Wade Ceramics LTD ©UKI Ceramics LTD Produced Exclusively for UKI Ceramics LTD in an Exclusive World-wide Edition" [name of model and UKI tel. no.]

Comm.	Name	Description	Issue	Price	Size	U.S. $	Can. $	U.K. £
UKI	British Lion	Tan, streaked brown mane	340	£30	160	50.	55.	30.
UKI	British Lion	Unknown	10	£30	160	—	—	—
Wade	Puppy Love "Ella"	White; tan patches	500	£20	70	40.	45.	23.
Wade	Seals (pair)	Grey/black	750	£30	40 x 70	50.	55.	28.
UKI	Shoal of Fish	Orange; white waves; blue base	340	£30	140	55.	60.	30.
UKI	Shoal of Fish	Unknown	10	£30	140	—	—	—

2002

Backstamp: Lil Witch and Union Bear: Printed "Ltd. Edit. 125 Lil Witch September 2002" and red "Wade" logo
Polar Bear: Embossed "Wade"

Comm.	Name	Description	Issue	Price	Size	U.S. $	Can. $	U.K. £
Wade	Lil Witch	Black cloak, white dress; black hat, red band/ribbon	125	N/A	98	100.	110.	55.
Wade	Polar Bear (EW)	Pearlised	—	Free	30 x 50	12.	13.	7.
Wade	Union Bear	White bear; red/white/blue Union Jack flag	125	N/A	78	50.	55.	30.

2003

Backstamp: Unknown

Comm.	Name	Description	Issue	Price	Size	U.S. $	Can. $	U.K. £
Wade	Buttercup (Horse)	Amber horse; brown base	—	£20	85	30.	35.	17.
Wade	Lil' Cricketer	White , blue, red, gold and green	125	N/A	95	70.	80.	40.
Wade	Pearl Snail	Pearl	125	Free	30 x 35	13.	15.	8.
Wade	Shep the Sheepdog	Black/white; green base	—	£20	90	30.	33.	18.

DUNSTABLE FAIRS (cont.)

2004

Blackbird

Football Bear

Comm.	Name	Description	Issue	Price	Size	U.S. $	Can. $	U.K. £
Wade	Blackbird	Black bird; green base	—	—	Unk.	35.	40.	20.
Wade	Football Bear	Honey bear; red, white, blue football strip	—	—	—	—	—	—
Wade	Penguin Whimsie	See Pearl Lustre Whimsies, page 82	—	—	—	—	—	—

2005

Antique
Bully

Comm.	Name	Description	Issue	Price	Size	U.S. $	Can. $	U.K. £
Wade	Antique Bully	Black jacket; grey trousers;	125	—	80	—	—	—
Wade	Giraffe Whimsie	See Pearl Lustre Whimsies, page 82	—	—	—	—	—	—

2006

Comm.	Name	Description	Issue	Price	Size	U.S. $	Can. $	U.K. £
Wade	Halloween Felix the Cat	See Felix the Cat Series, page 106	—	—	—	—	—	—
Wade	Puppy Whimsie	See Pearl Lustre Whimsies, page 82	—	—	—	—	—	—

OLYMPIA INCENTIVE EXHIBITION

1998

The 1997 *Bear Ambitions* model "Admiral Sam" was reissued for the Trade Exhibition, and was handed out at random to visitors to the Wade Stand. Surplus models were placed in the Bran Tub at the San Antonio show.

Backstamp: Embossed "Wade Eng" on back rim

Date	Name	Description	Issue	Price	Size	U.S. $	Can. $	U.K. £
1998	Admiral Sam	Pale blue	200	—	50	60.	65.	35.

Note: 1. A dash in any of the technical data columns of the table indicates that we do not have the required information, if you do, we would be pleased to hear from you.
2. Dashes in the pricing columns indicate one of two things: firstly, there was insufficient market pricing available, and secondly, pieces issued in small quantities of 10 or 20 pieces will be subject to wide pricing swings.

RIPLEY VILLAGE FETE and TEDDY BEARS' PICNIC

1998

The Wade Village fete and Teddy Bears' Picnic was held on Sunday June 7th, 1998, at The Castle Flatts, Ripley Castle, Warwickshire.

Backstamp: **Camping Bear:** Printed "Camping Bear 1998 The Official International Wade Collectors Club" with OIWCC logo
Teddy Bear Plaque: Gold printed "Wade England Ripley 1998"

Date	Name	Description	Issue	Price	Size	U.S. $	Can. $	U.K. £
1998	Camping Bear	Dark green jacket; grey trousers	2,000	£15	115	35.	40.	20.
1998	Teddy Bear Plaque	Honey bear; white plaque	1,500	£20	195	55.	60.	30.

Bear Ambitions, 1998

Admiral Sam and Alex the Aviator   Artistic Edward and Beatrice Ballerina   Locomotive Joe and Musical Marco

Backstamp: **Artistic Edward:** Embossed "Wade England"
All other Bear Ambition figures: Embossed "Wade Eng"

Date	Name	Description	Issue	Price	Size	U.S. $	Can. $	U.K. £
1998	Admiral Sam	Green	2,000	£18	55	14.	16.	8.
1998	Alex the Aviator	Green	2,000	£18	45	14.	16.	8.
1998	Artistic Edward	Green	2,000	£18	40	14.	16.	8.
1998	Beatrice Ballerina	Green	2,000	£18	50	14.	16.	8.
1998	Locomotive Joe	Green	2,000	£18	50	14.	16.	8.
1998	Musical Marco	Green	2,000	£18	40	14.	16.	8.

Note: For *Bear Ambitions* in different colourways, see Wade regular issue, page 102, and Tom Smith and Company, page 318.

STOKE FAIRS

1997, TRENTHAM GARDENS

Kangaroo (1997)

Rufus (1997)

Backstamp: Kangaroo: Black printed "The Kangaroo 1 of 1,500 Exclusive Limited Edition For The Trentham Gardens Wade Fair 1997 ©UK Fairs LTD & Wade Ceramics LTD"
Kangaroo: Printed "The Kangaroo 1 of 50 Exclusive Limited Edition Trentham Gardens 1997 Wade Fair Special Produced solely for overseas Wade Collectors ©UK Fairs Ltd & Wade Ceramics Ltd"
Rufus: Printed "The Official International Wade Collectors Club Wade on Tour 1997"

Comm.	Name	Description	Issue	Price	Size	U.S. $	Can. $	U.K. £
UKI	Kangaroo	Orange-brown; green base	1,650	£18.00	127	70.	80.	40.
Wade	Mr. Snowman Pepper	Black hat; green striped scarf	100	£17.50	100	18.	20.	10.
Wade	Mrs. Snowman Salt	Black hat; brown collar, muff	100	Pair	95	18.	20.	10.
Club	Rufus	Red-brown; cobalt blue cushion	—	£15.00	65	35.	40.	20.

1998, TRENTHAM GARDENS

Backstamp: City Gent Catkins: Printed "The City Gent Catkins ® 1 of 1,500 Exclusive Limited Edition For The Trentham Gardens Wade Fair 1998 © UK Fairs LTD & Wade Ceramics LTD"
Travelling Badger: Printed "The Official International Wade Collectors Club Travelling Badger Wade on Tour 1998"

Comm.	Name	Description	Issue	Price	Size	U.S. $	Can. $	U.K. £
UKI	City Gent Catkins	Light grey coat; dark grey pants	1,500	£25	115	50.	55.	30.
Club	Travelling Badger	Blue coat, hat; brown case	—	£15	90	35.	40.	20.

1999, TRENTHAM GARDENS

Backstamp:
Gypsy Catkins: Printed "Gypsy Catkins 1 of 1,000 Exclusive Limited Edition for the Trentham Wade Fair 1999 UKWCO3 ©UK Fairs & Wade® Ceramics Ltd"
Penguins: Printed "Wade Made in England"
Puppy Love "Sidney": Black paw print with black and red lettering "Puppy L♥ve By Wade Puppy L♥ve Limited Edition 500 1999 Sidney"

Comm.	Name	Description	Issue	Price	Size	U.S. $	Can. $	U.K. £
UKI	Gypsy Catkins	Maroon waistcoat; blue pants	1,000	£20	140	50.	55.	30.
Wade	Penguins (pair)	Black/white; yellow beaks	750	£35	80 x 60	80.	90.	45.
Wade	Puppy Love "Sidney"	Tan/white; blue cushion	500	£20	50	40.	45.	23.

2000,TRENTHAM GARDENS

Backstamp: Red printed "Wade Made in England"

Comm.	Name	Description	Issue	Price	Size	U.S. $	Can. $	U.K. £
Wade	Roly Poly Rabbit	Yellow dress; white apron	500	£20	75	40.	45.	23.

2000, STAFFORD SHOW GROUNDS

In 2000, the Spring Wade Fair (May 7th) was moved from Trentham Gardens to the Show Grounds at Stafford. There were two Wade Show specials, "Fireman Catkins" and "Millennium Catkins." The "Millennium Teddy" was designed by Stoke-on-Trent schoolgirl Helen Bourne, it was sold at the fair by Wade Ceramics.

Fireman Catkins (2000)

Millennium Catkins (2000)

Millennium Teddy (2000)

Backstamp: **Fireman Catkins:** Printed "Fireman Catkins Exclusive Limited Edition of 250 No. 7 in the series WADE © UKI CERAMICS LTD. © WADE CERAMICS LTD."
Millennium Catkins: Printed "Millennium Catkins Exclusive Limited Edition of 250 (No.) in the series WADE England © UKI CERAMICS LTD. © WADE CERAMICS LTD."
Millennium Teddy: Printed "May 2000" with International Wade Club logo.

Comm.	Name	Description	Issue	Price	Size	U.S. $	Can. $	U.K. £
UKI	Fireman Catkins	Dark blue uniform; yellow helmet gold nozzle, badge	250	£38.50	128	60.	65.	35.
UKI	Millennium Catkins	White shirt; grey trousers; multicoloured balloons	250	£38.50	125	60.	65.	35.
OWICC	Millennium Teddy	Brown; white/pewter/blue numeral 2000	500	£20.00	90	60.	65.	35.

2001, TRENTHAM GARDENS

Owl (2001)

Lil' Devil (2001)

Hector the Owl (2001), Pedro the Donkey (2001), Major the Lion (2001), Poppy the Pig (2001)

Backstamp: **Australia Olympic Catkins:** Unknown
Clown Catkins: Unknown
Hector the Owl: Printed red and white "Wade" decal
Lil' Devil: Printed "Lil' Devil Extravaganza Special 2001 Ltd Ed 100" with red "Wade" logo
Major the Lion: Printed white "Wade" in red decal
Pedro the Donkey: Printed red and white "Wade" decal
Poppy the Pig: Printed red and white "Wade" decal

Comm.	Name	Description	Issue	Price	Size	U.S. $	Can. $	U.K. £
UKI	Australia Olympic Catkins	Yellow/green suit; gold medal	100	£50	120	85.	95.	50.
UKI	Clown Catkins	Red/black/white /gold	22	£45	120	85.	95.	50.
Wade	Duck (WL)	Pearl	—	Free	45 x 35	25.	28.	15.
UKI	Gypsy Catkins	Red/maroon/blue/brown	70	£45	120	85.	95.	50.
Wade	Hector the Owl	Tan, black mortar board cap	250	£20	80 x 40	45.	50.	25.
Wade	Hector the Owl	Tan, gold mortar board cap	25	Special	80 x 40	85.	95.	50.
Wade	Lil' Devil	Red horns, bow; black cloak	100	£39.50	95	140.	160.	80.
Wade	Major the Lion	Honey; brown mane	250	£20	52 x 86	35.	40.	20.
Wade	Major the Lion	Honey; gold	20	£50	52 x 86	115.	125.	65.
Wade	Owl (WL)	Gold	—	Free	35 x 25	14.	16.	8.
Wade	Pedro the Donkey	Brown; yellow/blue hat	250	£20	57 x 70	60.	65.	35.
Wade	Pedro the Donkey	Brown, gold hat	25	Special	57 x 70	115.	125.	65.
Wade	Poppy the Pig	Pink; red/ yellow lollipop	250	£20	58 x 74	45.	50.	25.
Wade	Poppy the Pig	Pink; gold lollipop	20	£50	58 x 74	115.	125.	65.

2002, KINGS HALL CIVIC CENTRE

The Pearl Bunny, which is from the Tom Smith *Family Pets* (1988-1989) rabbit mould, was given free of charge to collectors as they entered the show. The Donkey, which was modelled by Simon Millard, was introduced at the this show.

Lil' Easter Bear
(2002)

Donkey
(2002)

Backstamp:
Donkey: Printed "C&S Wade Official Collectors Centre"
Lil' Easter: Printed "Ltd. Edt. 125 April 2002 Lil Easter Bear" and red "Wade" logo
Pearl Bunny: Embossed "Wade England"

Comm.	Name	Description	Issue	Price	Size	U.S. $	Can. $	U.K. £
C&S	Donkey	Honey; black eyes	100	£22	78 x 88	50.	55.	30.
Wade	Lil' Easter Bear	Blue/white dress; blue bonnet; pink ribbon, bow; yellow chick; brown basket	125	£45	95	90.	100.	50.
Wade	Pearl Bunny (TS)	Pearl	—	Free	30 x 25	20.	23.	12.

PIG STYLES

In the Pig Styles Series, please note the name "Caesar" is incorrectly spelled "Ceaser" in Wade advertising, and on the certificate of authenticity.

Arnie , Ceasar, Topsy-Turvey, Twirly Whirly (2002)

Backstamp: Printed "Pig Styles 2002 Ltd Edition of 200 [name of model]" and "Wade" logo

Comm.	Name	Description	Issue	Price	Size	U.S. $	Can. $	U.K. £
Wade	Arnie	Pink; green shorts; black weights	200	—	60	35.	40.	20.
Wade	Ceasar	Pink; white toga; green laurel wreath	200	—	65	35.	40.	20.
Wade	Topsey-Turvey	Pink; yellow t-shirt; blue pants; red nose	200	—	70	35.	40.	20.
Wade	Twirly Whirly	Pink; blue dress	200	—	73	35.	40.	20.

2003, NORTH STAFFORDSHIRE HOTEL

The site of the Wade UK Collectors Show, formerly held at Trentham Gardens, was moved again, this time to the North Stafford Hotel, Stoke-on-Trent, Staffordshire. The show held April 13th, 2003, offered many new models and show specials. Lil' Footballer was the fifth model in the Wade Lil' Bears series. It was produced in a limited edition of 125. Overseas collectors who could not attend the show could send a postcard to the Wade Club to be entered into a draw for 25 of the models. A set of ponies was introduced at various Wade shows throughout the year. The first model "Bluebell" was introduced at the North Stafford show. Also available at the show was the Dalmatian Key Chain, and Beau the Greyhound. The entry model was the Pearl Seahorse, originally from *English Whimsies* series, at a cost of £6.00.

Bluebell the Pony (2003)

Dalmatian Key Chain (2003)

Lil' Footballer Bear (2003)

Beau the Greyhound (2003)

Backstamp: **Beau the Greyhound:** Printed "Beau 2003" and red "Wade" logo
Bluebell: Embossed "Wade"
Brandy: Printed "Brandy 125 Limited Edition" and red "Wade" logo
Budgie: Printed "Fair Special Budgie Limited Edition 125" and red "Wade" logo
Lil' Footballer: Printed "Ltd. Edt. 125 April 2002 Lil Footballer" and red "Wade" logo
Pearl Seahorse: Embossed "Wade"

Comm.	Name	Description	Issue	Price	Size	U.S. $	Can. $	U.K. £
Wade	Beau the Greyhound	Beige; checkered blue/beige base	—	—	55	35.	40.	20.
Wade	Bluebell the Pony	Tan; brown base	—	—	90	35.	40.	20.
Wade	Brandy, St. Bernard	White; red brown markings; gold barrel	125	—	70	35.	40.	20.
Wade	Budgie	Green/white/yellow bird, brown base	125	—	68	60.	65.	35.
Wade	Dalmatian Key Chain	White; black markings; chrome key chain	—	—	40	9.	10.	5.
Wade	Lil' Footballer Bear	Brown; white/blue/red shirt; black/gold ball	125	—	85	50.	55.	30.
Wade	Pearl Seahorse (EW)	Pearl	—	Free	50	15.	17.	8.

Note: The Wade glaze colour for the tan pony is 'rock'.

2004, NORTH STAFFORDSHIRE HOTEL

Hungry Spot, the Dalmatian (2004)

Jonno Bear (2004)

Kingfisher (2004)

Backstamp: **Hungry Dalmatian:** Printed "Wade Made in England"
Jonno Bear: Printed "Jonno Bear Wade Made in England, April 2004, Ltd Edition 125"
Kingfisher: Printed "Kingfisher Wade Made in England"

Comm.	Name	Description	Issue	Price	Size	U.S. $	Can. $	U.K. £
Wade	Dolphin Whimsie	See Pearl Lustre Whimsies, page 82	—	Free	30x40	18.	20.	10.
C&S	Easter Bunny	Fawn, pink inner ears; black eyes	125	£25	78	45.	50.	25.
Wade	Hungry Spot, the Dalmation	White, black markings; brown boot	500	£25	35	45.	50.	25.
Wade	Jonno Bear	Honey; white shirt, black shorts	125	£55	155	90.	100.	55.
Wade	Kingfisher	Blue, orange, white bird; pale blue base	500	£25	78	35.	40.	20.
Wade	Kingfisher	Blue; bronze breast, wings	20	£20	78	—	—	—

2005, KINGS HALL CIVIC CENTRE

British Bulldog (2005)

Goodnight Spot (2005)

Maisie (2005)

Comm.	Name	Description	Issue	Price	Size	U.S. $	Can. $	U.K. £
Wade	British Bulldog	Black suit; brown hat; red/white/blue waistcoat	100	—	90	100.	110.	60.
Wade	Goodnight Spot	White, black dog; brown basket	500	£25	35	45.	50.	25.
Wade	Maisie	White, black dog; brown basket; green cover	250	£25	65	45.	50.	25.
Wade	Puppy Whimsie	See Pearl Lustre Whimsies, page 82	—	—	—	—	—	—

2006, KINGS HALL CIVIC CENTRE

Sydney
Tetley Tea Whimsie
(2006)

Maurice
Tetley Tea Whimsie
(2006)

Backstamp: Wade England Tetley

Comm.	Name	Description	Issue	Price	Size	U.S. $	Can. $	U.K. £
Wade	English Bull Terrier	See Pearl Lustre Whimsies, page 82	—	—	—	—	—	—
Wade	Felix the Cat	See Felix the Cat Series, page 106	—	—	—	—	—	—
Wade	Maurice	See Tetley Tea Folk Whimsies, page 84	—	—	—	—	—	—
Wade	Sydney	See Tetley Tea Folk Whimsies, page 84	—	—	—	—	—	—

2007, DISCOVER TRENTHAM

Timid Mouse

Backstamp: Unknown

Comm.	Name	Description	Issue	Price	Size	U.S. $	Can. $	U.K. £
Wade	Bluebird Whimsie	Pale blue	—	Free	—	28.	30.	15.
Wade	Cocktail Felix	See Felix the Cat Series, page 106	—	—	—	—	—	—

WADE CHRISTMAS EXTRAVAGANZA

2000

Bear Cub (2000)

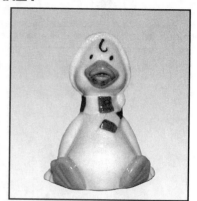

Quackers the Duck, Style One (2000)

Backstamp: **Bear Cub:** Embossed "Wade"
Quackers the Duck: Red printed "Wade Made in England"

Comm.	Name	Description	Issue	Price	Size	U.S. $	Can. $	U.K. £
Wade	Bear Cub (EW)	Gold	1,500	Free	30	20.	22.	12.
Wade	Quackers the Duck, Style One	Red/white hat; blue/white scarf	500	£20	70	45.	50.	25.

FAMILY FAVOURITES

The Family Favourites set was still available on-line and from the Wade Factory Shop in September 2003, at the U.K. prices listed below.

Backstamp:: Red printed "Wade Made in England"

Comm.	Name	Description	Issue	Price	Size	U.S. $	Can. $	U.K. £
Wade	Boots the Rabbit	Brown rabbit; blue/white boot	—	£15	90 x 75	25.	30.	15.
Wade	Dribbles the Dog	Brown dog; white/black football	—	£15	70 x 90	25.	30.	15.
Wade	Hattie the Squirrel	Honey squirrel; grey hat	—	£15	85 x 70	25.	30.	15.
Wade	Priscilla the Pig	Pink pig; brown bed; blue blanket	—	£15	60 x 75	25.	30.	15.
Wade	Tiny the Mouse	Brown mouse; grey/platinum can	—	£15	95 x 40	25.	30.	15.
Wade	Tubby the Bear	Brown bear; blue/pewter barrel	—	£15	82 x 55	25.	30.	15.

U.S.A. WADE COLLECTORS SHOWS

The four U.S. Wade Collectors Shows (Seattle 1996, Oconomowoc 1997, Buffalo 1998, and San Antonio 1999) were all held in conjunction with The International Association Jim Beam Bottles Society Collectors Club.

Madison Mouse (1997)

New York Tourist (1998)

Oscar the Christmas Teddy Bear (1998)

1996, SEATTLE, WA

Backstamp: Printed black and red "The Official International Wade Collectors Club," and black "Seattle 1996"

Comm.	Name	Description	Issue	Price	Size	U.S. $	Can. $	U.K. £
Wade	Westie the West Highland Terrier	White	3,000	$20 US	75 x 78	40.	45.	23.

1997, OCONOMOWOC, WI

Backstamp: Black and red circular "The Official International Wade Collectors Club Wisconsin 1997"

Comm.	Name	Description	Issue	Price	Size	U.S. $	Can. $	U.K. £
OIWCC	Madison Mouse	Beige; yellow cheese	—	$30 US	95 x 60	40.	45.	23.

1998, BUFFALO, NY

Backstamp: **New York Tourist:** Printed "Buffalo Fair Special 1998" with OIWCC logo
Oscar the Christmas Teddy Bear: Printed "Oscar Special Colourway Buffalo 1998 The Official International Wade Collectors Club" with OIWCC logo
Teddy Bear Plaque: Gold printed "Wade England Buffalo 1998"

Comm.	Name	Description	Issue	Price	Size	U.S. $	Can. $	U.K. £
Wade	New York Tourist	Blue t-shirt; black trousers	—	$24 US	110	45.	50.	25.
Wade	Oscar , Christmas Teddy Bear	Honey; green hat; lustre sack	75	$85 US	110	300.	325.	175.
Wade	Teddy Bear Plaque	Chocolate brown bear, plaque	1,500	$40 US	195	50.	55.	30.

1999, SAN ANTONIO, TX

Backstamp: **Prairie Dog:** Printed "The Prairie Dog with OIWCC logo"
Puppy Love "Shelby": Black paw print with black and red lettering "Puppy L♥ve by Wade Puppy L♥ve Limited Edition 500 1999 Shelby"
Rufus on Tour: Printed "Genuine Wade Porcelain limited edition of 100"

Comm.	Name	Description	Issue	Price	Size	U.S. $	Can. $	U.K. £
Wade	Prairie Dog	Brown/white; yellow rose	500	$20 US	120	75.	85.	40.
Wade	Puppy Love "Shelby"	White; brown patches	500	$20 US	50	45.	50.	28.
Wade	Rufus on Tour	Beige; pearlised beige base	100	Set	84	70.	75.	40.
Wade	Rufus on Tour	Grey; gold base	100	of	84	70.	75.	40.
Wade	Rufus on Tour	Honey; platinum base	100	Four	84	70.	75.	40.
Wade	Rufus on Tour	Tan; copper base	100	$200 US	84	70.	75.	40.

KANSAS WADE SHOW

2000

Armadillo (2000)

Backstamp: Armadillo: Embossed "Wade England"

Comm.	Name	Description	Issue	Price	Size	U.S. $	Can. $	U.K. £
Rucker	Armadillo (TS)	Copper lustre	917	$10 US	25 x 45	20.	22.	12.
Rucker	Armadillo (TS)	Light green	1,000	$10 US	25 x 45	20.	22.	12.

2001

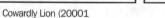

Cowardly Lion (20001

Dorothy and Toto (2001)

Ozma (2001)

Backstamp: Wizard of Oz Series: Hand written "Oz No [number of model in series]" with printed "Wade Est 1810 England"

Comm.	Name	Description	Issue	Price	Size	U.S. $	Can. $	U.K. £
KSWader	Cowardly Lion	Honey; brown mane	500	$35 US	67	50.	55.	28.
KSWader	Cowardly Lion	White	25	Prizes	67	175.	190.	90.
KSWader	Dorothy and Toto	White, blue check dress; grey dog	500	$70 US	60	90.	100.	50.
KSWader	Dorothy and Toto	White	25	Prizes	60	175.	190.	90.
KSWader	Ozma	Pearlised dress	500	$50 US	65	60.	65.	35.
KSWader	Ozma	White	25	Prizes	65	175.	190.	90.

Notes: 1. The Armadillo models sold at the Kansas Wade Show were commissioned by Ed and Bev Rucker.
2. For other models in the Wizard of Oz series, see page 267.

RED ROSE TEA FAIR, CONNECTICUT

2006

The Red Rose Tea Fair was held November 4th and 5th, 2006.

Flamingo Whimsie

Gingerbread Man Tree Ornament

Squirrel Whimsie

Backstamp: Printed "Made in England" with red Wade logo

Date	Name	Description	Issue	Price	Size	U.S. $	Can. $	U.K. £
C&S	Flamingo Whimsie	Pink flamingo; bronze base	250	Set of	—	18.	20.	10.
C&S	Flamingo Whimsie	Pink flamingo; gold base	250	Three	—	18.	20.	10.
C&S	Flamingo Whimsie	Pink flamingo; silver base	250	£28.50	—	18.	20.	10.
Red Rose	Gingerbread Man Tree Ornament	Brown	300	$50 US	175	45.	50.	25.
Wade	Squirrel Whimsie	Honey; black nut	—	—	35 x 30	—	—	—
Wade	Squirrel Whimsie	Honey; green nut	—	—	35 x 30	—	—	—
Wade	Squirrel Whimsie	Honey; gold nut	—	—	35 x 30	—	—	—
Wade	Squirrel Whimsie	Honey; red-brown nut	—	—	35 x 30	—	—	—

Note: 1. A dash in any of the technical data columns of the table indicates that we do not have the required information, if you do, we would be pleased to hear from you.

2. Dashes in the pricing columns indicate one of two things: firstly, there was insufficient market pricing available, and secondly, pieces issued in small quantities of 10 or 20 pieces will be subject to wide pricing swings.

ROSEMONT TRADE SHOW
ROSEMONT, ILLINOIS

1999

Backstamp: Black paw print with black and red lettering "Puppy L♥ve
By Wade Puppy L♥ve Limited Edition 500 1999 Henry"

Comm.	Name	Description	Issue	Price	Size	U.S. $	Can. $	U.K. £
Wade	Puppy Love "Henry"	White/ grey	500	$20 US	85	35.	40.	20.

MINI WADE FAIR
YORK, PENNSYLVANIA

1999

The Mini Wade Fair, organized by Pat and Gary Keenan, was held August 1999, at Harrisburg, Pennsylvania. "Jenny the Black Poodle" was complimentary with admission to fair, additional models were sold at $5.00 US.

Backstamp: Embossed "Wade England"

Comm.	Name	Description	Issue	Price	Size	U.S. $	Can. $	U.K. £
Wade	Jenny the Black Poodle (RRC)	Black	40	$15 US	40 x 45	25.	28.	15.

SUMMER WADE FEST
HARRISBURG, PENNSYLVANIA

Organized by Pat and Gary Keenan, the Summer Wade Fest (formerly the Mini Wade Fair) is held at the Radisson Convention Centre, Camp Hill, Harrisburg, Pennsylvania.

2000

Backstamp: Embossed "Wade England"

Comm.	Name	Description		Issue	Price	Size	U.S. $	Can. $	U.K. £
Wade	Cat/Thunder (TS/RRU)	Black		1,200	$6 US	25 x 33	18.	20.	10.
Wade	Cat/Lightning (TS/RRU)	White		800	$6 US	25 x 33	18.	20.	10.
Wade	Cat/Goldie (TS/RRU)	Gold		100	Prizes	25 x 33	100.	110.	60.

2001

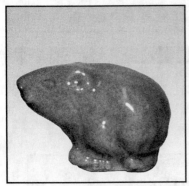

Guinea Pig (2001)

Nibbles the Bunny (2001)

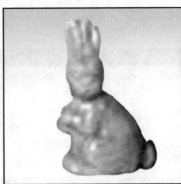

Little Bunnies [Lil' Bits] (2001)

Backstamp: **Arthur Hare Wizhared:** Embossed "Wade / C&S" on back rim
Guinea Pig: Embossed "Wade England"
Leprechaun Riding Snail: Printed "Wade"
Little Bunnies (Lil' Bits): Embossed "Wade England"
Nibbles the Bunny: Impressed "Wade"

Comm.	Name	Description	Issue	Price	Size	U.S. $	Can. $	U.K. £
C&S	Arthur Hare Wizhared	See Wizhared Whimsie, page 215	—	—	—	—	—	—
Wade	Guinea Pig (TS)	Black	500	$7 US	20 x 30	20.	22.	12.
Wade	Guinea Pig (TS)	Gold	100	Prizes	20 x 30	100.	110.	55.
Wade	Guinea Pig (TS)	White	1,000	$6 US	20 x 30	20.	22.	12.
Keenan	Leprechaun Riding Snail	Honey; brown/amber	650	$25 US	50 x 53	50.	55.	30.
Keenan	Little Bunnies (Lil' Bits)	Blue	450	$8 US	22	18.	20.	10.
Keenan	Little Bunnies (Lil' Bits)	White/pink streaks	250	Goodie	22	25.	30.	15.
Keenan	Little Bunnies (Lil' Bits)	Coronation green	450	$8 US	22	35.	40.	20.
Keenan	Little Bunnies (Lil' Bits)	Gold	50	Prizes	22	85.	95.	50.
Keenan	Little Bunnies (Lil' Bits)	Pink	450	$8 US	22	20.	22.	12.
Keenan	Little Bunnies (Lil' Bits)	White	450	$8 US	22	20.	22.	12.
Wade	Nibbles the Bunny	Honey	135	£20, $30 US	85	55.	60.	30.
Wade	Nibbles the Bunny	White	15	£20, $30 US	85	—	—	—

SUMMER WADE FEST, 2002

American Eagle (2002)

Mischief the Chimp (2002)

Leprechaun with Wheelbarrow

Lil' Uncle Sam (2002)

Lil' Bit Mice (2002)

Puppy (2002)

Backstamp: **American Eagle:** Printed "American Eagle July 2002 150 Limited Edition" with blue "C&S" and red "Wade" logo**s**
Leprechaun with Wheelbarrow of Gold: Printed red "Wade" logo
Lil' Bit Mice: None
Lil' Uncle Sam: Printed "Lil Uncle Sam Ltd. Edit. 125 July 2002" and red "Wade" logo
Mischief the Chimp: Printed "Mischief the Chimp USA July 2002"
Puppy: Embossed "Wade England"

Comm.	Name	Description	Issue	Price	Size	U.S. $	Can. $	U.K. £
C&S	American Eagle	Brown/white; gold base	20	Prizes	90	110.	120.	65.
C&S	American Eagle	Brown/white; off-white base	150	$38 US	90	40.	45.	23.
Keenan	Leprechaun / wheelbarrow	Honey coins	350	$28 US	50	35.	40.	20.
Keenan	Leprechaun / wheelbarrow	Gold coins	30	Prizes	50	120.	130.	70.
Keenen	Lil' Bit Mouse	Blue	500	$7 US	18	10.	11.	6.
Keenan	Lil' Bit Mouse	Gold	50	Prizes	18	70.	80.	40.
Keenan	Lil' Bit Mouse	Grey	500	$7 US	18	10.	11.	6.
Keenan	Lil' Bit Mouse	Honey	500	$7 US	18	10.	11.	6.
Keenan	Lil' Bit Mouse	White	500	$7 US	18	10.	11.	6.
Keenan	Lil' Uncle Sam	Blue coat; white waistcoat; red pants; red/white hat	125	$60 US	90	85.	95.	50.
Wade	Mischief the Chimp	Grey	50	$35 US	80	60.	65.	35.
Wade	Mischief the Chimp	Honey	100	$35 US	80	35.	40.	20.
Wade	Puppy	Black	650	$6 US	35 x 35	10.	11.	6.
Wade	Puppy	Gold	100	Prizes	35 x 35	50.	55.	30.
Wade	Puppy	White	650	$6 US	35 x 35	10.	11.	6.

Note: The base of the Lil' Bit Mouse is too small to hold a backstamp. The backstamp on the gold colourway Puppy is difficult to see.

SUMMER WADE FEST, 2003

Leprechaun on Rock [grey rock] (2003)

North American Bear (2003)

Lil' American Footballer (2003)

Harrisburg Straw Draw (gold specials) prizes: Kitten, Puppy, Guinea Pig, Lil' Bit Mouse, Lil' Rabbit, Reindeer (2003)

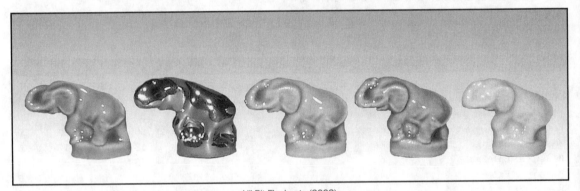

Lil' Bit Elephants (2003)

SUMMER WADE FEST, 2003

Backstamp: **Bulgie the Frog:** Embossed "Wade England"
Crocodile/Alligator: Embossed "Wade England" in recessed base
Leprechaun on a Rock: Printed red "Wade England" logo
Frog: Embossed "Wade England" in recessed base
Lil' American Footballer: Printed "Lil' American Footballer Limited Edition 125 July 2003" and red "Wade" logo
Lil' Bit Elephants: Embossed "Wade Eng"
North American Bear: Printed "American Bear Limited Edition of 150 July 2003" with blue "C&S"/red "Wade" logos
North American Bear: (Special) Printed red "Wade" logo
Reindeer: Embossed "Wade Eng" on front and back rims
Terrapin: Embossed "Wade England"s in recessed base

Comm.	Name	Description	Issue	Price	Size	U.S. $	Can. $	U.K. £
Wade	Bulgie the Frog	Blue	25	$30 US	50 x 90	70.	80.	40.
Wade	Bulgie the Frog	Green	125	$30 US	50 x 90	50.	55.	30.
Wade	Crocodile/Alligator (RR)	Honey	Unk.	Prizes	14 x 40	5.	6.	3.
Keenan	Leprechaun on a Rock	Brown/beige/blue-grey	300	$30 US	65	30.	35.	18.
Keenan	Leprechaun on a Rock	Brown/beige/gold	100	Prizes	65	50.	55.	30.
Wade	Frog (RR)	Light green	Unk.	Prizes	15 x 30	5.	6.	3.
Wade	Lil' American Footballer	Honey/dark blue/white/gold/red	125	$60 US	80	85.	95.	50.
Keenan	Lil' Bit Elephants	Blue	500	$7 US	22 x 33	10.	11.	6.
Keenan	Lil' Bit Elephants	Gold	100	Prizes	22 x 33	70.	75.	40.
Keenan	Lil' Bit Elephants	Green	500	$7 US	22 x 33	10.	11.	6.
Keenan	Lil' Bit Elephants	Grey	500	$7 US	22 x 33	10.	11.	6.
Keenan	Lil' Bit Elephants	White	500	$7 US	22 x 33	10.	11.	6.
C&S	N. American Bear	Dark brown; black eyes, nose	150	$35 US	70	50.	55.	30.
C&S	N. American Bear	White; black eyes, nose	20	Prizes	70	—	—	—
Wade	Reindeer, no gap (TS)	Gold	100	Prizes	30 x 35	—	—	—
Wade	Reindeer, no gap (TS)	Honey	600	—	30 x 35	14.	15.	8.
Wade	Reindeer, no gap (TS)	Honey, red nose	70	Prizes	30 x 35	—	—	—
Wade	Reindeer, no gap (TS)	White	600	—	30 x 35	14.	15.	8.
Wade	Terrapin (RR)	Grey	Unk.	Prizes	10 x 40	5.	6.	3.

Note: 1. A dash in any of the technical data columns of the table indicates that we do not have the required information, if you do, we would be pleased to hear from you.

2. Dashes in the pricing columns indicate one of two things: firstly, there was insufficient market pricing available, and secondly, pieces issued in small quantities of 10 or 20 pieces will be subject to wide pricing swings.

SUMMER WADE FEST, 2004

PA Pup

Leprechaun with Sign

Lil' Bit Duck

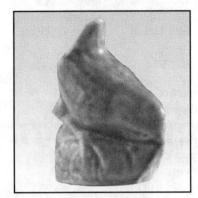
Wren Whimsies

Backstamp: **American Bear Cub:** Unknown
Leprechaun: Printed red "Wade" logo
Lil' Bit Duck: None
PA Pup: Unknown
Wren Whimsies: Embossed "Wade Eng"

Comm.	Name	Description	Issue	Price	Size	U.S. $	Can. $	U.K. £
C&S	American Bear Cub	Tan, brown; black eyes, nose	125	—	Unk.	50.	55.	25.
Keenan	Leprechaun with Sign	Grey hat, coat; honey trousers, base	300	—	65	35.	40.	20.
Keenan	Leprechaun with Sign	Grey hat, coat; honey trousers; gold base	40	—	65	60.	65.	35.
Keenan	Lil' Bit Duck	Blue	500	—	22	9.	10.	5.
Keenan	Lil' Bit Duck	Honey	500	—	22	9.	10.	5.
Keenan	Lil' Bit Duck	Gold	100	Prizes	22	60.	65.	35.
Keenan	Lil' Bit Duck	Green	500	—	22	9.	10.	5.
Keenan	Lil' Bit Duck	White	500	—	22	9.	10.	5.
Keenan	PA Pup	Honey; black eyes; red tongue	125	—	30 x 75	50.	55.	25.
Keenan	PA Pup	White; black eyes; pink tongue	25	—	30 x 75	175.	190.	100.
Wade	Wren Whimsie	Blue	600	$6 US	33	10.	11.	6.
Wade	Wren Whimsie	Gold	100	Prizes	33	60.	65.	35.
Wade	Wren Whimsie	White	600	$6 US	33	10.	11.	6.

SUMMER WADE FEST, 2005

Billy the Bottle Oven

PA Dragon

Gingerbread Girls

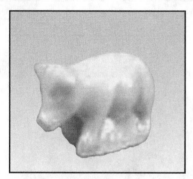
Lil' Bit Pig

Whimsieland Rabbit

Backstamp: **Billy the Bottle Oven:** Embossed "Wade Eng"
Gingerbread Girl: Embossed "Wade Eng"
Lil' Bit Pig: Embossed "Wade"
PA Dragon: Unknown
Whimsieland Rabbit: Embossed "Wade Eng"

Comm.	Name	Description	Issue	Price	Size	U.S. $	Can. $	U.K. £
Wade	Billy the Bottle Oven	White, light blue, red, black	250	$25 US	60 x 40	26.	28.	15.
Keenan	Gingerbread Girl	Red brown; blue skirt; green base	600	$15 US	70	18.	20.	10.
Keenan	Gingerbread Girl	Red brown; green skirt, base	600	$15 US	70	18.	20.	10.
Keenan	Gingerbread Girl	Red-brown; red skirt; green base	600	$15 US	70	18.	20.	10.
Keenan	Gingerbread Girl	Red-brown; yellow skirt; green base	600	$15 US	70	18.	20.	10.
Keenan	Lil' Bit Pig	Blue	500	$12 US	16	12.	13.	7.
Keenan	Lil' Bit Pig	Gold	100	Prizes	16	—	—	—
Keenan	Lil' Bit Pig	Green	500	$12 US	16	12.	13.	7.
Keenan	Lil' Bit Pig	Pink	500	$12 US	16	12.	13.	7.
Keenan	Lil' Bit Pig	Yellow	500	$12 US	16	12.	13.	7.
Keenan	PA Dragon	Pale blue	125	$25 US	90	55.	60.	33.
Keenan	PA Dragon	White	15	$25 US	90	—	—	—
Wade	Whimsieland Rabbit	Gold	100	Prizes	50	—	—	—
Wade	Whimsieland Rabbit	Grey	225	$10 US	50	10.	11.	6.
Wade	Whimsieland Rabbit	Honey	225	$10 US	50	10.	11.	6.

SUMMER WADE FEST, 2006

American Bald Eagle

Eagle Whimsie

Lil' Bit Cat

Bulldog Whimsies

Rabbit Whimsie

Backstamp: **American Bald Eagle:** Unknown
Bulldog: Embossed "Wade Eng"
Lil' Bit Cat: Embossed "Wade"

Comm.	Name	Description	Issue	Price	Size	U.S. $	Can. $	U.K. £
Keenan	American Bald Eagle	White head; brown body; blue base	Unk.	Unk.	45	30.	35.	14.
Keenan	Eagle Whimsie	Brown; grey base	—	Set of	45	25.	28.	12.
Keenan	Eagle Whimsie	Grey; dark green base	—	Three	45	25.	28.	12.
Keenan	Eagle Whimsie	White; blue base	—	$80 US	45	25.	28.	12.
Wade	Bulldog Whimsie (TS)	Gold	100	Prizes	35	100.	110.	55.
Wade	Bulldog Whimsie (TS)	Honey	600	$10 US	35	10.	11.	6.
Wade	Bulldog Whimsie (TS)	White	600	$10 US	35	10.	11.	6.
Keenan	Lil' Bit Cat	Black	500	$9.50	22	10.	11.	6.
Keenan	Lil' Bit Cat	Grey	500	$9.50	22	10.	11.	6.
Keenan	Lil' Bit Cat	Honey	500	$9.50	22	10.	11.	6.
Keenan	Lil' Bit Cat	White	500	$9.50	22	10.	11.	6.
Keenan	Lil' Bit Cat	Gold	100	Prizes	22	—	—	—
KSWader	Rabbit Whimsie	White; red Wade logo	100	£15 US	30	18.	20.	10.

WEST COAST WADE COLLECTORS FAIR
WASHINGTON

2002-2003

See also page 169 for colourways of "Lil' Uncle Sam" and "Mischief the Chimp."

| American Patriotic Eagle (2002) | Lil' Uncle Sam (2003) | Mischief the Chimp (2002) |

Backstamp: **American Patriotic Eagle:** Embossed "Wade England"
Lil' Uncle Sam: Printed "Lil' Uncle Sam Ltd. Edit. 125 June 2002"
Mischief the Chimp: Printed "Mischief the Chimp USA June 2002"

Comm.	Name	Description	Issue	Price	Size	U.S. $	Can. $	U.K. £
Wade	American Patriotic Eagle (TS)	Black	100	Prizes	25x45	18.	20.	10.
Wade	American Patriotic Eagle (TS)	Blue	300	Unk.	25x45	18.	20.	10.
Wade	American Patriotic Eagle (TS)	Gold	8	Prizes	25x45	—	—	—
Wade	American Patriotic Eagle (TS)	Red	300	Unk.	25x45	18.	20.	10.
Wade	American Patriotic Eagle (TS)	White	300	Unk.	25x45	18.	20.	10.
Wade	Lil' Uncle Sam	Brown, red, white and blue	125	$60 US	90	85.	95.	50.
Wade	Mischief the Chimp	Grey	50	$35 US	80	60.	65.	35.
Wade	Mischief the Chimp	Honey	100	$35 US	80	35.	40.	20.

Note: **1.** A dash in any of the technical data columns of the table indicates that we do not have the required information, if you do, we would be pleased to hear from you.
  2. Dashes in the pricing columns indicate one of two things: firstly, there was insufficient market pricing available, and secondly, pieces issued in small quantities of 10 or 20 pieces will be subject to wide pricing swings.

WEST COAST WADE COLLECTORS FAIR
2003

The Portland, Oregon, Airport Holiday Inn, was chosen for this years venue. The black and white Orca, also known as the Killer Whale is often seen in the oceans off the West Coast of the USA. The black, and black and white whales were produced in a limited edition of 300 each; the white whale was produced in a limited edition of 100. The black and white whale on a black base was given free of charge to collectors who stayed at the hotel, and the black whale on a blue base was in the show package. The original price of the models was $37.00 for three. The white model was given free in the fair package, and was also sold at the fair for $15.00. These models, in grey and blue colourways, were previously used in the Great Universal Stores and Tom Smith Crackers UK promotions, and were named Baleen Whale.

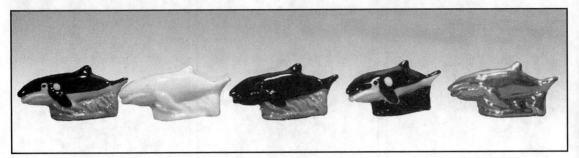

Whimsical Whales (2003)

Backstamp: Embossed: "Wade England"

Comm.	Name	Description	Issue	Price	Size	U.S. $	Can. $	U.K. £
Wade	Whale (TS)	Black; blue base	300	$11 US	22 x 52	18.	20.	10.
Wade	Orca / Killer Whale (TS)	Black/white; black base	300	$11 US	22 x 52	18.	20.	10.
Wade	Orca / Killer Whale (TS)	Black/white; blue base	300	$11 US	22 x 52	18.	20.	10.
Wade	Whale (TS)	Gold	10	Prizes	22 x 52	—	—	—
Wade	Whale (TS)	White	100	$15 US	22 x 52	25.	27.	15.

ONE-OF-A-KIND MODELS

These one-of-a-kind models were auctioned, used as prizes, or given away at various venues. In most cases, these figures are colourways of previously issued models, and carry a backstamp naming the event at which they appeared. They are not priced for one simple reason, they are unique.

Name	Date	Event	Colourway
Alice in Wonderland	2000	Trentham	Unknown
Alligators (Water Life)	1997	Arundel	Unknown
Amelia Teddy Bear	1999	San Antonio	Black; multicoloured floral body; gold eyes
Amelia Teddy Bear	2000	Trentham	Unknown
Amelia Teddy Bear	2003	Portland	Pink dress; white collar, cuffs; blue trim; blue/yellow flowers
Andy Capp	2000	Trentham	Black suit; yellow scarf
Annabelle Waiting For Christmas	2000	Trentham	Pale blue dress; red bow, yellow cracker
Arundel Bunny	1999	San Antonio	Multicolourel floral body; platinum ears, tail
Arundel Bunny	2000	Trentham	Purple; red ears
Arundel Bunny	2000	Trentham	White; green patch
Arundel Cat	2000	Arundel	Black
Arundel Cat	2000	Arundel	Blue
Arundel Cat	2000	Arundel	Floral chintz
Arundel Cat	2000	Arundel	Gold
Arundel Cat	2000	Arundel	Pewter
Arundel Cat	2000	Trentham	Honey; red collar; gold bell; black patches
Arundel Cat	2000	Trentham	White; black collar; silver bell; black patches
Arundel Chick	2000	Trentham	Red; green base
Arundel Duck	1997	Arundel	Blue duck; greenish base
Arundel Duck	1997	Arundel	Green duck; greenish base
Arundel Duck	1997	Arundel	Orange duck; greenish base
Arundel Duck	2000	Trentham	Beige/yellow; blue eyes; beige beak
Arundel Duck	2000	Trentham	Yellow; brown eyes, beak
Baby Bear in Pyjamas	2000	Trentham	Blue/white striped pyjamas, blue slippers
Baby Bear in Pyjamas	2000	Trentham	White/red pyjamas; red slippers; gold base
Betty Boop Beach Belle	1998	Arundel	Black swimsuit, hair; green hat; pink towel; olive base
Betty Boop Beach Belle Bikini	1998	Buffalo	Black bikini with yellow spots; black hat; pink towel
Betty Boop Ringmaster	2000	Arundel	Red jacket, garter, shoes; black skirt, top hat; gold base
Betty Boop Classic Wall Plaque	1997	Arundel	White moon, pearlised dress
Big Bad Wolf	2000	Trentham	Brown; white face, chest, feet
Bookend Bear	1999	Arundel	Multicoloured chintz on a white background
Boots the Rabbit	2000	Trentham	Unknown
Brick House Pig	2000	Trentham	Unknown
Bulgie the Frog	2003	Harrisburg	Green; red coat with green/yellow lines; black headphones
Camping Bear	1998	Arundel	Pale blue jacket; black trousers; brown boots
Camping Bear	1998	Bufalo	Light green jacket; dark green trousers; pale blue boots
Camping Bear	2000	Trentham	Unknown
Cheshire Cat	2000	Trentham	Black; pink inside ears; green eyes; gold base
Chintz Bear	2001	Kansas City	Black; multicoloured chintz
Christmas Puppy	1997	Trentham	Dark brown; matt
Christmas Puppy	2001	Wade Fest	Brown; matt
Christmas Teddy Bear	1997	Arundel	Brown; red/white hat; blue sack
Chuckles the Clown	1998	Arundel	Green coat; yellow spotted trousers
Chuckles the Clown	1998	Buffalo	Red coat, nose; yellow trousers
Chuckles the Clown	1998	Buffalo	Black coat, shoes, hat; yellow trousers

EXAMPLES OF ONE-OF-A-KIND MODELS

Daddy Bear (Arundel)

Mummy and Daddy Bears (Arundel)

Daddy Bear (Arundel)

Arundel Bunny (San Antonio)

Bookend Bear (Arundel)

Amelia Teddy Bear (San Antonio)

Chuckles the Clown (Buffalo)

Emily the Doll (Arundel)

English Whimsies

Set One: Fawn, Rabbit, Mongrel, Kitten, Spaniel
1971 (P. 54)

Set Eight: Donkey, Barn Owl, Cat, Mouse, Ram
1977 (P. 58)

Set Eleven: Bison. Bluebird, Wild Boar, Bullfrog, Racoon
1979 (P. 60)

Set Twelve: Penguin, Seal Pup, Husky, Walrus, Polar Bear
1980 (P. 61)

First Whimsies

Set One: English Animals; Leaping Fawn, Horse, Spaniel with Ball, Poodle, Squirrel
1954-1958 (P. 63)

Set Two: English Animals; Bull, Lamb, Kitten, Hare, Dachshund
1954-1958 (P. 64)

Set Three: English Country Animals; Badger, Fox Cub, Stoat, Shetland Pony, Retriever
1955-1958 (P. 64)

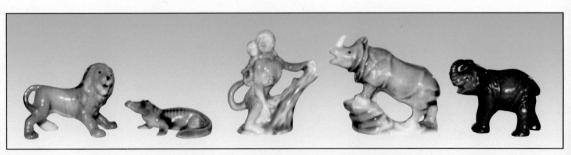

Set Four: African Jungle Animals; Lion, Crocodile, Monkey and Baby, Rhinoceros, Baby Elephant
1955-1958 (P. 65)

First Whimsies

Set Five: Horses; Light Brown Mare, White Mare, Light Brown Foal, White Foal, Light Brown Colt, White Colt, Beagle
1956-1959 (P. 65)

Set Six: Polar Animals; King Penguin, Husky, Polar Bear, Baby Seal, Polar Bear Cub
1956-1959 (P. 66)

Set Seven: Pedigree Dogs; Alsatian, West Highland Terrier, Corgi, Boxer, Dark Brown Saint Bernard, Light Brown Saint Bernard
1957-1961 (P. 67)

Set Eight: Zoo Animals; Llama, Lion Cub, Giant Panda, Bactrian Camel, Cockatoo
1957-1961 (P. 68)

First Whimsies

Set Nine: North American Animals; Snowy Owl, Raccoon, Grizzly Bear, Cub in Light brown, brown and white, Cougar
1958-1961 (P. 68)

Set Ten: Farm Animals; Pig, Italian Goat, Beige Shire Horse, White Shire Horse, Foxhound, Swan
1957-1961 (P. 69)

First Whimsies Derivatives Whimtrays

Yellow Tray with Grizzly Cub

Black Tray with Corgi

Black Tray with Bactrian Camel
(P. 347)

Yellow Tray with Cockatoo
1958-1965 (P. 71-73)

Yellow Tray with Llama

Red Rose Tea (Canada) Ltd.
Miniature Nurseries

Baa Baa Black Sheep, Cat and the Fiddle, Dr. Foster, Gingerbread Man, Goosey Goosey Gander, Hickory Dickory Dock
(P. 292)

House that Jack Built, Humpty Dumpty, Jack, Jill, Little Bo-Peep, Little Boy Blue
(P. 292-293)

Little Jack Horner, Little Miss Muffet, Little Red Riding Hood, Mother Goose, Old King Cole, Old woman Who Lived in a Shoe
(P. 293-294)

Pied Piper, Puss in Boots, Queen of Hearts, The Three Bears, Tom Tom the Piper's Son, Wee Willie Winkie
(P. 294)

Red Rose Tea U.S.A Ltd.
Miniature Animals

**First Issue: Chimpanzee, Elephant, Hare, Hippo, Squirrel, Turtle, Wild Boar
Bear Cub, Bison, Bluebird, Bushbaby, Lion, Otter, Owl, Seal on Rock,** 1983-1985 (P. 298)

**Second Issue: Beaver, Camel, Giraffe, Leopard, Orang-outan, Pine Marten, Polar Bear,
Gorilla, Kangaroo, Koala, Langur, Raccoon, Rhino, Tiger, Zebra,** 1985-1990 (P. 299)

**Fourth Issue: Kangaroo, Koala, Langur, Persian Kitten, Orang-outan, Pine Marten, Polar Bear, Pony, Raccoon,
Beaver, Cock-a-teel, Giraffe, Gorilla, Camel, Rabbit, Puppy, Tiger, Zebra, Rhino,** 1992 (P. 300-301)

Red Rose Tea U.S.A. Ltd.
Noah's Ark

Noah and his Wife with the Ark
(P. 305)

Noah and his Wife
Base Varieties – Oval and Peanut (P. 305)

Animals of the Ark
Top Row: Female Rhino, Hen, Rooster, Female Elephant, Male Elephant
Middle Row: Goose, Gander, Lioness, Lion
Bottom Row: Male Rhino, Ewe, Ram, Female Zebra, Male Zebra, 2002 (P. 305)

Tom Smith and Company Ltd.
Wildlife

Goat, Hare, Squirrel, Zebra, Bison, Collie, Duck, swimming
1986-1987 (P. 331)

Colourways

Goat in two colourways
from the **Farmyard Animals Set**, 1982-1983 (P. 321)

Swimming Duck in three colourways
Farmyard and Wildlife Sets, 1982-1987 (P. 321, 325, 331)

Whelk from the **Sealife Set**
1998 (P. 322)

Koala from the **Safari Park
Set**, 1976-1977 (P. 326)

West Highland Terrier
from the **World of Dogs**,
1990-1991 (P. 332)

Old King Cole from the
Recoloured Models
of 1990 (P. 324)

ONE-OF-A-KIND MODELS

Name	Date	Event	Colourway
Chuckles the Clown	1999	Arundel	Yellow coat; blue trousers; green/black spotted bowtie; black hat
Chuckles the Clown	2000	Trentham	Unknown
Clorinda, Ugly Sister	2002	Harrisburg	Green blouse; pearl skirt with red flowers
Clown, banjo	2000	Arundel	Blue/red striped trousers; yellow collar, cuffs; black hat, green dots
Clown, banjo	2000	Trentham	Blue/red diamond trousers; blue buttons
Clown, banjo	2000	Trentham	Green/pink patch trousers; blue jacket
Clown, banjo	2000	Trentham	Grey check trousers; red buttons
Clown, singing	2000	Arundel	Blue/yellow bowtie; green coat; blue/red/yellow patched trousers
Clown, singing	2000	Trentham	Black hat; blue cuffs; black buttons
Clown, singing	2000	Trentham	Black hat; pink ruff, cuffs; gold buttons
Clown, singing	2000	Trentham	Yellow hat, ruff, cuffs; black buttons
Cornish Tin Mine Pixie	1997	Trentham	Green coat; brown trousers; black hat; silver buckles
Cornish Tin Mine Pixie	1998	Arundel	Dark green coat; brown trousers, hat; gold buckles
Cornish Tin Mine Pixie	1999	Sab Antonio	Black coat, trousers, hat, shoes; silver buckles
Cornish Tin Mine Pixie	2000	Trentham	Unknown
Cross-eyed Bear	2001	Arundel	Honey; red spotted jacket, trousers; black/white bee on face
Daddy Bear	1997	Arundel	Dark blue jacket; green/blue striped trousers
Daddy Bear	1997	Arundel	Dark blue jacket; dark/light blue striped trousers
Daddy Bear	1997	Dunstable	Blue jacket, red spots; black trousers
Daddy Bear	1997	Trentham	Unknown
Daddy Bear	1997	Oconomowoc	Black suit
Daddy Bear	1997	Uxbridge	Royal blue coat; red/yellow striped trousers
Daddy Bear	1999	Arundel	Pale blue waistcoat; black trousers
Daddy Bear	1999	San Antonio	Pale blue jacket; yellow trousers
Daddy Bear	2000	Trentham	Unknown
Dick Whittington's Cat	1997	Arundel	Unknown
Dick Whittington's Cat	2000	Trentham	Unknown
Dribbles the Dog	2000	Trentham	Unknown
Elizabeth Tedwina	2000	Trentham	Unknown
Emily the Doll	1998	Arundel	Green dress, pink bands; white hat; yellow hair
Emily the Doll	1998	Buffalo	White dress, dark blue edging; yellow hat; brown hair
Emily the Doll	2000	Trentham	Unknown
Felicity Squirrel	1997	Arundel	Light grey
Felicity Squirrel	1997	Arundel	Orange
Fizzy the fawn	2000	Trentham	Dark brown; brown/honey base
Fizzy the fawn	2000	Trentham	Red brown; green/brown base
Goldfish (Water Life)	1997	Arundel	Orange
Golly Gosh Bear	2000	Trentham	Beige; blue dungarees; black buckles
Green Man	2000	Trentham	Unknown
Hattie the Squirrel	2000	Trentham	Unknown
Honey Bear	2000	Trentham	Beige; black suit; pearlised collar, cuffs
King Velveteen	2000	Trentham	Unknown
King Arthur	2000	Trentham	Cream; red cloak; gold gauntlets, base
Lady of the Lake	2000	Trentham	Unknown
Library Bear	2000	Trentham	Green hat/trousers; gold neck bow; brown book
Library Bear	2000	Trentham	Yellow hat/trousers; blue spotted neck bow; blue/green book
Lil' American Footballer	2003	Harrisburg	Honey; pale blue jersey, gold trim; pearl pants, helmet; brown football

EXAMPLES OF ONE-OF-A-KIND MODELS

Prince Tedward (Trentham)

Palace Guard (Trentham)

Princess Plushette

King Arthur (Trentham)

Guinevere (Trentham)

Felicity Squirrel

Big Bad Wolf (Trentham)

Christmas Puppy (Arundel)

ONE-OF-A-KIND MODELS

Name	Date	Event	Colourway
Lil' Devil	2001	Trentham	Honey; black horns; red cloak
Long-neck Cat	2000	Trentham	Grey-blue
Mad Hatter	2000	Trentham	Black coat; purple trousers; yellow/black bow tie
Madison Mouse	2000	Trentham	Unknown
Merlin	2000	Trentham	Unknown
Mermaid	2000	Trentham	Unknown
Millennium Teddy	2000	Trentham	Brown; red/blue/gold numerals
Millennium Teddy	2001	Wade Fest	Green/brown/blue/yellow numbers
Mischief the Chimp	2002	Harrisburg	Brown; red shirt; red/green spotted bandana; brown tool belt
Mother Badger	2003	Arundel	Gold
Mother Goose	1997	Arundel	Green bonnet, ribbon; white bloomers; red/white socks
Mother Goose	2000	Trentham	Unknown
Mummy Bear	1999	Arundel	Pale blue dress; white/black cap, apron
Nanny Fluffins	2000	Trentham	Unknown
New York Tourist	2000	Trentham	Unknown
Oops! The Bear, Style Three	2001	Vancouver, WA	Beige; dark green blanket
Oops! The Bear, Style Three	2002	Vancouver, WA	Honey; gold blanket
Oscar Christmas Teddy Bear	2000	Trentham	Unknown
Pantomime Dame	1997	Arundel	Blue dress, bag; green bow, shoes; brown hair
Pantomime Dame	1997	Arundel	Green dress
Pantomime Horse	1998	Trentham	Yellow; black stripes; green patch
Pantomime Horse	2000	Trentham	Unknown
Pantomime Horse	2002	Vancouver, WA	White; black patches, hooves, tail; yellow/red eyes; red/blue blanket
Pocket Pals (complete set)	2000	Trentham	Unknown
Prairie Dog	2000	Trentham	Unknown
Prince George Tedward	2000	Trentham	Blue shirt; red trousers, hat
Prince George Tedward	2000	Trentham	Green/white sailor suit; black shoes
Prince George Tedward	2000	Trentham	Red/white sailor suit
Princess Plushette	2000	Trentham	Rose pink dress
Princess Plushette	2000	Trentham	Yellow dress with red hearts
Priscilla the Pig	2000	Trentham	Unknown
Priscilla the Pig	2000	Vancouver, WA	(Lavender) Light blue; multicoloured flowers
Puck	1998	Buffalo	White horns, hooves, blue-grey legs; gold flute
Puck	1999	Arundel	Gold legs, flute; black horns, hooves
Puck	2000	Trentham	Unknown
Puppy Love "Ella"	2000	Trentham	Unknown
Puppy Love "Shelby"	2000	Trentham	Honey
Puppy Love "Sidney"	2000	Trentham	Unknown
Queen Guinevere	2000	Trentham	Maroon/ black dress; gold hood, cloak
Quackers the Duck	2000	Trentham	Black/red spotted hat, blue rim
Quackers the Duck	2000	Trentham	Blue hat
Quackers the Duck	2000	Trentham	Red Santa suit; white/blue scarf
Queen Beatrice	2000	Trentham	Green dress; pale green cloak; green/gold crown
Queen Beatrice	2000	Trentham	Pink dress; red cloak; pink/gold crown
Ratty	2000	Trentham	Unknown
Roly Poly Rabbit	2000	Trentham	Pale green dress; white apron with pink flowers
Roly Poly Rabbit	2000	Trentham	Yellow dress with red flowers

ONE-OF-A-KIND MODELS

Name	Date	Event	Colourway
Rosie the Kitten	2000	Trentham	Unknown
Royal Guard	2000	Trentham	Red coat; green hat, belt, boots
Rufus	1997	Arundel	Red-brown dog; green cushion; gold trim
Smudger	1997	Trentham	Matt black; glossy eyes
Snow Children	1998	Arundel	White; maroon hat, scarf; blue hat, scarf
St. George and the Dragon	1998	Buffalo	Brown cloak; gold armour, lance; blue-grey dragon
St. George and the Dragon	2000	Trentham	Unknown
Straw House Pig	2000	Trentham	Unknown
Ted"E" Bear	2001	Kansas City	Honey; dark brown marking; gold book
Tiny the Mouse	2000	Trentham	Unknown
Togetherness	2000	Trentham	Unknown
Toy Soldier	1998	Arundel	Red jacket, helmet; green trousers; pale blue plume
Toy Soldier	2000	Trentham	Unknown
Travelling Badger	2000	Trentham	Unknown
Travelling Badger	2002	Vancouver, WA	Purple coat. hat, gold trim; brown suitcase; green base
Tubby the Bear	2000	Trentham	Unknown
Wade Baby	2000	Trentham	Unknown
Welcome Home	2000	Trentham	Unknown
Whale (Water Life)	1997	Arundel	Unknown
White Rabbit	2000	Trentham	Red coat; white/brown striped waistcoat

THE OFFICIAL INTERNATIONAL WADE COLLECTOR'S CLUB FIGURES

Membership Figures   184
Enrol a Friend   185
Membership Series   185
Christmas Models   198

MEMBERSHIP FIGURES

Starting in 1994, complimentary membership figures were given to new and renewing members. *Truly the Puppy* was available to members who had four years continuous membership in the OIWCC. First seen at the October Wade Christmas Extravaganza, the model was not available until January 2002 when membership renewals were due. The issue price was £9.99.

The membership model for 2004 was changed to celebrate the 50th anniversary of the *First Whimsies*. Wade produced a blow-up model of the Lamb from Set Two: English Animals, which was introduced in 1954.

Work's Cat Burslem (1994-95)

Christmas Puppy (1995-96)

Smudger (1996-97

Truly the Puppy (2002)

Blow Up Lamb (2004)

Shetland Pony Blow Up (2005)

Date	Name	Description	Size	U.S. $	Can. $	U.K. £
1994-95	Work's Cat Burslem	White; black patches	75	160.	175.	90.
1995-96	Christmas Puppy	Amber	57	70.	80.	40.
1996-97	Smudger	Black; grey shading	70	50.	55.	30.
1997-98	Wade Baby	White vest and pants; green shoes	83	35.	40.	20.
1999	Alice in Wonderland	See Membership Series, page 189	—	—	—	—
2000	Toad of Toad Hall	See Membership Series, page 190	—	—	—	—
2001	Cinderella in Rags	See Membership Series, page 191	—	—	—	—
2002	Peter Pan	See Membership Series, page 192	—	—	—	—
2002	Truly the Puppy	Honey; yellow bow, collar	60	20.	22.	12.
2003	Beauty	See Membership Series, page 193	—	—	—	—
2004	Blow Up Lamb	White; fawn muzzle, lower legs; grey hooves	85	50.	55.	30.
2005	Shetland Pony Blow Up	White; blue mane, tail, hooves	82	40.	45.	25.
2006	Gaffer and Sydney	See Tetley Tea Folk Whimsies, page 84	—	—	—	—
2007	Felix the Cat (right arm up)	See Felix the Cat Series, page 106	—	—	—	—

ENROL A FRIEND

In 1996 the "Enrol A Friend" scheme was introduced. Both the renewing and newly enrolled member in the OIWCC received a complimentary figure. In 1998-1999, the firs t 10,000 members to renew/enrol received the Blue Angelfish.

A new Enrol A Friend model named "Firm Friends" was introduced in Spring 2003, this model of a teddy bear with a rabbit was sent to new members, plus the member who recommended them to join the Wade Collectors Club.

Firm Friends (2003-2006)

Best Friend Bears (2006-2007)

Backstamp: Embossed "Wade England"

Date	Name	Description	Size	U.S. $	Can. $	U.K. £
1996-97	Seal Pup (EW, TS)	White; blue base	17 x 30	25.	28.	15.
1998-99	Angel Fish (EW)	Dark blue	35 x 30	25.	28.	15.
2001-03	Ruffles the Bear	Honey; red ruffles	58 x 54	25.	28.	15.
2003-06	Firm Friends	Honey; brown ears, feet pads	70	45.	50.	25.
2006-07	Best Friends Bears	Honeybear; brown bear	Unk.	—	—	—

MEMBERSHIP SERIES

1995 – BIG BAD WOLF AND THE THREE LITTLE PIGS

Big Bad Wolf

Brick House Pig

Straw House Pig and Wood House Pig

Backstamp: Red print "Wade England" with two lines and black printed "The Official Wade International Collectors Club [name of model] 1995"

Date	Name	Description	Issue	Price	Size	U.S. $	Can. $	U.K. £
1995	Big Bad Wolf	Mottled-grey; white chest	1,500	£15	140	80.	90.	45.
1995	Brick House Pig	Red-brown trousers	1,500	£15	130	80.	90.	45.
1995	Straw House Pig	Dark blue dungarees	1,250	£15	125	90.	100	55.
1995	Wood House Pig	Dark green dungarees	1,250	£15	117	90.	100.	55.

1996 – GOLDILOCKS AND THE THREE BEARS, Style Two

The first figurine in this series was *Mummy Bear,* and originally the production was intended to be 1,500 of each model but due to the increasing club membership numbers the production was increased to 2,750. For *Goldilocks and the Three Bears,* Style One, see page 32.

Backstamp:
Circular black and red printed "Official International Wade Collectors Club," black printed "[name] 1996"

Mummy Bear and Daddy Bear

Baby Bear and Goldilocks

Date	Name	Description	Issue	Price	Size	U.S. $	Can. $	U.K. £
1996	Mummy Bear	Dark blue dress; white apron, cap	2,750	£15	102	60.	65.	35.
1996	Daddy Bear	Dark blue suit; red bow tie	2,750	£15	105	60.	65.	35.
1996	Goldilocks	Pink dress; brown chair	2,750	£15	85	60.	65.	35.
1996	Baby Bear	Dark blue dungarees; white shirt	2,750	£15	60	60.	65.	35.

1997 – PANTOMIME SERIES

This series was available to club members only, and limited to one per member.

Backstamp:
Circular black and red printed "[Name] The Official International Wade Collectors Club 1997"

Pantomime Horse and Mother Goose

Dick Whittington's Cat and Pantomime Dame

Date	Name	Description	Issue	Price	Size	U.S. $	Can. $	U.K. £
1997	Pantomime Horse	White; brown patch	4,000	£15	90	35.	40.	20.
1997	Mother Goose	Pale blue bonnet, bloomers	4,000	£15	110	45.	50.	25.
1997	Dick Whittington's Cat	Light blue trousers; black boots	4,000	£15	110	50.	55.	30.
1997	Pantomime Dame	Sea green dress; red/white bloomers; light blue hair	4,000	£15	110	35.	40.	20.

1997 – THE CAMELOT COLLECTION

This new series of slip cast models based on the legend of King Arthur was introduced at the Wade/Jim Beam fair held in Wisconsin in July 1997. Two hundred of each figure had the C & S logo added to the Wade backstamp.

| Sir Lancelot and King Arthur | The Lady of the Lake | Queen Guinivere and The Wizard Merlin |

Backstamp: A. Black printed "Camelot Collection" logo and "[name] The Camelot Collection Wade"
B. Black printed "C&S logo, Camelot Collection logo" and '[name] The Camelot Collection Wade"

Date	Name	Description	Issue	Price	Size	U.S. $	Can. $	U.K. £
1997	King Arthur	Brown cloak; yellow crown	2,000	£20	108	35.	40.	20.
1997	Queen Guinivere	Brown dress; dark green collar	2,000	£20	108	35.	40.	20.
1997	Sir Lancelot	Brown cloak	2,000	£20	108	35.	40.	20.
1977	The Wizard Merlin	Blue-grey hooded cloak	2,000	£20	108	35.	40.	20.
1997	The Lady of the Lake	Light/dark brown robes	2,000	£20	83	35.	40.	20.

1998 – TOY BOX SERIES

This series was created by Sue Ames, winner of a competition run by The Wade Collectors Club. The *Toy Soldier* (first in the series) was released at the Trentham Gardens Wade Fair in March 1998.

Backstamp:
Printed "The Official Wade Collectors Club 1998," OIWCC logo and [name of model]

| Toy Soldier and Amelia Teddy Bear | Chuckles the Clown and Emily the Doll |

Date	Name	Description	Issue	Price	Size	U.S. $	Can. $	U.K. £
1998	Amelia Teddy Bear	Blue/white dress; yellow ducks	3,000	£20	90	45.	50.	25.
1998	Chuckles the Clown	Red coat; white shirt, trousers	3,000	£20	115	45.	50.	25.
1998	Emily the Doll	Blue dress, bonnet; maroon bow	3,000	£20	85	45.	50.	25.
1998	Toy Soldier	Yellow jacket; blue helmet	3,000	£20	110	45.	50.	25.

1998-99 – BRITISH MYTHS AND LEGENDS SERIES

This series released in 1998-1999 depicts characters from British Folklore. The sixth model, *King Canute,* was sent free of charge (upon application) to club members who had previously purchased a *Myths and Legends* set.

Cornish Tin Mine Pixie and Green Man

King Canute and Mermaid

Puck and St. George and the Dragon

Backstamp: Printed "British Myths and Legends Wade" and [name of model]

Date	Name	Description	Issue	Price	Size	U.S. $	Can. $	U.K. £
1998-99	Cornish Tin Mine Pixie	Brown suit; gold hammer head	2,000		108	35.	40.	20.
1998-99	Green Man	Green-white figure; brown tree	2,000	£115	114	35.	40.	20.
1998-99	King Canute	Dark brown cloak; silver crown	2,000	per	120	35.	40.	20.
1998-99	Mermaid	Honey; green-blue tail	2,000	set	120	35.	40.	20.
1998-99	Puck	Amber body, horns; gold flute	2,000		114	35.	40.	20.
1998-99	St. George and the Dragon	Brown cloak; grey armour	2,000		101	35.	40.	20.

1999 – ALICE IN WONDERLAND

In late 1998, the O.I.W.C.C. changed their membership renewal system so that all memberships started January 1st and ended December 31st. *Alice in Wonderland* is the first in a series of six models that members had the opportunity to purchase.

The membership model for 1999 was *Alice in Wonderland,* the first in the series. Members could purchase the other models in the series at quarterly intervals throughout the 1999 membership year. Those members having purchased the four models by February 14th, 2000, could complete their set by purchasing The Queen of Hearts. Only 1,484 Queen of Hearts models were produced, the production number being based on the number of orders received by the cut off date.

Alice and Membership Badge

Mad Hatter and White Rabbit

Cheshire Cat

Dormouse

Queen of Hearts

Backstamp: **A.** Printed "Alice in Wonderland Collection Alice 1999 Membership Piece made in England ©MacMPub 1999" with OIWCC logo

B. Printed "Alice in Wonderland Collection made in England ©MacMPub 1999" with OIWCC logo and [name of model]

Date	Name	Description	Issue	Price	Size	U.S. $	Can. $	U.K. £
1999	Alice	Blue dress; white pinafore	—	Memb.	120	60.	65.	35.
1999	Mad Hatter	Purple coat; red/blue trousers	2,000	£28.50	110	60.	65.	35.
1999	White Rabbit	Olive green coat; yellow/red striped waistcoat	2,000	£28.50	113	80.	90.	45.
1999	Dormouse	Amber; platinum teapot	2,000	£28.50	90	60.	65.	35.
1999	Cheshire Cat	Brown; green eyes	2,000	£28.50	60	80.	90.	45.
1999	Queen/Hearts	Red/blue/white/gold dress	1,484	£39.95	130	125.	135.	70.

2000 – WIND IN THE WILLOWS

The membership model for 2000 was *Toad of Toad Hall*. Members could purchase the other models in the series at intervals throughout the year. Those members having purchased all four models by December 31st, 2000, had the opportunity to purchase "Ratty and Mole in a Rowing Boat."

Toad of Toad Hall

Ratty and Mole in a Rowing Boat

Mole, Ratty, Badger, Weasel

Backstamp: **A.** Printed "The Wind in the Willows Toad ©EHS"
B. Printed "The Wind in the Willows © EHS 2000" with OIWCC logo and [name of model]

Date	Name	Description	Issue	Price	Size	U.S. $	Can. $	U.K. £
2000	Toad of Toad Hall	Brown coat; yellow/black checked waistcoat	—	Memb	105	50.	55.	30.
2000	Mole	Pale blue dressing gown	2,000	£25	108	60.	65.	35.
2000	Ratty	Olive green coat; white trousers	2,000	£25	115	60.	65.	35.
2000	Badger	Khaki coat; red waistcoat	2,000	£25	125	60.	65.	35.
2000	Weasel	Brown satchel; red fez	2,000	£25	110	60.	65.	35.
2000	Ratty / Mole in a Rowing Boat	Ratty: White suit, hat; Mole: White shirt; blue waistcoat	2,000	£25	85	100.	110.	60.

2001 – CINDERELLA

The first figure in the series "Cinderella in Rags," was the membership model for 2001. Members could then purchase the other models in the series at intervals throughout the year. The Cinderella special, "The Fairy Godmother," (1,818 models produced) was available to all members who purchased the other four models by January 18th 2002.

The ugly sisters Clorinda and Thisbe are named after the original characters who appeared in the first Cinderella Pantomime performed in Covent Garden, London, England in 1820. Models are listed in order of issue.

Cinderella in Rags

Clorinda (Ugly Sister)

Thisbe (Ugly Sister)

Prince Charming

Cinderella, Ready for the Ball

Fairy Godmother

Backstamp: Printed "Cinderella 2001" and OIWCC logo. [name of model]

Date	Name	Description	Issue	Price	Size	U.S. $	Can. $	U.K. £
2001	Cinderella in Rags	Yellow dress; white/brown apron	—	Memb.	100	50.	55.	30.
2001	Clorinda	Pearl/green dress; gold highlights	2,000	£25	110	50.	55.	30.
2001	Thisbe	Orange/pearl dress; gold highlights	2,000	£25	105	50.	55.	30.
2001	Prince Charming	Green tunic; pearl cloak, slipper	2,000	£25	90	50.	55.	30.
2001	Cinderella, Ready for the Ball	Pearl dress; gold bow/necklace/tiara	2,000	£25	100	50.	55.	30.
2001	Fairy Godmother	Pearl dress; orange pumpkin	1,818	£39.95	110	100.	110.	60.

2002 – PETER PAN

Peter Pan was the membership figure for 2002, and the first model in this series. The other four models were produced at intervals throughout the year, and Club members who purchased all four of the *Peter Pan* models could then order the special figure "Captain Hook and the Crocodile." The issue size of the special figure was 1,532 models, which was based on the number of orders received by February 14th, 2003.

Peter Pan

Tinkerbell

Michael

Wendy

John

Captain Hook and Crocodile

Backstamp: Captain Hook and the Crocodile: Printed "Peter Pan Collection 2002 Captain Hook Limited Edition The Official Wade Collectors Club" with red "Wade" logo
Peter Pan: Printed "Peter Pan Collection Peter Pan Membership Piece 2002" and OIWCC logo
Tinkerbell: Printed "Peter Pan Collection 2002 Limited Edition Tinkerbell Official Wade Collectors Club"

Date	Name	Description	Issue	Price	Size	U.S. $	Can. $	U.K. £
2002	Peter Pan	Green/brown	—	Memb.	115	50.	55.	27.
2002	Tinkerbell	Pink dress; gold thimble	—	£27	75	50.	55.	27.
2002	John	White/blue pyjamas; black top hat	—	£27	85	50.	55.	27.
2002	Wendy	Pearl/blue dress; brown dog	—	£27	95	50.	55.	27.
2002	Michael	Blue nightshirt; white blanket	—	£27	65	50.	55.	27.
2002	Captain Hook and Crocodile	Captain Hook: Blue/black coat Crocodile: Green/white	1532	£27	130	125.	135.	70.

2003 – BEAUTY AND THE BEAST

The membership model for 2003 was "Beauty", from *Beauty and the Beast*. The model was sent free of charge to club members in a special presentation box; a club badge was included with the model. The other models from the series could then be purchased from the club at intervals throughout the year. The special model, "Beauty and the Beast Dancing," was available to all members who purchased the other four models from the series, the edition size being based on orders received.

Beauty

The Beast

Beauty's Father

Enchanted Witch

Prince

Beauty and the Beast Dancing

Backstamp: Printed "Beauty & the Beast 2003 The Official International Collectors Club" with red "Wade" logo and [name of model]

Date	Name	Description	Issue	Price	Size	U.S. $	Can. $	U.K. £
2003	Beauty	Pearlised coat, blue trim; pink/pearl ruffled dress; brown hair; pink rose	—	£27	98	50.	55.	27.
2003	The Beast	Grey; dark blue cloak; pearlised shirt; green trousers; pink rose	—	£27	112	50.	55.	27.
2003	Beauty's Father	Black cloak; white pants; purple hat; green band; tan gloves, shoes; grey hair, beard	—	£27	110	50.	55.	27.
2003	Enchanted Witch	Black coat, hat, grey trim; ochre green dress; brown staff, basket; pink roses	—	£27	110	50.	55.	27.
2003	Prince	Black cloak, red lining; white shirt; ochre green trousers; tan boots; yellow hair	—	£27	Unk.	50.	55.	27.
2003	Beauty and Beast Dancing	Beauty: Red lustre/pearl dress, pink bow Beast: Grey; white shirt; gold epaulettes; brown lustre trousers; pearlised base	—	£27	Unk.	85.	95.	50.

2004 – SNAP, CRACK POP, COCO THE MONKEY and TONY TIGER SURFING

The first model issued in this series was "Pop." Members who purchase all four models in the series by December 31st, 2005, were eligible to purchase the speical edition piece "Tony Tiger Surfing."

Coco the Monkey

Crackle

Pop

Snap

Tony the Tiger Surfing

Date	Name	Description	Issue	Price	Size	U.S. $	Can. $	U.K. £
2004	Coco the Monkey	Brown, blue, white, beiges	—	£25	Unk.	45.	50.	25.
2004	Crackle	Green, white, brown, yellow	—	£25	Unk.	45.	50.	25.
2004	Pop	Red, white, brown, yellow	—	£25	Unk.	45.	50.	25.
2004	Snap	Blue, white, black, orange	—	£25	Unk.	45.	50.	25.
2004	Tony Tiger Surfing	Orange, black, white, green, grey-blue	1,254	£25	Unk.	60.	65.	35.

2005 – MR. MEN AND LITTLE MISS

Little Miss Splendid

Little Miss Tiny

Mr. Funny

Mr. Small

Mr Rush on his Skateboard

Date	Name	Description	Issue	Price	Size	U.S. $	Can. $	U.K. £
2005	Little Miss Splendid	Green; red/white/blue hat; red shoes	—	£25	Unk.	45.	50.	25.
2005	Little Miss Tiny	Pink; blue pail	—	£25	Unk.	45.	50.	25.
2005	Mr. Funny	Green; tan hat gloves; red/white shoes	—	£25	Unk.	45.	50.	25.
2005	Mr. Rush on his Skateboard	Purple; yellow hat; red skateboard	981	£25	Unk.	45.	50.	25.
2005	Mr. Small	Red; blue boot/hat	—	£25	Unk.	45.	50.	25.

Note: 1. A dash in any of the technical data columns of the table indicates that we do not have the required information, if you do, we would be pleased to hear from you.

2. Dashes in the pricing columns indicate one of two things: firstly, there was insufficient market pricing available, and secondly, pieces issued in small quantities of 10 or 20 pieces will be subject to wide pricing swings.

2006 – TEDDY BEARS PICNIC

This set was designed by Richard Wilson. The first model issed was Bug Hunt Bear. Members who purchased all four models in the series by December 31st, 2006, were eligible to purchase the special edition piece "Wakey, Wakey! Bears."

Bug Hunt Bear

Gone Fishin' Bear

Wakey, Wakey! Bears

We're Hungry Bears

Yum-Yum Bear

Date	Name	Description	Issue	Price	Size	U.S. $	Can. $	U.K. £
2006	Bug Hunt Bear	Tan/white/blue/red	500	£27	Unk.	50.	55.	27.
2006	Gone Fishin' Bear	Brown/ white/blue/tan/black	500	£27	Unk.	50.	55.	27.
2006	Wakey, Wakey! Bears	Tan/white/brown/green/blue	500	£27	Unk.	50.	55.	27.
2006	We're Hungry Bears	White/tan/brown/blue/red/yellow	500	£27	Unk.	50.	55.	27.
2006	Yum-Yum Bear	Tan/red/white	500	£27	Unk.	50.	55.	27.

2007 – WHIMSIES

For 2007 members will be offered a new set of twelve Whimsie models. They will be issued quarterly with the Collector's Club magazine. Members purchasing the complete set of twelve Whimsies will be eligible to purchase a special stand to hold the set.

SET ONE

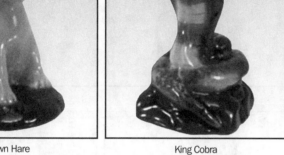

Brown Hare	King Cobra	Snowy Owl

SET TWO

African Lion	Palm Cockatoo	Toco Toucan

Date	Name	Description	Issue	Price	Size	U.S. $	Can. $	U.K. £
2007	Brown Hare	Light brown, white hare, green base	500	Three	Unk.	—	—	—
2007	King Cobra	Yellow, grey, brown cobra, green base	500	pieces	Unk.	—	—	—
2007	Snowy Owl	White bird, brown base	500	£28	Unk.	50.	55.	28.
2007	African Lion	Honey	500	Three	Unk.	—	—	—
2007	Palm Cockatoo	Blue bird, brown branch	500	pieces	Unk.	—	—	—
2007	Toco Toucan	Black, white, yellow bird, brown branch	500	£28	Unk.	50.	55.	28.

CHRISTMAS MODELS

1994-2006

Snowman (1994)

Snow Woman (1995)

Snow Children (1996)

Annabel Waiting for Christmas (1998)

Santa with Open Sack (1999)

Our Little Angel (2000)

Silent Night (2003)

Snowball Fight (2003)

Christmas Cheer (2004)

CHRISTMAS MODELS (cont.)

Backstamp: **Annabel Waiting for Christmas:** Printed "Christmas 1998" with OIWCC logo

Our Little Angel: Printed "Christmas 2000" with OIWCC logo

Oscar the Christmas Teddy: Printed circular "The Official International Wade Collectors Club Christmas Teddy 1997" with O.I.W.C.C. logo

Santa with Open Sack: Printed Red "Christmas 1999"

Snow Children: Black printed "Christmas 1996 Wade Made in England" with two black lines

Snow Woman: Black transfer "Christmas 1995 Wade Made in England"

Snowman: Black transfer "Wade England"

Snowman Silent Night: Printed "Silent Night Christmas 2002 limited edition 500" and red "OIWCC" logo

Snowman Snowball Fight: Unknown

Date	Name	Description	Issue	Price	Size	U.S. $	Can. $	U.K. £
1994	Snowman	Off-white/black/blue	1,000	—	125	110.	120.	60.
1995	Snow Woman	Off-white/dark blue/black	1,500	—	127	110.	120.	60.
1996	Snow Children	White/blue/brown	2,500	£15.00	120	75.	85.	45.
1997	Oscar, Christmas Teddy Bear	Honey; red hat	2,500	£20.00	110	40.	45.	25.
1998	Annabel Waiting For Christmas	Blue/white/red/green	2,000	£20.00	110	40.	45.	25.
1999	Santa with Open Sack	Red/white/brown/yellow	1,500	£15.00	80	50.	55.	30.
2000	Our Little Angel	White/yellow/gold	1,500	£20.00	90	30.	33.	17.
2001	Santa's Little Helper	Olive jacket; green pants, hat	500	£22.50	65	35.	40.	20.
2002	Silent Night	White; black hat; blue/white scarf; blue carol sheet; brown robin with red/white scarf	500	£25.00	90	35.	40.	20.
2003	Snowball Fight	White; black hat; blue/red scarf; white/pearl snowballs; brown robin with green/white scarf	500	£25.00	90	35.	40.	20.
2004	Christmas Cheer	White, yellow crown	500	£25.00	90	35.	40.	20.
2005	Seasonal Snow Greetings	White, pink, blue, black, brown	500	£27.50	Unk.	35.	40.	20.
2006	Felix's Seasonal Greetings	See Felix the Cat, page 106	—		—	—	—	—

We're Hungry Bears
Teddy Bears Picnic (page 196)

COMMISSIONERS ISSUES

Ameriwade	203
Arthur Price of England	204
Balding and Mansell	206
BJ Promotions	208
Blyth Ceramics	209
Brighton Corporation	209
Brooke Bond Oxo Ltd., England	210
C&S Collectables Direct	211
Cadbury World	234
Camtrak	235
Carryer Craft of California	237
Ceramica	238
CIBA Geigy	238
Collect It! Magazine	239
Collector (The)	242
Cotswold Collectables	242
Cricket Design Incorporated (CDI Imports)	243
David Trower Enterprises	247
E. and A. Crumpton	249
Father's Collection and Wades by Peg	250
Frisco Coffee	250
Fudge Collectables	251
G&G Collectables	252
Gamble, Peggy (formerly Gamble and Styles)	254
General Foods	255
Gold Star Gifthouse	256
Granada Television	256
Great Universal Stores	257
James Robertsons & Sons	261
K.P. Foods Ltd.	262
KS Wader / Happy Wad-ing	263
Keenan, Patty	268
Key Collectables Ltd.	269
King Aquariums Ltd	279
Langford, Keith	280
Latka, Sharon	281
Lever Rexona	282
Lux Soap	283

Memory Jars   283
New Victoria Theatre   284
Out of the Blue Ceramics   285
Pos-ner Associates   287
R & M Collectables   287
Red Rose Tea (Canada) Ltd.   288
Red Rose Tea U.S.A. Ltd. (Redco Foods Ltd)   298
Robell Media Promotions Ltd.   307
St. John Ambulance Brigade (U.K.)   308
Salada Tea Canada   308
Sharps Chocolate   309
Simons Associates Inc.   310
Spillers Dog Foods Ltd.   312
Staffordshire House Gifts   312
Thomas Waide & Sons Ltd.   313
Tom Smith and Company Ltd.   314
Traufler   333
21st Century Collectables   334
21st Century Keepsakes   335
UKI Ceramics Ltd.   336
Wade Watch USA   340
WadeUSA.com 2003   340
Warner Brothers   341
Whimisal Waders   341
Williamson, Robert and Peter Elson   342
Unknown Company   343

AMERIWADE

UNITED CAVES OF BEARICA

2002

"Li'Bearty" was the first model produced for Ameriwade.

Backstamp:
- **A.** Printed "United Caves of Bearica Statue of Li'Bearty Ameriwade LE of 250" [Name of model] and red "Wade Est. 1810 England" logo
- **B.** Printed "United Caves of Bearica Statue of Li'Bearty Ameriwade LE of 25" [Name of model] and red "Wade Est. 1810 England" logo

No.	Name	Description	Issue	Price	Size	U.S. $	Can. $	U.K. £
1	Li'Bearty	Brown bear; white robes; gold crown, torch	250	$55 US	112	60.	65.	35.
2	Li'Bearty	Green	25	Prizes	112	100.	110.	55.

BEARY CHRISTMAS

2002

The second model produced for Ameriwade was Beary Christmas. Each model was issued with a hand-signed and numbered certificate of authenticity.

Backstamp:
- **A.** Printed "United Caves of Bearica. Beary Christmas Ameriwade LE of 250" [model number] and red "Wade" logo
- **B.** Printed "United Caves of Bearica. Beary Christmas Ameriwade LE of 25" [model number] and red "Wade" logo

No.	Name	Description	Issue	Price	Size	U.S. $	Can. $	U.K. £
1	Beary Christmas	Honey bear; green wreath; red lettering	250	$49.95	70 x 35	60.	65.	35.
2	Beary Christmas	White bear; red wreath; green lettering	25	Prizes	70 x 35	100.	110.	55.

ARTHUR PRICE OF ENGLAND
THE WONDERFUL WORLD OF ANIMALS SERIES
Late 1970s-Early 1980s

Arthur Price of England commissioned an unknown quantity of Wade English *Whimsie* models to compliment his boxed sets of children's nursery ware of a spoon, fork and a napkin ring.

Backstamp: **A.** Embossed "Wade England" on back of model rim
B. Embossed "Wade England"

Jungle Babies

Photograph not available
at press time

No.	Name	Description	Size	U.S. $	Can. $	U.K. £
1	Bushbaby	Brown; blue ears; black nose	30 x 30			
2	Chimp	Dark brown; light brown face, patches	35 x 35			
3	Fawn	Brown; blue ears	30 x 30			
4	Koala	Yellow-brown; black nose; green base	35 x 25			
5	Langur, Type 1	Light brown; dark brown stump	35 x 30			
6	Pine Martin	Honey brown	30 x 30			
—	Boxed Set		—	75.	85.	45.

Jungle Kings

This set of Arthur Price Whimsies was titled *Jungle Kings* although it contained a polar bear! In the centre of the box is a silver-plated baby cup.

Jungle Babies Boxed Set with Silver-plate Baby's Cup

No.	Name	Description	Size	U.S. $	Can. $	U.K. £
1	Gorilla, standing	Grey; grey-green base	35 x 25			
2	Leopard	Yellow-brown; green base	17 x 45			
3	Lion	Brown mane; honey body	35 x 45			
4	Orang-outan	Ginger	30 x 30			
5	Polar Bear, head forward	White; blue base	30 x 30			
6	Tiger	Honey; green base	35 x 25			
—	Boxed Set		—	75.	85.	45.

On the Farm

Photograph not available
at press time

No.	Name	Description	Size	U.S. $	Can. $	U.K. £
1	Collie	Golden brown; green base	35 x 35			
2	Cow	Honey; green on base	35 x 35			
3	Horse	Dark grey; green base	45 x 35			
4	Lamb	Light beige; green base	35 x 25			
5	Pig	Beige; green base	25 x 35			
6	Ram	White; grey face; green base	30 x 30			
—	Boxed Set		—	75.	85.	45.

Pets and Companions

In the boxed set illustrated are the "Donkey" and the "Cat" from the *English Whimsies* Set No 8 which was produced in 1977: therefore a date of late 1970s-early 1980s has been estimated for this series. As the models are indistinguishable from *English Whimsies* a value has been given for a boxed set only. Models are listed in alphabetical order for ease of reference.

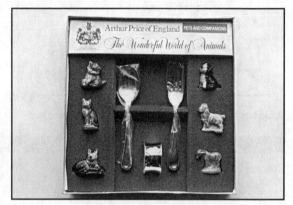

Pets and Companions Set with Spoon, fork and napkin ring set

No.	Name	Description	Size	U.S. $	Can. $	U.K. £
1	Alsatian	Grey; tan face	30 x 40			
2	Cat	Light brown/ginger; green base	40 x 17			
3	Donkey	Light brown; green base	30 x 30			
4	Kitten, seated	Dark/light brown; pink ball of wool	30 x 30			
5	Mongrel	Dark/light brown	35 x 35			
6	Spaniel	Honey; green on base	35 x 35			
—	Boxed Set		—	75.	85.	45

BALDING AND MANSELL

FLINTSTONES CHRISTMAS CRACKER PREMIUMS

1965

The four prehistoric Comic Animals (based on the television series *The Flintstones*) were only used in Balding & Mansell's Christmas Crackers. The "Bluebird," "Crocodile," "Hedgehog" and "Terrapin" were reissued in 1967 and were included in the Red Rose Tea of Canada promotion. The "Hedgehog" and the "Bluebird" were also used in the 1971-1984 *English Whimsies* series. For other Christmas cracker models, see Great Universal Stores and Tom Smith and Company.

Backstamp: **A.** Embossed "Wade England" in recessed base
B. Embossed "Wade England" on rim

No.	Name	Description	Size	U.S. $	Can. $	U.K. £
1	Bluebird	Beige and blue	15 x 35	9.	10.	5.
2	Bronti	Brown; beige face, feet, base; blue ears	20 x 35	18.	20.	10.
3	Crocodile	Brownish-green	14 x 40	10.	11.	6.
4	Dino	Beige; green eyes; black-brown base	35 x 35	18.	20.	10.
5	Hedgehog, Type 1	Dark red-brown; honey face; black nose	20 x 40	3.	4.	2.
6	Rhino	Beige; blue eyes, ears	23 x 40	18.	20.	10.
7	Terrapin	Beige; brown markings	10 x 40	10.	11.	6.
8	Tiger	Yellow brown; black stripes, nose; brown feet	38 x 28	25.	28.	14.
—	Boxed Set		—	130.	145.	75.

ANIMAL PARTY CRACKERS

Circa late 1960s

Backstamp: Embossed "Wade England"

No.	Name	Description	Size	U.S. $	Can. $	U.K. £
1	Brontosaurus	Brown; beige face, feet, base; blue ears	20 x 35	18.	20.	10.
2	Dinosaur	Beige; green eyes, black-brown base	35 x 35	18.	20.	10.
3	Giraffe	Beige	35 x 35	5.	6.	3.
4	Hippo	Honey	20 x 40	5.	6.	3.
5	Rhino	Beige; blue eyes, ears	23 x 40	18.	20.	10.
6	Tiger	Yellow brown; black stripes, nose; brown feet	38 x 28	18.	20.	10.
7	Wild Boar	Brown	30 x 40	5.	6.	3.
8	Zebra	Black	40 x 35	45.	50.	25.
—	Boxed Set		—	110.	120.	65.

BJ PROMOTIONS
THE BEANO COLLECTION
1999-2000

Commissioned by BJ Promotions *Dennis the Menace* is a character from the British children's comic *The Beano*. The other models in this series are Dennis' faithful dog *Gnasher*, and *Minnie the Minx*. Each model was issued with a certificate of authenticity and the original cost was £39.95.

Although issued in an edition of 1,500, only the first 1,000 subscribers to *Dennis the Menace* received a Beano Collection key ring

| Dennis the Menace and Beano Key ring | Gnasher | Minnie the Minx |

Backstamp: **A.** Circular printed "© D.C.Thomson & Co. Ltd, 1999 Wade England Limited Edition of 1,500"
B. Circular printed "© D.C.Thomson & Co. Ltd, 1999 Wade England Limited Edition of 1,000"
C. Circular printed "© D.C.Thomson & Co. Ltd, 1999 Wade England Limited Edition of 500"

Date	Name	Description	Issue	Price	Size	U.S. $	Can. $	U.K. £
1999	Dennis	Black/red	1,500	£39.95	130	70.	75.	40.
1999	Gnasher	Pink/black fur/green	1,000	£39.95	90	70.	75.	40.
2000	Minnie the Minx	Black/red/white	500	£39.95	135	70.	75.	40.

BLYTH CERAMICS
1998-2000

SID THE SEXIST AND SAN THE FAT SLAG

Sid the Sexist is the first of two characters from the British comic *Viz*. *San the Fat Slag* was the second model in the *Viz* collection.

Backstamp: Printed "Wade Viz 1998 © John Brown
Publishing House Viz © Blyth Ceramics Limited
Edition of 1000 with Certificate of Authenticity"
with name of model

Date	Name	Description	Issue	Price	Size	U.S. $	Can. $	U.K. £
1998	San the Fat Slag	Red/black; off-white base	1,000	£63	127	35.	40.	20.
1998	San the Fat Slag	Red/black; gold base	50	Unk.	127	75.	85.	40.
2000	San the Fat Slag	Red/black; platinum base	1,500	Unk.	127	45.	50.	25.
1998	Sid the Sexist	Black/red; grey base	1,000	£36	127	35.	40.	20.
1998	Sid the Sexist	Black/red; gold base	50	Unk.	127	75.	85.	40.
2000	Sid the Sexist	Black/red; platinum base	1,000	Unk.	127	45.	50.	25.

BRIGHTON CORPORATION
1988

BRIGHTON PAVILION

The *Brighton Pavilion* set consists of a circular pavilion and two oblong pavilions.

Backstamp: Unmarked

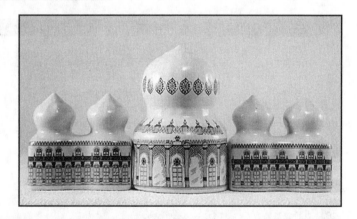

No.	Name	Description	Size	U.S. $	Can. $	U.K. £
1	Circular Pavilion	Blue/black/yellow	75 x 35	45.	50.	25.
2	Oblong Pavilion	Blue/black/yellow	50 x 53	45.	50.	25.

BROOKE BOND OXO LTD., ENGLAND
1969-1970

After the success of the *Miniature Animals* promotion by its sister company in Canada (Red Rose Tea), Brooke Bond Oxo Ltd. of London (England) offered nine figures from the same set in its 1969 promotion of Brooke Bond Teabags. One model was included in the 36 and 72-teabag box and two models in the 144-teabag box. The first models were so popular that a further six models from Red Rose Tea were added to the series in late 1969 and early 1970, for a total of 16 models. All these figures are in the same colours as the original Red Rose Tea Canada issue. Wade later used some of them in its *English Whimsies* series. As so few of the green-tipped butterflies have been found, it is believed they were samples and not put into full production. In a late 1960s advertisement the Fantail Goldfish model is misnamed the "Angel Fish."

Backstamp:
- **A.** Embossed "Wade England"
- **B.** Embossed "Wade" between front feet and "England" on back of model

No.	Name	Description	Size	U.S. $	Can. $	U.K. £
1	Bear Cub	Grey; beige face	30 x 40	7.	8.	4.
2	Beaver	Grey-brown; honey-brown face	35 x 45	5.	6.	3.
3	Bison, small	Honey; dark brown head, mane	30 x 40	7.	8.	4.
4	Bushbaby	Brown; blue ears; black eyes, nose	30 x 30	5.	6.	3.
5a	Butterfly	Honey; grey tips; raised circles	10 x 45	14.	16.	8.
5b	Butterfly	Green/brown; green tips; raised circles	10 x 45	14.	16.	8.
6	Corgi	Honey; black nose	30 x 35	10.	12.	6.
7	Duck	Blue/brown; yellow beak	30 x 40	10.	12.	6.
8	Fantail Goldfish	Green/yellow; blue rock	30 x 35	14.	16.	8.
9	Fox	Dark brown; fawn face, chest	30 x 30	9.	10.	5.
10a	Frog	Green	15 x 30	20.	22.	12.
10b	Frog	Green/yellow	15 x 30	20.	22.	12.
11	Otter	Beige; blue base	30 x 35	7.	8.	4.
12	Owl	Dark brown; light brown chest, face	35 x 20	7.	8.	4.
13	Pine Martin	Honey	30 x 30	7.	8.	4.
14	Seal on Rock	Light brown; blue rock	35 x 35	14.	16.	8.
15	Setter	Light brown; grey-green base	35 x 50	7.	8.	4.
16	Trout	Brown; red tail; grey-green base	30 x 30	7.	8.	4.

C&S COLLECTABLES DIRECT

ANDY CAPP AND FLO
1994-1995

Andy Capp depicts the cartoon character created by Reg Smythe in 1958 for the *British* Daily Mirror. *Flo* is Andy's long-suffering wife.

Backstamp:
  A. Black transfer "1994 © Mirror Group Newspapers Ltd C&S Collectables Wade England"
  B. Black transfer "1994 © Mirror Group Newspapers Ltd C&S Collectables Wade England Flo 1995"

Date	Name	Description	Issue	Price	Size	U.S. $	Can. $	U.K. £
1994	Andy Capp	Black/green/white	2,000	£12	75	50.	55.	30.
1994	Andy Capp	As above, with cigarette	100	Unk.	75	150.	165.	90.
1995	Flo	Green/black/white	2,000	£12	75	50.	55.	30.
1995	Flo	As above, with cigarette	100	Unk.	75	150.	165.	90.

ANIMALAND
2001-2005

Mama Otter, Baby Bear Cub, Snowy Owl

Elephant; Panda - black/white; Panda - white

Backstamp: A. Printed "Wade's Animaland 250 Limited Edition" [name of model] with "C&S" and "Wade" logos
B. Printed "Wade's Animaland Otter Collectors Meet Special 12th August 2001 Limited Edition 250" with "C&S" and "Wade" Logos
C. Printed "C&S 250 Limited Edition Wade's Animaland" [name of model] and "C&S" and "Wade" logo

Date	Name	Description	Issue	Price	Size	U.S. $	Can. $	U.K. £
2001	Baby Bear Cub	Honey/black; grey-green rock base	250	£25.00	65 x 55	60.	70.	35.
2001	Baby Bear Cub	White; gold base	25	Prizes	65 x 55	—	—	—
2001	Mama Otter	Brown; blue-grey rock base	250	£22.50	65 x 50	50.	55.	30.
2001	Mama Otter	Brown; gold rock base	20	Prizes	65 x 50	—	—	—
2001	Snowy Owl	White; brown log base	250	£25.00	68 x 68	60.	70.	35.
2001	Snowy Owl	Honey; gold base	25	Prizes	68 x 68	—	—	—
2002	Elephant	Honey; green grass; grey base	250	£25.00	85 x 65	45.	50.	25.
2002	Elephant	White	20	Prizes	85 x 65	—	—	—
2002	Panda	Black/white	250	£25.00	60	45.	50.	25.
2002	Panda	White	20	Prizes	60	—	—	—
2005	Panda Blow Up	Black, white	100	£70.00	100	85.	95.	50.
2005	Panda Whimsie	Black, white	100	Unk.	40	—	—	—

Note: 1. A dash in any of the technical data columns of the table indicates that we do not have the required information, if you do, we would be pleased to hear from you.
2. Dashes in the pricing columns indicate one of two things: firstly, there was insufficient market pricing available, and secondly, pieces issued in small quantities of 10 or 20 pieces will be subject to wide pricing swings.

AQUALAND

2002-2003

Backstamp:

A. Printed "Wade's Aqualand No. 1 Dolphin 250
Limited Edition" with blue "C&S" and red "Wade"
logos

B. Printed "Limited Edt 250 Seahorse" and red
"Wade" logo

Dolphin

Seahorse

Date	Name	Description	Issue	Price	Size	U.S. $	Can. $	U.K. £
2002	Dolphin	Grey; pearl white waves	250	£27.50	85	50.	55.	30.
2002	Dolphin	White lustre; blue waves	20	Prizes	85	—	—	—
2003	Seahorse	Honey; white spots; pearlised fin; honey base	250	£27.50	78	60.	65.	35.
2003	Seahorse	Honey; white spots; pearlised fin; gold base	20	Prizes	78	—	—	—

ARTHUR HARE
Series One

1993-1997

This series of comic animals is based on the characters from the British storybook *The Adventures of Arthur Hare and the Silent Butterfly*. The figures Arthur Hare and Holly Hedgehog were modelled by Ken Holmes, and Felicity Squirrel and Edward Fox by Robert Feather.

Edward Fox   Holly Hedgehog   Felicity Squirrel   Arthur Hare

Backstamp: **A.** Black transfer "Arthur Hare © C&S Collectables Wade England" (1a, 1b)
B. Black transfer "Holly Hedgehog © C&S Collectables Wade England" (2)
C. Black transfer "Felicity Squirrel 1250 Limited Edition © C&S Collectables 1995 Arthur Hare Productions Wade England" between two lines (3b)
D. Printed "Felicity Squirrel 250 Limited Edition Collectors Corner © 1995 Arthur Hare Productions Wade" with two lines
E. Printed in red "Genuine Wade" (3a)
F. Black printed "Edward Fox 1000 Limited Edition © C&S Collectables 1997 Arthur Hare Productions Wade" (4)

Date	Name	Description	Issue	Price	Size	U.S. $	Can. $	U.K. £
1993	Arthur Hare	Blue-grey/white/red	1,750	£16	130	45.	50.	25.
1993	Arthur Hare	Fawn/white/red	350	£25	130	75.	85.	40.
1993	Holly Hedgehog	Beige/brown/grey	2,000	£19.95	95	45.	50.	25.
1993	Felicity Squirrel	Grey/pink/white	1,250	£25	105	45.	50.	25.
1996	Felicity Squirrel	Dark red/pink/white	200	Unk.	105	90.	100.	50.
1997	Edward Fox	Light orange/pink/white	1,000	£25	115	45.	50	25.

ARTHUR HARE
Series Two
ARTHUR HARE TEENIES
1999-2000

The *Arthur Hare Teenies* are miniature, solid two-coloured variations of the hollow Village People Collection.

Harestronaut, Jesthare, P.C. Gotchare

Bravehare, The Shareriff

Backstamp: Embossed "Wade" on back rim

Date	Name	Description	Issue	Price	Size	U.S. $	Can. $	U.K. £
1999	Harestronaut	Pale blue; black boots	300	£20	58	20.	22.	12.
1999	Jesthare	Grey; red costume	300	set	58	20.	22.	12.
1999	PC Gotchare	Pale blue; dark blue uniform	300	3 pcs	58	20.	22.	12.
2000	Bravehare	Grey; dark green shirt	250	£25	60	40.	45.	25.
2000	The Shareriff	Pale blue; yellow shirt	250	Pair	60	40.	45.	25.

ARTHUR HARE WIZHARED WHIMSIE
2001-2006

The green colourway of Arthur Hare Wizhared Whimsie was issued at the Pennsylvania Wade Fest 2001.

Backstamp: Embossed "Wade / C&S" on back rim

Date	Name	Description	Issue	Price	Size	U.S. $	Can. $	U.K. £
2001	Wizhared Whimsie	Blue	1,650	£6.50	43	12.	14.	7.
2001	Wizhared Whimsie	Green	250	$10 US	43	18.	20.	12.
2006	Wizhared Whimsie	Pale blue, gold stars, silver moons	100	£18.00	43	30.	35.	18.

THE COLLECTHARE COLLECTION
1998-1999

Backstamp: Printed "With Certificate of Authenticity. 500 Limited Edition. Arthur Hare the Collecthare by Wade England © 1998 or 1999 C&S"

Date	Name	Description	Issue	Price	Size	U.S. $	Can. $	U.K. £
1998	Christmas Bonanza	Red shirt; *Christmas Bonanza*	400	£39.95	120	60.	65.	35.
1999	Jolly Potter	Purple T shirt; *Jolly Potter*	500	£39.95	120	60.	65.	35.
1999	Wade's World	Yellow T shirt; *Wade's World*	500	£39.95	120	60.	65.	35.

THE TRAVELHARE COLLECTION
1998-1999

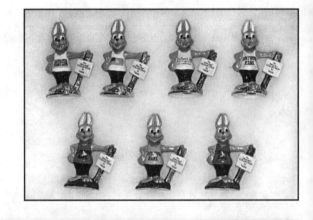

Backstamp: Gold circular printed "© 1998 C&S Collectables Fair Special Uxbridge, Trentham Gardens, Buffalo, Arundel Swapmeet, Dunstable. Modelled by Andy Moss Special Limited Edition C&S Arthur Hare with Certificate of Authenticity by Wade England"

Date	Venue	Description	Issue	Price	Size	U.S. $	Can. $	U.K. £
1998	Arundel Swap Meet	White vest, Union Jack; gold base	500	£35	115	90.	100.	50.
1998	Buffalo Fair	White vest, U.S.A. flag; gold base	250	£35	115	90.	100.	50.
1998	Dunstable Fair	Pearl lustre vest; dark green base	350	£39.95	115	90.	100.	50.
1998	Dunstable Fair	Pearl lustre vest; gold base	20	Prizes	115	—	—	—
1998	Collect It! Fair, Newark	White vest; gold base; *Collect It!*	400	£40	115	90.	100.	50.
1998	Mail Order Sp. Edition	Gold vest; green base	250	£39.95	115	90.	100.	50.
1998	Trentham Gardens	Red vest; dark green base	250	£35	115	130.	140.	75.
1999	Uxbridge Fair	Yellow vest; green base	250	£35	115	110.	140.	65.
1999	Uxbridge Fair	Purple vest; green base	250	£35	115	110.	120.	65.

THE VILLAGE PEOPLE COLLECTION

1997-2000

A new series of *Arthur Hare* models dressed in character clothes and modelled by freelance artist Andy Moss was introduced in December 1997. The Jesthares were issued as fair specials, the platinum version being introduced at the Brunel University, Uxbridge Show, in November 1998, and the gold version at the Alton Towers Christmas Extravaganza, November 1999. The "Harestronaut" was produced for the Wade/I.A.J.B.B.S.C. Show held in San Antonio, Texas, July 1999.

Big Chief Bravehare, Shareriff, Santhare Paws, PC Gotchare

Jesthare (gold base), Harestronaut

Harelloween, Wizhared

Backstamp: **A.** Printed black and red circular "© 1997 C&S Collectables Limited Edition With Certificate of Authenticity Modelled by Andy Moss Special Limited Edition (C&S) Arthur Hare™ Santhare Paws by Wade England"
B. Printed "With Certificate of Authenticity © 1998 C&S Wade England Arthur Hare The Jesthare 350 Special Edition C&S"
C. Printed "With Certificate of Authenticity. 500 Limited Edition. Harestronaut by Wade England © 1999 C&S"
D. Printed "©2000 C&S Collectables with certificate of authenticity [name of model] Wade England Modelled by Andy Moss 500 Limited Edition C&S"

Date	Name	Description	Issue	Price	Size	U.S. $	Can. $	U.K. £
1997	Santhare Paws	Grey/red/white/brown/black	500	£30.00	124	70.	75.	40.
1998	Big Chief Bravehare	Red/yellow/green	1,000	£33.00	115	60.	65.	35.
1998	Jesthare	Orange/yellow/platinum base	350	£39.95	115	85.	95.	50.
1998	Jesthare	Orange/yellow/gold base	350	£39.95	115	85.	95.	50.
1998	PC Gotchare	Dark blue/yellow/brown	1,000	£33.00	115	60.	65.	35.
1998	Shareriff	Grey/red/yellow/blue/brown	1,000	£33.00	110	60.	65.	35.
1999	Harestronaut	Grey/silver/black/gold	500	£39.95	115	70.	75.	40.
2000	Harelloween	Grey/black/gold; pearlised base	500	£39.95	110	70.	75.	40.
2000	Wizhared	Grey/purple; pearlised base	500	£39.95	115	70.	75.	40.

ARUN BEAR TOWN CRIER

2001

Backstamp: Printed "Wade Est 1810 England Arun Bear Town Cryer Arundel Wade Collectors Meet. August 2001" with "C&S" logo

Date	Name	Description	Issue	Price	Size	U.S. $	Can. $	U.K. £
2001	Arun Bear	Red coat; black tricorn hat; gold bell	250	£35	65 x 50	60.	65.	35.
2001	Arun Bear	Green coat; black tricorn hat; gold bell	20	Prizes	65 x 50	140.	150.	80.

BEARS WITH FLAGS

2002-2003

In October 2002, due to demand from Canadian collectors, C&S recoloured the Victor"E" Bear yellow, and renamed it "Maple the Canadian Bear." It was produced in a limited edition of 125 and cost £25.00.

In March 2003, a limited edition of 28 bears in a black colourway was produced for the Canadian on-line Wademad group. The cost was also £25.00.

Two special colourways of green bears with either the USA or UK flags were produced in a limited edition of 15 each. These were available as prizes throughout 2003.

Victor"E" Bear, USA Flag (2003)   Maple the Canadian Bear (2002)   Victor "E" Bear, UK Flag, (2003)

Backstamp: **Maple the Canadian Bear:** Printed "Maple Bear 125 Ltd. Edit." and "Wade" logo
              Maple the Canadian Bear: Printed gold "WADE" logo

Date	Name	Description	Issue	Price	Size	U.S. $	Can. $	U.K. £
2002	Maple the Canadian Bear	Yellow bear; red/white Canadian flag	125	£25	78	80.	90.	45.
2003	Maple the Canadian Bear	Black bear; red/white Canadian flag	28	£25	78	100.	110.	60.
2003	Victor"E" Bear, USA	Green bear; red/white/blue USA flag	15	Prizes	78	100.	110.	60.
2003	Victor"E" Bear, UK	Green bear; red/white/blue UK flag	15	Prizes	78	100.	110.	60.

BETTY BOOP

1996-2007

Originally created in 1930 by animator Grim Natwick and made famous by film producer Max Fleisher in 1931, *Betty Boop* was a popular North American cartoon character who was usually accompanied by her dog "Pudgy." King Features produced a comic strip cartoon of her in the mid-late 1930s, and her cartoons appeared on North American television in the late 1950s and 1970s.

The Christmas Surprise with a gold base was sold at the Collect It! Fair in 1998. For variations of "Betty Boop Wall Plaque," see *Collect It!* magazine, page 239, and for a variation of Betty Boop Beach Belle see page 177.

Backstamps: Black printed circular "© 1996 King Features Syndicate, Inc. Fleisher Studios, Inc. [No.of Limited Edition] (C&S) Betty Boop by Wade England"

Date	Name	Description	Issue	Price	Size	U.S. $	Can. $	U.K. £
1996	Betty Boop	Red dress; white collar; green base	1,500	£35.00	95	130.	145.	75.
1997	Betty Boop	Blue dress; pearlised collar, base	500	£35.00	95	150.	165.	85.
1997	Wall Plaque	White dress; pearlised moon	1,250	£37.00	225	100.	110.	60.
1997	Christmas Surprise	Red dress, hat; brown sack; pearlised base	1,750	£39.95	132	150.	165.	85.
1998	Christmas Surprise	Red dress, hat; green sack gold base	250	£45.00	132	175.	200.	100.
1998	Beach Belle	Black swimsuit with yellow spots	2,000	£41.00	152	130.	145.	75.
1999	Halloween	Black hat, dress, gloves, shoes	1,000	£42.00	152	175.	200.	100.
1999	Halloween	Platinum hat; black dress, gloves shoes	20	Prizes	152	425.	475.	250.
1999	Southern Belle	White flowered dress; pink hat, ribbons	500	£35.00	80	150.	165.	85.
1999	Southern Belle	White flowered dress; blue hat, gold ribbons	100	£35.00	80	350.	375.	200.
1999	Southern Belle	White flowered dress; gold hat, ribbons	20	Prizes	80	—	—	—
2000	Liberty (figure)	Dark blue dress; platinum crown, torch	980	£42.00	158	200.	225.	120.
2000	Liberty (figure)	Dark blue dress; gold crown, torch	20	Charity	158	425.	475.	250.
2000	Liberty (plaque)	Dark blue dress; pearl lustre	300	£65.00	200	75.	85.	60.
2000	Ringmaster	Red jacket, shoes; gold base	20	Charity	125	425.	475.	250.
2000	Ringmaster / Pudgy	Red jacket, shoes, base; white dog	480	£50.00	125	165.	18.0	95.
2000	Rose	Pink dress; bouquet of purple flowers	1,000	£45.00	132	175.	200.	100.
2000	Springtime	White dress, hat; pink bows; brown basket	1,000	£45.00	140	150.	165.	85.
2001	Graduate, UK	Black, blue outfit; pewter tassel	500	£55.00	132	130.	145.	75.
2001	Graduate, USA	Black, purple outfit; gold tassel	500	$78 US	132	130.	145.	75.
2001	Movie Queen	Red dress; black, white film	250	£99.00	230	425.	475.	250.
2001	Superstar	Blue dress; gold jewellery	750	£55.00	145	175.	200.	100.
2002	Christmas Morning	Red/white dress blue parcel; yellow ribbons	750	£55.00	90	95.	110.	55.
2002	Christmas Morning	Red/white dress; gold parcel, ribbons	20	Prizes	90	—	—	—
2002	Elegance	Black dress; red sash, bow	500	£99.00	230	275.	300.	150.
2002	Elegance	Black dress; gold sash, bow	20	Prizes	230	—	—	—
2002	Halloween	Mauve dress; orange pumpkin, black outlines	750	£55.00	153	175.	200.	100.
2002	Halloween	Mauve dress; orange pumpkin, gold outlines	20	Prizes	153	—	—	—
2002	Jubilee	Red, ermine cloak; blue dress	500	£99.00	230	175.	200.	100.
2002	Jubilee	Royal blue, ermine cloak; blue dress	25	Prizes	230	—	—	—
2002	Lazy Daze	White dress; blue cushion, gold tassel	750	£55.00	76	95.	110.	55.
2002	Lazy Daze	Gold dress; red cushion, gold tassel	20	Prizes	76	95.	110.	55.
2002	Queen of Hearts	Red swimsuit, shoes; purple, gold crown	2,000	£55.00	135	150.	165.	85.
2002	Queen of Hearts	Gold swimsuit; red shoes; purple, gold crown	20	Prizes	135	—	—	—
2002	St. Patrick's Day	Green tunic, hat; white dog	750	£55.00	140	175.	200.	100
2002	St. Patrick's Day	Green tunic; gold hat; white dog	20	Prizes	140	—	—	—
2002	Valentine	Black dress; red heart; pearl base	750	£55.00	150	175.	200.	100.
2002	Valentine	Black dress; gold heart; pearl base	20	Prizes	150	175.	200.	100.

Betty Boop

Betty Boop Christmas Surprise

Betty Boop Wall Plaque

Betty Boop Beach Belle

Betty Boop Halloween Trick or Treat

Betty Boop Southern Belle

Betty Boop Liberty

Betty Boop Wall Plaque

Betty Boop Springtime

Betty Boop Ringmaster

Pudgy

Betty Boop Rose

BETTY BOOP (cont.)

Date	Name	Description	Issue	Price	Size	U.S. $	Can. $	U.K. £
2003	Betty in Black	Black glitter dress; black hair	20	Prizes	140	—	—	—
2003	Betty in Red	Red dress; black hair	750	£55	140	125.	140.	70.
2003	Rainy Days	Dark blue jacket, boots; red dress	2,000	£55	155	130.	145.	75.
2003	Rainy Days	Dark blue Jacket, red dress, gold base	20	Prizes	155	275.	300.	150.
2003	Seasons Greetings	Green, red and white	750	£55	140	175.	200.	100.
2003	Swinging 60s	Black/white mini dress; white dog; red box	750	£55	145	220.	250.	125.
2003	Trick or Treat	Red dress; black hat; gold moon	750	£58	150	220.	250.	125.
2004	Juke Box	Red bodice, lilac skirt; white/lilac jukebox	750	£58	152	200.	225.	110.
2004	Juke Box	Red bodice, lilac skirt; silver jukebox	20	Prizes	152	—	—	—
2004	Material Girl	White dress	2,000	£55	152	100.	110.	55.
2004	Material Girl	Blue dress	250	£55	152	125.	140.	70.
2004	Material Girl	Red dress	12	Prizes	152	—	—	—
2004	Showtime	Black and pearl lustre dress; pearl stole	750	£58	152	150.	165.	80.
2004	Showtime	Red dress	20	Prizes	152	—	—	—
2004	Snow Queen	White dress, blue trim; silver crown	500	£99	225	200.	225.	110.
2004	Snow Queen	White dress, platinum trim; silver crown	20	Prizes	225	220.	250.	125.
2004	Sweetheart	Black dress; red heart; pearlised wrap	750	£58	140	90.	100.	50.
2005	Cheers Ten Years	Red dress; white goblet	1,250	£60	152	175.	200.	100.
2005	Cheers Ten Years	Blue dress; white champagne glass	300	£60	152	260.	290.	150.
2005	Christmas Time	Red, white dress; brown sack	500	£99	225	130.	145.	75.
2005	Christmas Time	Red, pearl dress; silver sack	150	£99	225	220.	250.	125.
2005	Hubble Bubble	Black witches costume, purple trim	750	£58	152	125.	140.	70.
2005	Ladies Day	Pale blue dress, hat; lustre feather boa	500	Unk.	225	200.	225.	110.
2005	Ladies Day	Black dress, hat	20	Prizes	225	—	—	—
2005	Uptown Girl	Pale blue dress	2,000	£58	152	100.	110.	60.
2005	Uptown Girl	Black dress	20	Prizes	152	—	—	—
2006	Air Hostess	Red kirt, jacket; blue luggage	750	£60	152	100.	110.	60.
2006	Air Hostess	Pink skirt, jacket	20	Prizes	152	—	—	—
2006	Christmas Present	Red, white Santa dress; green package	750	£60	152	100.	110.	60.
2006	Christmas Present	Red, white Santa dress; gold package	20	Prizes	152	250.	275.	150.
2006	Cool Breeze	Red dress	250	£60	152	150.	165.	85.
2006	Cool Breeze	White dress	2,000	£60	152	100.	110.	60.
2006	Nurse	Nurse's uniform; red cross	2,000	£60	152	100.	110.	60.
2006	Nurse	Nurse's uniform; green cross	20	Prizes	152	—	—	—
2006	Halloween	Black cloak, hat; red dress	500	£105	225	190.	210.	110.
2006	Halloween	Black cloak, hat; blue dress	20	Prizes	225	—	—	—
2006	Toy Box Betty	Red dress; white toy box, pink, blue letters	500	£105	Unk.	190.	210.	105.
2006	Satin and Lace	Blue dress	750	£60	152	100.	110.	60.
2006	Satin and Lace	Lustre dress	20	Prizes	152	350.	375.	200.
2006	Viva Las Vegas	Pale blue and white, gold trim	2,000	£60	152	100.	110.	60.
2006	World Cup Betty	Red jersey; white shorts; red, white flag	750	£60	152	130.	145.	75.
2006	World Cup Betty	Red Jersey, white shorts, gold base	20	Prizes	152	250.	275.	150.
2007	Cheerleader	Yellow dress, socks; blue ponpoms	750	£60	152	100.	110.	60.
2007	Elegant Betty	Pale blue dress	2,000	£60	152	100.	110.	60.
2007	Elegant Betty	Pink dress	300	Unk.	152	125.	140.	70.
2007	I Love You	Unknown	500	£105	225	190.	210.	105.
2007	Party Time	Pink dress; white cake, blue edging	750	£60	152	100.	110.	60.

Betty Boop Movie Queen

Betty Boop St. Patrick's Day

Betty Boop Superstar

Betty Boop Valentine

Betty Boop Christmas Morning

Betty Boop Elegance

Betty Boop Halloween

Betty Boop Jubilee

Betty Boop Lazy Daze

Betty Boop Queen of Hearts

Betty Boop Swinging 60s

Betty Boop Trick or Treat

BETTY BOOP WHIMSIES
2004

Date	Name	Description	Issue	Price	Size	U.S. $	Can. $	U.K. £
2004	Whimsie	Apricot	500	£8	45.	18.	20.	10.
2004	Whimsie	Beige	500	£8	45	18.	20.	10.
2004	Whimsie	Cobalt blue	500	£8	45	18.	20.	10.
2004	Whimsie	Christmas green	200	£6	45	18.	20.	10.
2004	Whimsie	Christmas burgundy	200	£6	45	18.	20.	10.
2004	Whimsie	Pink	500	£8	45	18.	20.	10.
2004	Whimsie	White	500	£8	45	18.	20.	10.

BRITISH HERITAGE COLLECTION
2003

This is the first model in an intended series named "British Heritage." It was produced in a limited edition of 250 and cost £22.00.

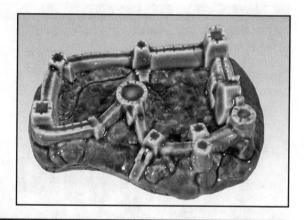

Backstamp: Printed "British Heritage Collection Arundel Castle Limited edition of 500" with blue "C&S" and red "Wade" logos

Date	Name	Description	Issue	Price	Size	U.S. $	Can. $	U.K. £
2003	Arundel Castle	Grey castle; green base	250	£22	30 x 80	45.	50.	25.

BUDGIE WHIMSIES

2003

Produced in a limited edition of 500, the budgies were issued in four colourways, priced at £22.00 for the set. For the 'pink' colourway see Wade Watch.

Backstamp: Embossed "Wade C/S"

Date	Name	Description	Issue	Price	Size	U.S. $	Can. $	U.K. £
2003	Budgie Whimsie	Blue	500	Set of	50			
2003	Budgie Whimsie	Green	500	four	50			
2003	Budgie Whimsie	Honey	500	models	50			
2003	Budgie Whimsie	White	500	£22.	50			
—	4 pce set		—	—	—	40.	45.	22.

A boxed set of six budgies in a special edition of two was offered as prizes in the C&S prize draw at the 2003 Harrisburg, PA, Wade Fest.

Backstamp: Embossed "Wade C/S"

Date	Name	Description	Issue	Price	Size	U.S. $	Can. $	U.K. £
2003	Budgie Whimsie	Blue			50			
2003	Budgie Whimsie	Green			50			
2003	Budgie Whimsie	Honey			50			
2003	Budgie Whimsie	Pink			50			
2003	Budgie Whimsie	White			50			
2003	Budgie Whimsie	White, gold base			50			
—	Boxed set		2	Prizes		—	—	—

C&S CRACKERS

October 2001

The C&S boxed set of six Christmas Crackers was produced in a limited edition of ten boxes. They contained a selection of the following Wade models: the *English Whimsies* Cow, 'Skip' the dog, a blue or green "Arthur Hare Wizhared" miniature, a "Betty Boop," "Wade Club" or a "Spooner's" whimble, a "Big Chief Bravehare Teenie", a "Miniature Teapot Key Ring," an "Arundel Otter" or the *Tiny Treasurers* 'Supergirl.' The cost of the box on the day was £29.95.

Date	Name	Description	Issue	Price	Size	U.S. $	Can. $	U.K. £
2001	C&S Crackers	Miscellaneous colours	10	£29.95	—	50.	55.	30.

CHARACTERS FROM CHARLIE BROWN
1999-2006

Snoopy and Woodstock

Snoopy Happy Holidays

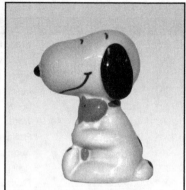
Snoopy Hugging Woodstock

Charlie Brown

Linus

Snoopy (standing)

Backstamp: Printed "With Certificate of Authenticity C&S 500 Special Edition Wade England"

Date	Name	Description	Issue	Price	Size	U.S. $	Can. $	U.K. £
1999	Snoopy and Woodstock	Snoopy: White/black/red Woodstock: Yellow/black	1,000 (pairs)	£38.00	65 58	140.	150.	80
2000	Snoopy Happy Holidays	White/green/ gold	1,000	£39.95	98	100.	110.	50.
2000	Snoopy Hugging Woodstock	White/black/yellow	1,000	£38.00	65	100.	110.	50.
2001	Charlie Brown and Linus	Charlie: Yellow/black/brown Linus: Blue/brown/white	500 (pairs)	£78.00	84 70	140.	155.	80.
2005	Snoopy (standing)	White, gold collar	20	Prizes	63	—	—	—
2005	Snoopy (standing)	White, red collar	500	£19.95	63	35.	40.	20.
2006	Snoopy (Santa hat)	White, red	100	£25.00	50	45.	50.	25.
2006	Witch Snoopy	White, black hat; red collar	100	£22.00	50	45.	50.	25.

eWADE

2001-2006

Although named Ted "E" Bear, the backstamp incorrectly reads TEDD "E" BEAR.

Date	Name	Description	Issue	Price	Size	U.S. $	Can. $	U.K. £
2001	Frost"E"	White snowman; blue scarf	150	£22.50	85	70.	80.	40.
2001	Frost"E"	Pearlised snowman; blue scarf	20	Prizes	85	250.	275.	150.
2001	Ted"E", Internet Guide	Honey, dark brown; *Internet Guide*	100	£22.00	85	80.	90.	45.
2001	Ted"E", Wade Handbook	Honey; dark brown; *Wade Handbook*	100	£22.00	85	80.	90.	45.
2001	Ted"E", Gold book	Honey; dark brown; gold book	20	Prizes	85	125.	140.	75.
2001	West"E"	White; black eyes, nose	100	£22.50	65	80.	90.	45.
2001	West"E"	Platinum	20	Prizes	65	—	—	—
2001	Scottie	Black; brown eyes, nose	100	£22.50	85	65.	75.	35.
2002	Donk"E"	Light grey; black eyes	125	£22.50	78 x 88	70.	80.	40.
2002	Donk"E"	Pearl lustre	20	Prizes	78 x 88	—	—	—
2002	Rud"E", Reindeer	Honey; dark brown antlers, red nose	150	£25.00	80	55.	60.	30.
2002	Rud"E", Reindeer	White; gold antlers; red nose	20	Prizes	80	—	—	—
2002	Victor"E" Bear	Blue bear; red/white/blue USA flag	125	£24.50	78	55.	60.	30.
2003	Brand"E" (St. Bernard)	White, brown dog; pewter barrel, collar	125	£25.00	70	35.	40.	20.
2003	Brand"E" (St. Bernard)	Pearl; gold barrel, collar	20	Prizes	70	—	—	—
2003	Budg"E"	Blue, white, yellow bird; grey base	125	£25.00	76	65.	75.	35.
2003	Budg"E"	Pearl white; gold beak, feet, base	20	Prizes	76	—	—	—
2003	Husk"E"	White	150	£25.00	57	30.	35.	17.
2004	Bunn"E"	Grey-black; red eyes	125	£25.00	78	55.	60.	30.
2004	Pon"E"	White; yellow mane, tail; grey base	125	£26.00	63	45.	50.	25.
2004	Pupp"E"	Honey; black eyes, nose	125	£26.00	90	45.	50.	25.
2005	Doll"E" the Sheep	White; green base	125	£26.00	60 x 76	45.	50.	25.
2005	Christmas Ging"E"	See Gingie Bear Series, page	—	—	—	—	—	—
2005	Spook"E" (Cat)	Black; green eyes	125	£27.50	90	70.	80.	40.
2005	Spook"E"	Pearl; green eyes	20	Prizes	90	120.	130.	70.
2006	Easter Bunn"E"	Beige	125	£27.50	63	30.	35.	17.
2006	Frost"E" Snowman II	Red hat; red, white striped scarf	100	£27.50	102	45.	50.	25.
2006	Ging"E" Trick or Treat	See Gingie Bear Series, page 229	—	—	—	—	—	—

Note:
1. A dash in any of the technical data columns of the table indicates that we do not have the required information, if you do, we would be pleased to hear from you.
2. Dashes in the pricing columns indicate one of two things: firstly, there was insufficient market pricing available, and secondly, pieces issued in small quantities of 10 or 20 pieces will be subject to wide pricing swings.

Frost"E" (2001)

Donk"E" [2002]

Rud"E" [2002]

Victor"E" (2002)

Brand"E" (2003)

Budg"E" (2003)

Ted"E" (2001)

West"E" (2001)

Doll"E" the Sheep (2005)

Frost"E" Snowman II (2006)

Pon"E" (2004)

Spook"E" (Cat) (2005)

FANTASYLAND

2002

The "Mermaid" and "Pegasus" were modelled by Ken Holmes, and the "Pixie on a Mushroom" by Cyril Roberts. The "Pegasus" model with the gold base was produced to mark the 10th Anniversry of C&S Collectables.

Mermaid (brown chest); Mermaid (gold chest); Pixie on a Mushroom (brown base) Pixie on a Mushroom (gold base)

Pegasus (gold base); Pegasus (blue base)

Backstamp: Printed "Wades Fantasy Land [name of model, limited edition number and number in series]" with blue "C&S" and red "Wade" logos

Date	Name	Description	Issue	Price	Size	U.S. $	Can. $	U.K. £
2002	Mermaid	Yellow hair; blue tail; brown trunk	250	£29.95	70	70.	75.	40.
2002	Mermaid	Yellow hair; blue tail; gold trunk	20	Prizes	70	—	—	—
2002	Pegasus	White; black hooves; blue base	250	£29.95	85	85.	95.	50.
2002	Pegasus	Pearlised white; black hooves; gold base	20	Prizes	85	150.	165.	85.
2002	Pixie on a Mushroom	Red coat; beige, brown mushroom	250	£29.95	75	70.	75.	40.
2002	Pixie on a Mushroom	Red coat; gold mushroom	20	Prizes	75	—	—	—

GARFIELD

1999

Backstamp: Printed "With Certificate of Authenticity C&S 500
Special Edition Wade England"

Date	Name	Description	Issue	Price	Size	U.S. $	Can. $	U.K. £
1999	Garfield	Orange, black, pink, yellow	500	£35	70	85.	95.	50.

GINGIE BEAR

2005-2007

For You

Traveller

Uncle Sam

Backstamp: Printed "Gingie Bear © 2005 little words limited"

Date	Name	Description	Issue	Price	Size	U.S. $	Can. $	U.K. £
2005	For You	Blue scroll	250	Unk.	40	35.	40.	20.
2005	For You	Silver scroll	75	Unk.	40	85.	95.	50.
2005	Christmas Ging"E"	Red,white hat; blue gift box, red ribbon	125	£28.50	75	50.	55.	30.
2005	Christmas	Red, pale blue hat; pale blue box, gold ribbon	20	Unk.	75	—	—	—
2005	Whimsie	Tan	500	£9.99	40	18.	20.	10.
2006	Halloween	Black hat	100	£15.00	40	25.	30.	15.
2006	Traveller	Gold knapsack	20	Unk.	40	—	—	—
2006	Traveller (Stoke Fair)	Orange spotted knapsack	100	Unk.	40	35.	40.	20.
2006	Traveller	Red/white/blue striped knapsack	100	Unk.	40	30.	35.	18.
2006	Traveller (Dunstable)	Silver knapsack	100	Unk.	40	80.	90.	45.
2006	Ging"E" Trick or Treat	Black hat; brown broom	100	£35.00	75	60.	65.	35.
2006	Whimsie, Gold Hat	Gold hat	10	Unk.	80	—	—	—
2006	Uncle Sam	Red, white and blue hat	100	Unk.	80	60.	65.	35.
2006	Whimsie, Silver Hat	Silver hat	10	Unk.	80	—	—	—
2007	Jet Set	Blue airplane	100	Unk.	75	60.	65.	35.

MR. MAGOO
1998

Backstamp: Printed "Mr Magoo Wade England ©1998 UPA
Pictures, Inc. With Certificate of Authenticity
1,000 Limited Edition C&S"

Date	Name	Description	Issue	Price	Size	U.S. $	Can. $	U.K. £
1998	Mr. Magoo	Dark green coat; white base	960	£37.50	105	80.	90.	45.
1998	Mr. Magoo	Dark green coat; gold base	40	£40.00	105	140.	150.	80.

MABEL LUCIE ATTWELL SERIES
2004-2006

Alice

Mad Hatter

Backstamp: Printed "LA Ltd 2005 Wade"

Date	Name	Description	Issue	Price	Size	U.S. $	Can. $	U.K. £
2004	Sam	Yellow shirt; fawn shorts; grey dog	750	£42	105	50.	55.	30.
2004	Sarah	White dress with blue spots	750	£42	105	50.	55.	30.
2005	Alice	Pink dress, white collar; white, blue bowl	500	£45	90	35.	40.	20.
2005	Alice	Pink dress, white collar; gold bowl	20	Unk.	90	—	—	—
2005	Mad Hatter	Blue jacket; brown trousers; white sandwich	500	£45	110	50.	55.	30.
2005	Mad Hatter	Blue jacket; brown trousers; gold sandwich	20	Unk.	110	100.	110.	60.
2006	Best Friends	Orange/white	250	£35	90	25.	28.	15.
2006	Best Friends	Lustre dress	20	Unk.	90	—	—	—

ORINOCO WOMBLE

1999

Orinoco is a well-known character from the British television cartoon series *The Wombles.*

Backstamp: Printed "With Certificate of Authenticity 1,000 limited edition C&S The Wombles Orinoco by Wade England.1,000 Limited Edition, © Elisabeth Berrisford / FilmFair Ltd 1999"

Date	Name	Description	Issue	Price	Size	U.S. $	Can. $	U.K. £
1999	Orinoco	Red hat, scarf; green base	750	£39.95	110	60.	65.	35.
1999	Orinoco	Red hat, scarf; gold base	250	£39.95	110	70.	75.	40.

POCKET PALS "TANGO"

1999

The mould used to make the Mother Cat in the *Happy Families Series* was also used to make "Tango." See also Pocket Pals, pages 122 and 240.

Backstamp: Gold Transfer "Wade Pp" in shield

Date	Name	Description	Issue	Price	Size	U.S. $	Can. $	U.K. £
1999	Tango	Apricot; blue eyes	1,000	£6.50	45 x 35	20.	22.	12.

THOMAS THE TANK ENGINE

STYLE TWO

2002

The engines "Thomas" and "Percy" were modelled by Simon Millard, and "Henry" and "James" by Cyril Roberts.

Henry the Engine

James the Engine

Percy the Engine

Thomas the Tank Engine

Backstamp: Printed blue "C&S" and red "Wade" logos, "©Gullane (Thomas) Limited 2002"

Date	Name	Description	Issue	Price	Size	U.S. $	Can. $	U.K. £
2002	Fat Controller	Black coat; grey trousers; green base	500	£29.95	62	65.	70.	35.
2002	Fat Controller	Black coat; grey trousers; gold base	20	Prizes	62	—	—	—
2002	Henry Engine	Green, black, red, grey, yellow	500	£30.00	50 x 100	70.	75.	40.
2002	James Engine	Red, black, yellow, grey	500	£30.00	50 x 90	70.	75.	40.
2002	Percy Engine	Green, black, red, grey, yellow	500	£30.00	50 x 76	70.	75.	40.
2002	Thomas the Tank Engine	Blue, black ,red, grey, yellow	500	£30.00	50 x 76	70.	75.	40.

Note: **1.** A dash in any of the technical data columns of the table indicates that we do not have the required information, if you do, we would be pleased to hear from you.

2. Dashes in the pricing columns indicate one of two things: firstly, there was insufficient market pricing available, and secondly, pieces issued in small quantities of 10 or 20 pieces will be subject to wide pricing swings.

WINTER WONDERLAND
2002-2004

Polar Bear Cubs on Ice (2002)

Polar Bear Cubs on Ice, silver ice block (2002)

Mother Polar Bear and Cub on Ice (2003)

Polar Bear Cub, standing (2004)

Polar Bear Cubs, hugging (2004)

WonderLand Penguin (2003)

Date	Name	Description	Issue	Price	Size	U.S. $	Can. $	U.K. £
2002	Polar Bearcubs on Ice	White; pearl ice block	250	Unk.	90 x 100	45.	50.	25.
2002	Polar Bearcubs on Ice	White; silver ice block	20	Unk.	90 x 100	—	—	—
2002	Polar Bear Cub, seated	White; black eyes, nose	100	£20.00	42	35.	40.	20.
2002	Polar Bear Cub, seated	Gold	20	Prizes	42	—	—	—
2002	Polar Bear Cub, walking	White; black eyes; blue base	100	Unk.	45	35.	40.	20.
2003	Mama Seal and Pup	Mama: Grey-blue; Pup: White	150	£25.00	90 x 50	45.	50.	25.
2003	Mother Polar Bear and Cub on Ice	White; grey base	250	£36.00	90 x 105	45.	50.	25.
2003	Mother Polar Bear and Cub on Ice	White; silver base	Unk.	Unk.	90 x 105	—	—	—
2003	Papa Seal	Grey-blue; silver rock	150	£25.00	80 x 60	45.	50.	25.
2003	Papa Seal	White; pale blue rock	Unk.	Unk.	80 x 60	—	—	—
2003	Polar Bear Cub, seated	White; pale blue base	100	£20.00	50 x 50	35.	40.	20.
2003	Polar Bear Cub, walking	White; pale blue base	100	£20.00	50 x 45	35.	40.	20.
2003	WonderLand Penguin	Black, white, yellow	150	£27.50	Unk.	50.	55.	28.
2003	WonderLand Penguin	Gold	20	Prizes	Unk	—	—	—
2004	Eskimo and Igloo	Eskimo: Olive green parka Igloo: Blue-grey	125 Pairs	£49.95 Pair	70 x 150 50 x 35	85.	90.	50.
2004	Eskimo and Igloo	Olive, blue-grey, lustre finish	20	Prizes	As above	150.	165.	85.
2004	Polar Bear Cub, standing	White; blue base	100	£25.00	55 x 35	50.	55.	25.
2004	Polar Bear Cubs, hugging	White; pinker inner ears, pads	100	£25.00	40 x 50	50.	55.	25.

CADBURY WORLD
2002-2005

Wade produced these Chucklebeans for Cadbury World in November 2002. Originally available only from Cadbury World Shop, in early 2003 they were available through the Wade Collectors Club.

| Chucklebean | Chucklebean Keyring | Hazelnut | Raisin |

Backstamp: **Chucklebean:** Embossed "Wade England"
Hazelnut / Raisin: Embossed "Wade Eng"

Date	Name	Description	Issue	Price	Size	U.S. $	Can. $	U.K. £
2002	Chucklebean	Beige; black shoes	—	—	40	4.	5.	2.
2002	Chucklebean	Beige; green shoes	—	—	40	4.	5.	2.
2002	Chucklebean	Beige; yellow shoes	—	—	40	4.	5.	2.
2005	Chucklenut Keyring	Honey	5,000	—	40	10.	11.	5.
2005	Hazelnut	Honey; black eyes	5,000	£1.99	45	6.	7.	3.
2005	Raisin	Blue-grey	5,000	£1.99	40	6.	7.	3.

Note: For the Cadbury World Train and Carriages Money Box see *Wade Collectables*, 4th edition.

CAMTRAK

CHILDHOOD FAVOURITES SERIES

1995-1999

Dougal, a cartoon dog from the British children's television series, *The Magic Roundabout,* was the first model of this series, produced for Camtrak of Nottingham, England. It was issued in a limited edition of 2,000 figures. The first 220 models were fired twice, leaving the model with a dark mushroom-coloured face, and is known as the brown-faced Dougal. The other 1,780 models were fired once only and have a lighter, pale ivory face.

Rupert and the Snowman was the fourth model in Camtrak's *Childhood Favourites* series and was also the first in an intended series of *Seasonal* models. A special limited edition of 110 models was produced with a pale blue Snowman's scarf for the City of London Police Fund (CLP).

Backstamp: **Dougal:** Transfer print "Camtrak's Childhood Favourites No.1 Dougal by Wade © Serge Danot/AB Productions SA 1995 Licensed by Link Licensing Ltd."
Paddington Bear: Printed "Camtrak's Childhood Favourites No 3 Paddington © Paddington and Company LTD 1997 Licensed by Copyrights Wade Made in England"
Paddington Bear: Printed "Camtrak Childhood Favourites by Wade No 7 Paddington's Snowy Day. ©Paddington and Company. Ltd 1999 Licenced by Copyrights"
Plaque: Printed "Camtrak's Childhood Favourites A Series Display Plaque 1997 by Wade"
Plaque: Gold printed limited edition of 120 with Official International Wade Club logo
Rupert and the Snowman: Printed "Camtrak's Childhood Favourites by Wade No.4 Rupert and the Snowman. Rupert Characters and ©Express Newspapers Plc 1997 Licenced by Nelvana Marketing Inc. UK representative Abbey Home Entertainment"
Rupert and the Snowman: Printed "Camtrak's Childhood Favourites by Wade No.4 Rupert and the Snowman. Rupert Characters and © Express Newspapers Plc 1997 Licenced by Nelvana Marketing Inc. UK representative Abbey Home Entertainment Limited Edition of 110 Exclusive to the CLP Fund" with print of policeman and child
Rupert Bear: Printed "Camtrak's Childhood Favourites by Wade No 2 Rupert © 1996 Express Newspapers plc Licensed by A.H.E/Nelvana"
Sooty: Printed "Childhood Favourites by Wade [model number and name] Sooty - Sooty ™" and "© Sooty international Limited 1998 Licenced by Chatsworth enterprises Ltd 50 Golden Years" with "50 Golden Years Sooty" logo
Tiny Clanger: Printed "Camtrak's Childhood Favourites by Wade No. 8 Tiny Clanger © 1999 Oliver Postgate and Peter Firmin. Licenced by Licencing by Design Limited"

Date	Name	Description	Issue	Price	Size	U.S. $	Can. $	U.K. £
1995	Dougal	Mushroom face	220	£27.50	84 x 155	60.	65.	35.
1995	Dougal	Pale ivory face	1,780	£27.50	84 x 155	85.	95.	50.
1996	Rupert Bear	Red , yellow, black; green base	900	£30.00	130	100.	110.	55.
1996	Rupert Bear	Red , yellow, black, gold base	100	Unk.	130	250.	275.	150.
1997	Paddington Bear	Blue coat; grey base	2,000	£33.00	90	50.	55.	30.
1997	Paddington Bear	Blue coat; gold base	Unk.	Unk.	90	200.	225.	120.
1997	Plaque	Brown/white; brown knobs	880	£11.00	70	45.	50.	25.
1997	Plaque	Brown/white; gold knobs	20	£16.00	70	50.	55.	30.
1997	Rupert and the Snowman	Rupert: Red coat, black buttons Snowman: Dark blue scarf	1,800	Unk.	120	100.	110.	55.
1997	Rupert and the Snowman	Rupert: Red coat; gold buttons Snowman: Dark blue scarf	100	Unk	120	275.	300.	150.
1997	Rupert and the Snowman	Rupert: Red coat; black buttons Snowman: Pale blue scarf	110	Unk.	120	275.	300.	150.
1998	Sooty	Amber bear; blue dungarees	2,000	£38.50	132	85.	95.	50.
1998	Sweep	Grey; red trousers; grey base	200	£38.50	136	85.	95.	50.
1998	Sweep	Grey; red trousers; gold base	120	Unk.	136	140.	155.	80.
1998	Tiny Clanger	Pink; Red jacket; black shoes	Unk.	£16.00	110	70.	80.	40.
1999	Paddington's Snowy Day	Red coat; pearlised base	2,000	£38.85	100	80.	90.	45.

CAMTRAK MODELS

Paddington Bear (1997)

Paddington's Snowy Day (1997)

Rupert Bear (1996)

Sooty (left); Sweep (right)

Dougal (1995)

Rupert and the Snowman (1997)

Tiny Clanger (1998)

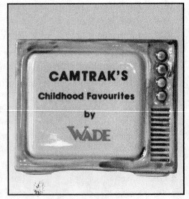

Childhood Favourites Plaque (1997)

CARRYER CRAFT OF CALIFORNIA
MINI MANSIONS
1984-1986

The beautiful Victorian houses of San Francisco survived the 1906 earthquake, but by the 1960s they had deteriorated badly. A few owners then decided to repaint their homes in the flamboyant colours of the original era, and the Painted Ladies were reborn. A Cable Car with different decals has been found: on one side of the car is a "Dewar's" decal and on the other "White Label" (the normal decals are "Fisherman's Wharf"). No information has been found to explain the change.

George Wade & Son Ltd. was commissioned by Carryer Craft of California (Iris Carryer was the elder daughter of Sir George Wade) to reproduce the Painted Ladies in porcelain. Because this short-lived series was made for export to the United States, only very limited quantities were released onto the British market.

All models are marked with "Wade England" in black on their side walls. The boxed set comprises six models, but the "Pink Lady," "Brown Lady," "White Lady" and the "Cable Car" are the most difficult to find. The original price was £10 for a box of eight models.

Original Box: Mini Mansions Set-1 San Francisco's Painted Ladies

Backstamp: Black transfer "Wade Porcelain England SF/[number of model]"

No.	Name	Description	Size	U.S. $	Can. $	U.K. £
SF/1	Pink Lady	Pink; black roof	55 x 25	85.	95.	50.
SF/2	White Lady	White; grey roof	55 x 25	85.	95.	50.
SF/3	Brown Lady	Brown; beige roof	65 x 30	85.	95.	50.
SF/4a	Yellow Lady	Yellow; grey roof; black apex	63 x 30	70.	80.	40.
SF/4b	Yellow Lady	Yellow; grey roof; blue apex	63 x 30	70.	80.	40.
SF/5	Blue Lady	Blue; grey roof	70 x 38	70.	80.	40.
SF/6a	Cable Car	Blue/green; red front; Fisherman's Wharf	20 x 38	120.	130.	70.
SF/6b	Cable Car	Blue/green; yellow front; Dewar's White Label	20 x 38	120.	130.	70.

CERAMICA

1999-2004

Ceramica is a museum in Burslem, Stoke-on-Trent, set in the historic Old Town Hall. The museum has many stunning displays of local pottery produced by such famous manufacturers as Moorcroft, Royal Doulton and Wade.

Backstamp:
   I'm On My Way: Printed "Wish You Were Here Collection I'm On My Way CERAMICA Limited Ed 750 With Certificate Wade England"
   Billy the Bottle Oven:
   Embossed "Ceramica Wade Eng"

I'm On My Way

Billy the Bottle Oven

Date	Name	Description	Issue	Price	Size	U.S. $	Can. $	U.K. £
1999	I'm On My Way	Green shirt; blue trousers	750	£29.00	130	60.	65.	35.
2004	Billy the Bottle Oven	Light green	—	£5.95	60 x 40	10.	11.	6.

CIBA GEIGY

SLOW FE AND SLOW K

1969

In 1969, George Wade was commissioned by the British drug company Ciba Geigy to produce models of tortoises with the words *Slow Fe* and *Slow K* on their backs. These models were presented to general practitioners by Ciba Geigy sales representatives as a promotional novelty to assist in marketing their iron and potassium preparations, Slow Fe (slow-release iron) and Slow K (slow-release potassium). Wade retooled the "Medium (Mother)" tortoise from the *Tortoise Family* by embossing either the name Slow Fe or Slow K in the top shell. See also page 130.

Slow Fe

Slow K

Backstamp: Embossed "Wade Porcelain Made in England"

Date	Name	Description	Issue	Price	Size	U.S. $	Can. $	U.K. £
1969	Slow Fe	Brown; blue markings	10,000	—	35 x 75	60.	65.	35.
1969	Slow K	Brown; blue markings	10,000	—	35 x 75	60.	65.	35.

COLLECT IT! MAGAZINE
1998 - 2006

BETTY BOOP
1998-2000

Backstamp: Unknown

Betty Boop Classic Wall Plaque

Betty Boop Liberty Wall Plaque

Date	Name	Description	Issue	Price	Size	U.S. $	Can. $	U.K. £
1998	Classic Plaque	Red dress; grey base	1,250	£41.95	225	120.	130.	70.
2000	Liberty Plaque	Red dress; gold crown, torch, book	250	£65.00	220	130.	140.	75.

COLLECT IT! FAIRIES
1998-1999

Backstamp:
  A. Black Printed "Collectania Made Exclusively for Collect it!
  By Wade Limited edition of 2,500"
  B. Black Printed "Collectus Made Exclusively for Collect it!
  By Wade Limited edition of 2,500"
  C. Black Printed "Collecteenie Made Exclusively for Collect
  it! By Wade Limited edition of 1,500"

Date	Name	Description	Issue	Price	Size	U.S. $	Can. $	U.K. £
1998	Collectania	Purple/yellow/pearl	2,500	£39.95	110	70.	80.	40.
1998	Collectus	White/purple/pearl	2,500	£39.95	105	70.	80.	40.
1999	Collecteenie	Red/blue/pearl	2,500	£39.95	65	70.	80.	40.

COLLECT IT! HONEY BEAR CUB

2000

A special colourway *English Whimsie* Bear Cub was given free with the October issue of *Collect It!* magazine. Some models have a thicker glaze than others producing a darker honey colour. For the gold colourway see Wade Christmas Extravaganza Figures, page 200.

Backstamp: Embossed "Wade" between front feet and "England" on back of model

Date	Name	Description	Issue	Price	Size	U.S. $	Can. $	U.K. £
2000	Bear Cub	Dark honey	—	—	40	10.	11.	6.
2000	Bear Cub	Light honey	—	—	40	10.	11.	6.

POCKET PALS

1999-2005

A special colourway Pocket Pal Frog named *Hopper* was given free with the November 1999 issue of *Collect It!* magazine. The frog was attached to the front cover of the magazine *Collect it!* In the same issue was an offer for a special colourway of the Wade Pocket Pal dog named *Woofit*. The original cost of *Woofit* was £5.95.

In 2004 *Collect It!* magazine offered a subscription special for new and renewing members, a set of three Pocket Pals in new colourways.

See also Pocket Pals, pages 122 and 231.

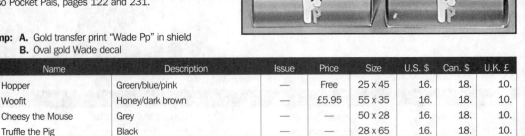

Backstamp: **A.** Gold transfer print "Wade Pp" in shield
B. Oval gold Wade decal

Date	Name	Description	Issue	Price	Size	U.S. $	Can. $	U.K. £
1999	Hopper	Green/blue/pink	—	Free	25 x 45	16.	18.	10.
1999	Woofit	Honey/dark brown	—	£5.95	55 x 35	16.	18.	10.
2005	Cheesy the Mouse	Grey	—	—	50 x 28	16.	18.	10.
2005	Truffle the Pig	Black	—	—	28 x 65	16.	18.	10.
2005	Bounce the Rabbit	Honey	—	—	55 x 30	16.	18.	10.

FELIX THE CAT
2006

Backstamp: Felix Christmas Surprise. Limited Edition 75.
TM and © 2006 Felix the Cat Productions, Inc.
All rights reserved. Felix the Cat is a registered
trademark of Felix the Cat Productions Inc.

Date	Name	Description	Issue	Price	Size	U.S. $	Can. $	U.K. £
2006	Felix Christmas Surprise	Black, red, white, brown, gold	75	£95	140	225.	250.	125.

THE COLLECTOR
IN THE FOREST DEEP
1997-1999

Backstamp: **A.** Printed "In The Forest Deep Series [name of model] for The Collector London Limited Edition of 1000 Wade"
  B. Printed "In The Forest Deep Series Santa Hedgehog for The Collector London Limited Edition of 2000 Wade"

Date	Name	Description	Issue	Price	Size	U.S. $	Can. $	U.K. £
1997	Morris Mole	Grey/buff mole	1,000	£39.95	105	70.	80.	40.
1997	Oswald Owl	Dark/light brown owl	1,000	£39.95	113	70.	80.	40.
1997	Santa Hedgehog	Brown hedgehog; red/white Santa suite	2,000	£39.95	132	70.	80.	40.
1998	Bertram Badger	Black/white badger; black coat	1,000	£39.95	135	70.	80.	40.
1998	Tailwarmer Squirrel	Brown squirrel; blue/green striped tailwarmer	1,000	£39.95	110	70.	80.	40.
1999	Huntsman Fox	Red brown fox; red waistcoat; white shirt, jodhpurs	1,000	£39.95	115	70.	80.	40.
1999	Gentleman Rabbit	Beige rabbit; light grey suit	1,000	£39.95	115	70.	80.	40.

COTSWOLD COLLECTABLES

TUFTY AND HIS FURRYFOLK FRIENDS
1998-1999

"Tufty the Red Squirrel" is a character created by Elsie Mills, M.B.E. in her storybooks of *Tufty and his Furryfolk Friends*. Commissioned by Stuart Mitchell and Caroline Murray, of Cotswold Collectables, Tufty was first introduced in 1998. A model with a gold base was released in 1999 at the *Collect It!* fair held in Wembley, U.K.

Note: A Belisha Beacon is a bright yellow lighted globe on top of a black and white striped pole and mounted at British zebra crossings (road crossings).

Backstamp: Circular printed "©Tufty and his Furryfolk Friends by Cotswold Collectables 1998 Wade 'Tufty' ©RoSPA Enterprises Ltd. Limited Edition 1,500"

Date	Name	Description	Issue	Price	Size	U.S. $	Can. $	U.K. £
1998	Tufty	Dark blue jacket; grey base	1,500	£39.95	140	70.	80.	40.
1999	Tufty	Dark blue jacket; gold base	150	£37.00	140	120.	130.	70.

CRICKET DESIGN INCORPORATED
(CDI IMPORTS)
ANIMAL FAMILIES

Cricket Design Incorporated is an import company in Costa Mesa, California. They imported a number of previously issued Wade models to be sold in the U.S.A. The sets were given new names and packaging: Wade's Nursery Favourites became "Fairytale Friends;" the Cat and Puppy Dish set became "Pups in a Basket;" Dogs and Puppies became "Doggy Family;" Happy Families became "Happy Family;" and the Tortoise Family became "Turtle Family."

The English issues of these models ended in the early 1980s, it is estimated that a limited number of surplus models were distributed to CDI for sale in the USA during the early 1980s. All the models are in the same colourways as the original issues.

Although the Whoppas were advertised under their original Wade England name, no evidence has been seen to indicate which, if any, models were issued. The author would welcome any information on this issue.

Not all models from the original Wade series were issued. The CDI name is given with Wade's original name in parenthesis.

DOGGY FAMILY

C.1980

Only three sets of the original series of five were issued: Alsatian (renamed German Shepherd), Cairn and Red Setter (renamed Irish Setter). The Mother and Pups were issued in two separate boxes in the U.K., but were packaged in one box for CDI.

Cairn Terriers

German Shepherds

Irish Setters

Backstamp: Label "Genuine Wade Porcelain Made in England"

No.	Name	Description	Size	U.S. $	Can. $	U.K. £
1	Cairn Terrier Mother	Honey brown; brown ears, nose	65 x 70	35.	40.	20.
2	Pup, lying	Honey brown; brown ears, nose	35 x 50	18.	20.	10.
3	Pup, standing	Honey brown; brown ears, nose	40 x 50	18.	20.	10.
4	German Shepherd Mother	Brown/honey brown	60 x 75	35.	40.	20.
5	Pup, lying	Brown/honey brown	35 x 45	18.	20.	10.
6	Pup, sitting	Brown/honey brown	40 x 45	18.	20.	10.
7	Irish Setter Mother	Red-brown	60 x 75	35.	40.	20.
8	Pup, lying, facing left	Red-brown	40 x 45	18.	20.	10.
9	Pup, lying, facing right	Red-brown	40 x 45	18.	20.	10.

FAIRYTALE FRIENDS

C.1980

These models are the original U.K. large size Nursery Favourites. All 20 of the English series were issued under the name Fairytale Friends. The majority of the models were advertised with the original Wade England names and set number, but with the 'Little,' 'Wee' or 'Old,' etc. removed. Little Boy Blue was advertised as "Blue Boy." The models were issued in Happy Family style boxes.

Cricket Design Incorporated packaging, and advertisement for Fairytale Friends

Backstamp: Embossed "Wade England"

No.	Name	Description	Size	U.S. $	Can. $	U.K. £
1	Jack	Brown hair, waistcoat; green trousers	75 x 30	40.	45.	23.
2	Jill	Green dress, bonnet	75 x 40	40.	45.	23.
3	Miss Muffett	Grey-green dress; yellow hair	60 x 50	40.	45.	23.
4	Jack Horner	Green jacket; yellow trousers; brown hair	70 x 40	40.	45.	23.
5	Humpty Dumpty	Honey brown; green suit; red tie	65 x 43	40.	45.	23.
6	Willie Winkie	Grey nightshirt; yellow hair	75 x 35	40.	45.	23.
7	Mary Lamb	Blue skirt, bonnet; grey-blue jacket	75 x 40	40.	45.	23.
8	Polly Kettle	Brown; pink cap, kettle	75 x 35	40.	45.	23.
9	King Cole	Yellow/grey hat; blue-grey cloak	65 x 50	40.	45.	23.
10	Tom Piper	Grey hat, kilt; brown jacket	65 x 55	40.	45.	23.
11	Blue Boy	Blue jacket, trousers, cap	75 x 30	40.	45.	23.
12	Mary Mary	Blue dress; pink shoes; yellow hair	75 x 45	40.	45.	23.
13	Cat and Fiddle	Brown/grey cat; yellow fiddle	70 x 50	40.	45.	23.
14	Queen of Hearts	Beige dress; pink hearts, crown	75 x 48	40.	45.	23.
15	Tommy Tucker	Blue pantaloons; yellow hair	75 x 45	40.	45.	23.
16	Puss in Boots	Beige; blue boots	70 x 30	40.	45.	23.
17	Three Bears	Grey; green base	70 x 60	40.	45.	23.
18	Goosey Gander	Beige; pink beak; blue-brown steps	66 x 55	40.	45.	23.
19	Bo Peep	Beige dress, bonnet; pink ribbon	70 x 40	40.	45.	23.
20	Old Woman in Shoe	Blue dress, bonnet; brown roof, door	60 x 55	40.	45.	23.

HAPPY FAMILY

C.1980

These *Happy Family* models were marketed in similar boxes to the third style box used in the U.K. edition. Only four sets of the original eleven were advertised: Giraffe, Hippo, Mouse and Rabbit.

Giraffe Family

Hippo Family

Mouse Family

Rabbit Family

Backstamp: **A.** Embossed "Wade England"
B. Black transfer "Wade Made in England" (some with cricket in large C)

No.	Name	Description	Size	U.S. $	Can. $	U.K. £
1	Giraffe Mother	Beige; turquoise eyelids; dark grey horns	60 x 45	45.	50.	28.
2	Baby, upright	Beige; turquoise eyelids; dark grey horns	40 x 28	25.	28.	15.
3	Baby, lying	Beige; turquoise eyelids; dark grey horns	15 x 30	25.	28.	15.
4	Hippo Mother	Smokey blue; brown eyes	35 x 50	45.	50.	28.
5	Baby, eyes open	Smokey blue; brown eyes	28 x 25	25.	28.	15.
6	Baby, eyes closed	Smokey blue	20 x 25	25.	28.	15.
7	Mouse Mother	White; grey patch; pink ears, tail	50 x 28	45.	50.	28.
8	Baby, eyes closed	White; grey patch; pink ears, tail	28 x 28	25.	28.	15.
9	Baby, eyes open	White; grey patch; pink ears, tail	25 x 30	25.	28.	15.
10	Rabbit Mother	White; blue patches	55 x 30	45.	50.	28.
11	Baby, sitting	White; blue patches	34 x 28	25.	28.	15.
12	Baby, standing	White; blue patches	30 x 35	25.	28	15.

PUP-IN-A-BASKET

C.1980

Only five of the original ten puppy dishes were issued by CDI: the two Cairn Terriers, the Alsatian (renamed German Shepherd for the American market), and one Red Setter pup, which was renamed Irish Setter. Some of the poses are listed differently in the CDI advertising, e.g.: the "Lying Cairn Pup" is advertised as 'sitting', and the "Sitting Alsatian" (German Shepherd) is advertised as standing, etc. This may cause some collectors to believe that they were different models in this series, which is not the case.

German Shepherd, sitting; German Shepherd, standing; Cairn Terrier, sitting; Cairn Terrier, standing

Backstamp: Embossed "Wade England"

No.	Name	Description	Size	U.S. $	Can. $	U.K. £
1	Cairn Terrier, sitting	Honey brown	35 x 75	35.	40.	20.
2	Cairn Terrier, standing	Honey brown	40 x 75	35.	40.	20.
3	German Shepherd, sitting	Brown/honey brown	35 x 75	35.	40.	20.
4	German Shepherd, standing	Brown/honey brown	40 x 75	35.	40.	20.
5	Irish Setter, lying, facing right	Red-brown	40 x 75	35.	40.	20.

TURTLE FAMILY

C.1980

The Father Tortoise Trinket Box with the lift-off shell is advertised as "Mother" turtle, and the two smaller tortoises, which in the U.K. are known as Mother and Baby, are advertised as baby turtles.

Backstamp: Embossed "Wade Porcelain Made in England"

No.	Name	Description	Size	U.S. $	Can. $	U.K. £
1	Mother Turtle	Brown/blue	50 x 105	35.	40.	20.
2	Baby Turtle	Brown/blue	35 x 75	18.	20.	10.
3	Baby Turtle	Brown/blue	25 x 45	18.	20.	10.

DAVID TROWER ENTERPRISES
POPEYE COLLECTION
1997-1998

Modeled by Ken Holmes and produced by Wade Ceramics for David Trower Enterprises.

Popeye, Wimpey, Brutus, Olive Oyl and Swee'Pea

Backstamp: **A.** Printed "Wade Popeye ™ & © 1997 King Features Synd Inc. Limited Edition of 2000 © David Trower Enterprises"
B. Printed "Wade Brutus ™ & © 1997 King Features Synd Inc. Limited Edition of 1500 © David Trower Enterprises"
C. Printed "Wade Olive Oyl and Swee'Pea ™ & © 1998 King Features Synd Inc. Limited Edition of 2000 © David Trower Enterprises"
D. Printed "Wimpy TM & © 1998 King Features Synd Inc Wade"

Date	Name	Description	Issue	Price	Size	U.S. $	Can. $	U.K. £
1997	Popeye	Dark blue navy suit	2,000	£35	120	150.	165.	85.
1997	Brutus	Orange T-shirt; blue trousers, hat	1,500	£36.	129	100.	110.	55.
1998	Olive Oyl and Swee'Pea	Olive Oyl: Red blouse; black skirt Swee'Pea: Red suit; white hat	2,000	£36.	Unk.	80.	90.	45.
1998	Wimpy	Dark blue jacket; orange trousers	1,500	£36.	130	80.	90.	45.

THE NURSERY RHYME COLLECTION

1998-2001

Humpty Dumpty, Goosey Gander

Little Bo-Peep

Little Jack Horner

Little Miss Muffett

Backstamp: **A.** Printed "Wade from the Nursery Rhyme Collection World Wide Limited Edition of 1,000 © 1998 Wade Ceramics Ltd © 1998 D.T.Ents" with name of model and year
B. Printed [Name of model] & ©2001 D.T. Ltd Worldwide Limited Edition of 150" and Wade logo est 1810

Date	Name	Description	Issue	Price	Size	U.S. $	Can. $	U.K. £
1998	Humpty Dumpty	Dark green/blue trousers; red hat	1,000	£32	115	80.	90.	45.
1999	Goosey Gander	Black jacket; red waistcoat	1,000	£32	127	80.	90.	45.
1999	Little Bo-Peep	White/blue dress; grey bonnet	1,000	£32	127	80.	90.	45.
2000	Little Jack Horner	Dark blue suit; pale blue shirt	250	£48	130	70.	80.	40.
2000	Little Miss Muffett	Pink jacket; blue skirt	250	£48	110	70.	80.	40.
2001	Cat and Fiddle	Brown cat; tan fiddle	250	£48	130	70.	80.	40.
2001	Jack	Green coat; brown trousers	150	—	135 x 60	85.	95.	50.
2001	Jill	Orange dress; white apron; grey pail	150	—	135 x 55	85.	95.	50.
2001	Mary Had a Little Lamb	Blue dress; white lamb	150	—	95 x 75	85.	95.	50.
2001	Wee Willie Winkie	Blue nightgown; black/red lantern	150	—	130 x 55	85.	95.	50.

E. AND A. CRUMPTON

THE LONG ARM OF THE LAW

1993-1995

The Long Arm Of The Law set was commissioned and designed by Elaine and Adrian Crumpton and modeled by Ken Holmes, in a limited edition of 2,000 each. "The Burglar" was issued in June 1993, the "Policeman" followed in October, the "Barrister" in August 1994 and the "Prisoner" in June 1995. The prisoner was produced with either black or brown hair. Due to production problems the first 400 Policeman models have impressed faces; the next 1,600 have hand-painted faces. A mislaid Policeman mould resulted in the unauthorized production of a black-suited earthenware version which has an embossed Wade backstamp but was not produced by Wade Ceramics.

Painted Face (left), Impressed Face (right)

Backstamp: **A.** Large embossed "Wade" (1)
B. Embossed "Wade" (2a, 2b, 4a, 4b)
C. Red transfer "Wade Made in England" (3)

Date	Name	Description	Issue	Price	Size	U.S. $	Can. $	U.K. £
1993	The Burglar	Black/white	2,000	Unk.	85	60.	65.	35.
1993	Policeman	Impressed face; dark blue uniform	400	Unk.	90	80.	90.	45.
1993	Policeman	Painted face; dark blue uniform	1,600	Unk.	90	60.	65.	35.
1994	Barrister	Black gown, shoes; grey trousers	2,000	Unk.	80	60.	65.	35.
1995	Prisoner	Black hair; grey shoes	2,000	Unk.	70	60.	65.	35.
1995	Prisoner	Brown hair, shoes	2,000	Unk.	70	80.	90.	45.
1995	Prisoner	Brown hair, grey shoes	2,000	Unk.	70	80.	90.	45.

FATHER'S COLLECTION and WADES BY PEG

Y2K PINK ELEPHANT

2000

Originally produced as an *English Whimsie* in 1973, the Y2K Pink Elephant was a joint commission by Peg and Roger Johnson (Wades by Peg) and Father's Collection (Father David Cox). The models were first available at the Kansas City Wade Show.

Backstamp: Embossed "Wade England" on rim

Date	Name	Description	Issue	Price	Size	U.S. $	Can. $	U.K. £
2000	Elephant, left	Pink; black decal	1,500	$10 US	35 x 45	25.	28.	15.
2000	Elephant, right	Pink; black decal	485	$12 US	35 x 45	25.	28.	15.

FRISCO COFFEE

ENGLISH WHIMSIES

1973-1974

During 1973-1974 Frisco Coffee (a division of Liptons Tea) of Cape Town, South Africa, distributed *Whimsie* models wrapped in cellophane packets in their boxes of Frisco Coffee. Seven models have been reported, but it is believed there may have been more. The models are the same colours as the original *English Whimsies,* and are listed in alphabetical order.

Backstamp: **A.** Embossed "Wade England" on rim
B. Embossed "Wade" between front feet and "England" on back of model

No.	Name	Description	Size	U.S. $	Can. $	U.K. £
1	Bear Cub	Grey; beige face	30 x 40	5.	6.	3.
2	Bushbaby	Brown; blue ears; black nose	30 x 30	5.	6.	3.
3	Duck	Blue/brown; yellow beak	30 x 40	5.	6.	3.
4	Fawn	Brown; blue ears	30 x 30	5.	6.	3.
5	Kitten, seated	Dark/light brown; pink wool	30 x 30	5.	6.	3.
6	Owl	Dark/light brown	35 x 20	5.	6.	3.
7	Rabbit	Beige open ears	30 x 30	5.	6.	3.

FUDGE COLLECTABLES

THE ENGLISH INNS COLLECTIONS

2004-2005

Fudge Collectables introduced the English Inns Collection, a series of models representing the names of traditional English pubs, at the Arundel Collectors Meet. Each model was to be a limited edition of 250 pieces, however due to production problems only 240 of the Anchor were produced.

Backstamp: "[Name of model] English Inns for Fudgecollectables Ltd Edt of 250" and "Wade Made in England"

Date	Name	Description	Issue	Price	Size	U.S. $	Can. $	U.K. £
2004	The Anchor	White, blue, brown	240	£23.95	90 x 55	35.	40.	20.
2004	The Lion	Gold and green	250	£23.95	85 x 60	35.	40.	20.
2005	The Bull	Honey and green	250	£23.95	65 x 105	35.	40.	20.

G&G COLLECTABLES
HANNA-BARBERA CHARACTERS
1997-1998

Scooby-Doo

Scrappy Doo

Pixie and Dixie

Boo Boo

Yogi Bear

Huckleberry Hound and Mr. Jinks

Backstamp: **Huckleberry Hound:** Printed "Wade England Huckleberry Hound © 1998 H.B. Prod Inc Worldwide Edition of 1500 G & G Collectables"
Mr. Jinks: Printed "Wade England Mr. Jinks © 1997 H.B. Prod Inc G & G Collectables"
Pixie/Dixie: Printed "Wade England © 1997 H.B. Prod Inc Worldwide edition of 1,500 G & G Collectables" [name]
Scooby-Doo: Black transfer "© H/B Inc Scooby-Doo Limited Edition of 2,000 Wade England G&G Collectables"
Scrappy Doo: Transfer print "© H/B Inc Scrappy Doo Limited Edition of 2,000 Wade England G&G Collectables"
Yogi Bear / Boo Boo: Printed black "Wade England [name of model]" "©1997 H.B.Prod Inc Worldwide Edition of 1500 G & G Collectables"

Date	Name	Description	Issue	Price	Size	U.S. $	Can. $	U.K. £
1994	Scooby-Doo	Brown; blue collar; gold medallion	2,000	Unk.	115	95.	110.	55.
1995	Scrappy Doo	Brown; blue collar	2,000	£29.95	90	90.	100.	50.
1997	Mr. Jinks	Orange cat; blue bow tie	1,500	£35.00	152	70.	80.	40.
1997	Pixie	Grey mouse; red tomato	1,500	£37.50	115	70.	80.	40.
1997	Dixie	Grey mouse; chocolate cupcake	1,500	£37.50	115	70.	80.	40.
1997	Boo Boo	Brown bear; black waistcoat	1,500	£34.00	114	70.	80.	40.
1997	Yogi Bear	Green hat, tie; dark blue waistcoat	1,500	£34.00	130	70.	80.	40.
1998	Huckleberry Hound	Blue hound; yellow hat; black drum base, gold lines	1,500	£38.00	135	70.	80.	40.

SANTA CLAUS

1997

Santa Claus was modelled by Nigel Weaver.

Backstamp: Unknown

Date	Name	Description	Issue	Price	Size	U.S. $	Can. $	U.K. £
1997	Santa Claus	Red/white suit; grey chimney	1,000	£36	133	60.	65.	35.

LITTLE RED RIDING HOOD AND THE BIG BAD WOLF

1998-1999

Little Red Riding Hood and the Big Bad Wolf

Backstamp: Printed "Limited Edition 1,000 ©G & G
Collectables & Wade [name of model]"

Date	Name	Description	Issue	Price	Size	U.S. $	Can. $	U.K. £
1998	Big Bad Wolf	Blue cape; white nightdress	1,000	£30	92	60.	65.	35.
1999	Little Red Riding Hood	Red cloak; blue dress	1,000	£30	100	60.	65.	35

PEGGY GAMBLE (Formerly Gamble and Styles)
MR. PUNCH and JUDY
1996-1999

Mr. Punch   Toby   Judy

Judy's ghost

Backstamp: **A.** Black transfer outline of a corgi, "P&S" stamped on the body, "Wade" between two black lines and the issue number (1)
B. Black transfer outline of a Corgi, "P&S" stamped on the body, "Modelled by K Holmes Wade" and the issue number (2)
C. Black transfer outline of a Corgi, "PG" stamped on the body, "Modelled by Simon Millard Wade"

Date	Name	Description	Issue	Price	Size	U.S. $	Can. $	U.K. £
1996	Mr. Punch	Burgundy suit	1,800	£45	165	70.	80.	40.
1996	Mr. Punch	Green suit	200	£45	165	200.	220.	115.
1997	Judy	Pale blue dress	1,800	£42	150	70.	80.	40.
1997	Judy	Green dress	200	£45	150	200.	220.	115.
1998	Toby	Red hat	1,500	£35	122	70.	80.	40.
1998	Toby	Green hat	200	£35	122	120.	130.	70.
1999	Judy's Ghost	Pearlised ghost; gold base	800	£35	143	70.	80.	40.
1999	Judy's Ghost	Pearlised ghost; green base	200	£35	143	100.	110	55.

GENERAL FOODS

CIRCA 1990

A planned promotion for General Foods of England that included miscellaneous animals of two or three colours and *Miniature Nursery Rhymes* characters in one-colour glazes was cancelled before it began. A number of models that had been intended for the promotion were released onto the market for a short time in late 1990. The Chimpanzee, in the olive/green-brown glaze has also been found in the USA, and may have been included in the Red Rose Decaffeinated Tea promotions.

MISCELLANEOUS ANIMALS

1990

Backstamp: Embossed "Wade England"

Note: (TS) Tom Smith
(EW) English Whimsies
(WL): *Whimsie-land*

Owl

Penguin

No.	Name	Description	Size	U.S. $	Can. $	U.K. £
1	Badger (TS British Wildlife)	Light grey/white; green base	25 x 40	12.	14.	7.
2	Chimpanzee (EW)	Olive/green-brown	35 x 35	12.	14.	7.
3	Owl (WL)	White; orange beak; green base	35 x 25	18.	20.	10.
4	Panda (WL)	Black/white	37 x 20	20.	22.	12.
5	Penguin (EW, TS 1987)	Black/white; orange beak	45 x 17	35.	40.	20.
6	Rabbit (EW)	White; pinky-beige; pink nose	30 x 30	18.	20.	10.
7	Zebra (EW)	Black; green grass	40 x 35	50.	55.	30.

MINIATURE NURSERY RHYMES

1990

These models are in an all-over solid colour.

Photographs not available at press time

Backstamp: Embossed "Wade England"

No.	Name	Description	Size	U.S. $	Can. $	U.K. £
1	Jack	Beige	34 x 33	7.	8.	4.
2	Jill	Beige	28 x 39	7.	8.	4.
3	Little Bo-Peep	Green	44 x 24	18.	20.	10.
4	Little Jack Horner	Beige	37 x 21	7.	8.	4.
5	Little Red Riding Hood	Pink	44 x 24	18.	20.	10.
6	Mother Goose	Beige	41 x 31	7.	8.	4.
7	Old King Cole	Light blue	37 x 32	18.	20.	10.
8	Old Woman Who Lived in a Shoe	Beige	35 x 40	7.	8.	4.
9	Pied Piper	Green	46 x 28	18.	20.	10.
10	Tom the Piper's Son	Blue	39 x 33	18.	20.	10.
11	Wee Willie Winkie	Blue	44 x 24	18.	20.	10.

GOLD STAR GIFTHOUSE

NURSERY FAVOURITES

1990-1991

Only five of the original 20 *Nursery Favourites* models were reissued for the Gold Star Gifthouse, a California Wade dealer. The Old Woman Who Lived in a Shoe and Goosey Goosey Gander are the hardest to find of the original *Nursery Favourites*, see page 34.

Backstamp:

A. Embossed "Wade England 1990" (1, 2, 3)

B. Embossed "Wade England 1991" and ink stamp "GSG" (4)

C. Embossed "Wade England 1991" (5)

No.	Name	Description	Size	U.S. $	Can. $	U.K. £
1	Mary, Mary	Brighter than original; blue dress; yellow hair; pink shoes; green base	75 x 45	40.	45.	25.
2	Polly Put the Kettle On	Same colours as original; brown; pink cap, kettle	75 x 35	40.	45.	25.
3	Tom Tom the Piper's Son	Brighter than original; blue-grey kilt; yellow/honey jacket	65 x 55	40.	45.	25.
4	Old Woman in a Shoe	Blue bonnet, dress; beige dog, door	60 x 55	85.	95.	50.
5	Goosey Goosey Gander	Same as original; beige; pink beak	66 x 55	85.	95.	50.

GRANADA TELEVISION

CORONATION STREET HOUSES

1988-1989

The *Coronation Street Houses* set was commissioned by Granada Television as a promotional item for its long-running television series, *Coronation Street*, and sold at the studio gift shop and by mail order. Only three models of the set were produced, although others were planned. The figures are very similar to the *Whimsey-on-Why* houses. They were sold on cards with details of the series printed on the back.

Backstamp: Embossed "Wade England"

No.	Name	Description	Size	U.S. $	Can. $	U.K. £
1	The Rovers Return	Brown; grey roof	45 x 48	20.	22.	12.
2	No. 9 The Duckworths	Yellow/grey windows, door	45 x 33	20.	22.	12.
3	Alf's Corner Shop	Brown; grey roof	45 x 33	20.	22.	12.
4	Jack (Salt)	Brown hair, trousers; dark green shirt; black shoes	110	18.	20.	10.
5	Vera (Pepper)	Yellow hair; red blouse; green skirt	120	18.	20.	10.

GREAT UNIVERSAL STORES

For a number of years, Tom Smith and Company marketed a line of Christmas crackers through Great Universal Stores (G.U.S.).

SET ONE: MISCELLANEOUS MODELS

1990-1993

The Miscellaneous Models, listed on page 312 of the 7th edition Wade Whimsical Collectables, have now been dated to 1990-1993. The models are all previous *English Whimsies* or Tom Smith models (most of which were re-issued in new colourways for Red Rose Tea U.S.A. Ltd. between the years 1990-1993). The first known issue of the model is indicated in brackets after the name of the model.

Backstamp: Embossed "Wade England"

No.	Name	Description	Size	U.S. $	Can. $	U.K. £
1	Beaver (RR 1992)	Dark brown	35 x 45	5.	6.	3.
2	Camel (RR 1985-90)	Beige	38 x 35	5.	6.	3.
3	Circus Lion (TS 1978-79 / RR 1993-98)	Honey	40 x 22	10.	12.	6.
4	Giraffe (EW 1973 / RR 1985-90)	Beige	35 x 35	3.	4.	2.
5	Langur, Type 3 (RR 1992)	Dark brown	35 x 30	5.	6.	3.
6	Pine Marten (EW 1974 / RR 1985-90)	Honey	30 x 30	5.	6.	3.
7	Raccoon (RRU 1985-90)	Dark brown	25 x 35	5.	6.	3.
8	Pony (Shetlandl) (TS 1988-89 / RR 1990)	Beige	25 x 30	5.	6.	3.
9	Spaniel Puppy (TS 1988-89 / RR 1990)	Honey	30 x 25	5.	6.	3.
10	Zebra (RR 1992)	Light grey	40 x 35	5.	6.	3.

Note: The following initials indicate the origin of the models:
  EW: *English Whimsies*
  RR: *Red Rose*
  TS: *Tom Smith*

SET TWO: SNOW LIFE

1993-1994

The Tom Smith *Snow Animals* series was reissued for G.U.S., with the addition of the Tom Smith *Survival Animals* "Whale" in grey, and the Red Rose *Miniature Nurseries* "Goosey Goosey Gander," coloured white and renamed the "Snow Goose." There are two types of the "Reindeer" model: Type 1 has a gap between the legs; Type 2 has no gap. For Type 2 see Tom Smith Crackers page 327.

Although there are ten models in this set, the box only contains eight crackers. This can cause problems for collectors wishing to complete a set and will cause a future rise in price for some figures.

Backstamp: Embossed "Wade England"

No.	Name	Description	Size	U.S. $	Can. $	U.K. £
1	Fox (WL)	Red-brown/honey	35 x 36	16.	18.	10.
2	Penguin (EW)	Blue-grey	49 x 21	12.	13.	7.
3	Polar Bear, head forward (EW)	White	27 x 45	12.	13.	7.
4	Reindeer, Type 1 (TS)	Beige	34 x 35	16.	18.	10.
5	Seal Pup (EW)	Blue-grey	26 x 39	12.	13.	7.
6	Snow Goose (RR)	White	33 x 37	12.	13.	7.
7	Snowshoe Hare (TS)	White	45 x 33	12.	13.	7.
8	Snowy Owl (WL)	White	35 x 25	12.	13.	7.
9	Walrus (EW)	Beige	34 x 36	12.	13.	7.
10	Whale (Baleen TS)	Grey	22 x 52	12.	13.	7.

Note: The following initials indicate the origin of the models:
    EW: *English Whimsies*
    RR: Red Rose *Miniature Nurseries*
    TS: Tom Smith
    WL: *Whimsie-land* Series

SET THREE: ENDANGERED SPECIES
1994

Backstamp: Embossed "Wade England"

No.	Name	Description	Size	U.S. $	Can. $	U.K. £
1	Cockatoo (TS)	Green	41 x 47	5.	6.	3.
2	Fox (WL)	Light brown	35 x 36	16.	18.	10.
3	Gorilla, standing (EW)	Brown	37 x 28	5.	6.	3.
4	Koala Bear (EW)	Beige	35 x 29	7.	8.	4.
5	Leopard (EW)	Honey	20 x 47	3.	4.	2.
6	Orang-outan (EW)	Brown	30 x 34	5.	6.	3.
7	Polar Bear, head forward (EW)	White	27 x 45	12.	13.	7.
8	Rhino (EW)	Grey	25 x 43	3.	4.	2.
9	Tiger (EW)	Honey	37 x 30	5.	6.	3.
10	Whale (Baleen TS)	Grey	22 x 52	8.	10.	5.

Note: The following initials indicate the origin of the models:
    EW: *English Whimsies*
    TS: *Tom Smith*
    WL: *Whimsie-land* Series

SET FOUR: TALES FROM THE NURSERY

1994-1995

Also reissued for G.U.S. was the Tom Smith *Tales from the Nurseries* set. There are slight colour variations from the previous set in "Hickory Dickory Dock," "Little Bo-Peep," "Humpty Dumpty," "Queen of Hearts," "Little Jack Horner" and "Ride a Cock Horse." The remaining models are the same colour as before.

Backstamp: Embossed "Wade England"

No.	Name	Description	Size	U.S. $	Can. $	U.K. £
1	Cat and the Fiddle (RR)	Grey	47 x 33	7.	8.	4.
2	Dr. Foster (RR)	Dark brown	43 x 26	7.	8.	4.
3	Hickory Dickory Dock (RR)	Beige	44 x 20	7.	8.	4.
4	Humpty Dumpty (RR)	Blue-grey	36 x 23	7.	8.	4.
5	Little Bo-Peep (RR)	Wine	44 x 24	7.	8.	4.
6	Little Boy Blue (TS)	Blue	41 x 25	7.	8.	4.
7	Little Jack Horner (RR)	Honey	37 x 21	7.	8.	4.
8	Queen of Hearts (RR)	Apricot	42 x 25	7.	8.	4.
9	Ride a Cock Horse (TS)	Green	36 x 41	7.	8.	4.
10	Tom Tom the Piper's Son (RR)	Honey	39 x 33	7.	8.	4.

Note: The following initials indicate the origin of the models:
RR: Red Rose
TS: Tom Smith

JAMES ROBERTSON & SONS

ROBERTSON'S JAM GOLLIES AND BANDSTAND

1963-1965

Golliwogs became the trademark of James Robertson & Sons after one of Mr. Robertson's sons visited the United States in the early 1900s. He purchased a golliwog doll for his children, and it was so loved by the family that they decided to use it as their trademark. In 1910 a golliwog first appeared on items from James Robertson Preserve Manufacturers Limited, such as labels and price lists.

Beginning in 1963 a Robertson's promotional campaign offered a series of eight golliwog musicians in exchange for ten paper golliwog labels per model and 6d in postage stamps. George Wade and Son Ltd. produced five models for a trial period only. At some time in 1965, Robertson's changed from using the Wade model to the cheaper Portuguese one.

None of the Golliwogs is marked with a Wade stamp or label, but it is relatively easy to spot a Wade model amongst the hundreds of Golliwogs seen at antique and collector shows. Only the Wade figures are standing on white bases. All the models have a raised "Robertson" mark on the front rim of the base, and all the *Gollies* are black, with blue coats and red trousers.

Wade records confirm that, out of the eight promotional models, it only produced five golliwog musicians: "Accordian Golliwog," "Clarinet Golliwog," "Bass Golliwog," "Saxophone Golliwog" and "Trumpet Golliwog." The three additional models, not confirmed by Wade and most likely produced by another manufacturer, are "Drum Golliwog," "Guitar Golliwog" and "Vocalist Golliwog."

Due to changing race relations laws in Great Britain during the late 1970s and early 1980s, the original name, *Golliwog*, was changed to *Golly Doll* or *Gollies*. The models below are listed by their original names.

Backstamp: **A.** Embossed "Robertson" (1-5)
B. Red transfer print "Wade England" (6)

No.	Name	Description	Size	U.S. $	Can. $	U.K. £
1	Accordion Golliwog	Blue jacket; red pants; white/yellow accordion	65 x 25	170.	180.	100.
2	Clarinet Golliwog	Blue jacket; red pants; black clarinet	65 x 25	170.	180.	100.
3	Bass Golliwog	Blue jacket; red pants; white/yellow/brown bass	65 x 25	170.	180.	100.
4	Saxophone Golliwog	Blue jacket; red pants; yellow saxophone	65 x 25	170.	180.	100.
5	Trumpet Golliwog	Blue jacket; red pants; yellow trumpet	65 x 25	170.	180.	100.
6	Bandstand	White	50 x 230	170.	180.	100.

K.P. FOODS LTD.

K.P. FRIARS

1983

The *K.P. Friars* set was commissioned by K.P. Foods Ltd. to promote the sales of its potato crisps (chips). The first model, the "Father Abbot," was free with a given number of tokens from the packets. The remaining five models could be obtained with tokens, plus a small charge of £1.30. The offer expired November 1, 1983, and was available to U.K. collectors .

The "Father Abbot" came either in a cardboard box with a friar's design on it or in a small box with a cellophane front. The rest of the figures were issued together as a set of five, in a box with a folding cardboard lid or one with a cellophane sleeve. Although K.P. Friars was first issued as a set of five and in late 1983, as a set of six, with the inclusion of the "Father Abbot," for some reason three of the models — "Brother Crispin," "Brother Angelo" and "Brother Francis" — are the hardest to find, so have higher collector's prices. Each model stands on a square base, with the name of the friar embossed on the front.

The origin of the two models with grey robes is unknown.

Backstamp: Embossed "Wade"

No.	Name	Description	Size	U.S. $	Can. $	U.K. £
1a	Brother Francis	Beige head, base; brown robes	42 x 20	35.	40.	20.
1b	Brother Francis	Honey head, base; grey robes	42 x 20	35.	40.	20.
2a	Brother Peter	Beige head, base; brown robes	40 x 18	18.	20.	10.
2b	Brother Peter	Honey head, base; grey robes	40 x 18	25.	28.	15.
3	Brother Angelo	Beige head, base; brown robes	48 x 20	35.	40.	20.
4	Brother Benjamin	Beige head, base; brown robes	40 x 18	18.	20.	10.
5	Brother Crispin	Beige head, base; brown robes	40 x 20	35.	40.	20.
6	Father Abbot	Beige head, base; brown robes	45 x 18	35.	40.	20.

KS WADER / HAPPY WAD-ING

2001-2006

A HORSE OF A DIFFERENT COLOUR

2003

The first solid Whimsie produced for KS Wader, the horse was originally used for the Tom Smith Crackers, 1982-83 Farmyard Horse. It was produced in five colourways, hence the name "A Horse of a Different Colour."

Backstamp: Embossed "Wade England"

Date	Name	Description	Issue	Price	Size	U.S. $	Can. $	U.K. £
2003	Horse	Burgundy	250	Set	40 x 30	10.	11.	6.
2003	Horse	Cobalt blue	250	of	40 x 30	10.	11.	6.
2003	Horse	Light green	250	Four	40 x 30	10.	11.	6.
2003	Horse	Orange; green base	250	$32 US	40 x 30	10.	11.	6.
2003	Horse	White; gold base	250	$15 US	40 x 30	35.	40.	20.

BARNYARD CAT WHIMSIES

2005

The mould for the Barnyard Cat Whimsie is taken from Set Eight of the *English Whimsies* which was introduced in 1977.

Backstamp: Embossed "Wade Eng" on back rim

Date	Name	Description	Issue	Price	Size	U.S. $	Can. $	U.K. £
2005	Barnyard Cat (Tuxedo)	Black and white	400	Set	14	14.	15.	8.
2005	Barnyard Cat (Calico)	Orange, black, white (Calico)	400	of	14	14.	15.	8.
2005	Barnyard Cat (Ginger)	Orange	400	Four	14	14.	15.	8.
2005	Barnyard Cat (Siamese)	Cream, black, blue eyes	400	$40 US	14	14.	15.	8.
2005	Barnyard Cat	Black; gold base	100	$22 US	14	35.	40.	20.
2005	Barnyard Cat	Gold	25	Prizes	14	—	—	—

CALVES

2003

The Calves, an Angus (black) and a Holstein (black and white) were produced in a limited edition of 125 each. The cost direct from KS Wader was $35.00 each or $68.00 for the pair.

A limited edition of 25 calves in an all-over white colourway was available for promotions and prizes. KS Wader auctioned one of the special white calves on e-Bay for $98.00 U.S., with the proceeds going to the American Red Cross.

Backstamp: Printed "Calf KS Wader 2003 Regular Edition of 125" and "Wade" logo
Printed "Calf KS Wader 2003 Special Edition of 25" and red "Wade" logo

Date	Name	Description	Issue	Price	Size	U.S. $	Can. $	U.K. £
2003	Calf (Angus)	Black	125	$35 US	40 x 30	35.	40.	20.
2003	Calf (Holstein)	Black and white	125	$35 US	40 x 30	35.	40.	20.
2003	Calf	White	25	Prizes	40 x 30	—	—	—

CHRISTMAS CAT

2003

Based on the popular 1950s Wade ABC Cats, this model is of a cat playing with a Christmas ornament.

The original colour of the ribbon and ball for the cobalt blue colourway was to be gold, however, due to production problems the colour was changed to silver.

Backstamp: KS Wader 2003 Christmas Cat Ltd Edt 250, and red Wade logo

Date	Name	Description	Issue	Price	Size	U.S. $	Can. $	U.K. £
2003	Christmas Cat	White; green bow; red ornament	250	$32 US	50	35.	40.	25.
2003	Christmas Cat	Cobalt blue; silver ribbon, ornament	25	Prizes	50	—	—	—

Note: 1. A dash in any of the technical data columns of the table indicates that we do not have the required information, if you do, we would be pleased to hear from you.
2. Dashes in the pricing columns indicate one of two things: firstly, there was insufficient market pricing available, and secondly, pieces issued in small quantities of 10 or 20 pieces will be subject to wide pricing swings.

DRAGON WHIMSIES

2004

A limited edition of 500 sets of Dragon Whimsies were produced in four colourways: cobalt blue, orange, grey and burgundy. The cost from KS Wader was $15 each or $50 for the set. One hundred models were produced in a silver colourway and reserved for collectors on the KS Wader mailing list. Twenty five models were produced in a gold colourway and given as prizes or promotions.

Backstamp: Impressed "KS Wader 2004 Wade"

Date	Name	Description	Issue	Price	Size	U.S. $	Can. $	U.K. £
2004	Dragon Whimsie	Burgundy	500	$15.00 US	40	18.	20.	10.
2004	Dragon Whimsie	Colbalt blue	500	$15.00 US	40	18.	20.	10.
2004	Dragon Whimsie	Gold	25	Prizes	40	100.	110.	55.
2004	Dragon Whimsie	Grey; green base	500	$15.00 US	40	18.	20.	10.
2004	Dragon Whimsie	Orange; green base	500	$15.00 US	40	18.	20.	10.
2004	Dragon Whimsie	Platinum	100	$22.50 US	40	100.	110.	55.

FANTASY SERIES

2002

Unicorns (black and white colourways)

Gargoyle

Backstamp: **Unicorn:** Printed "Wade Ltd. Edition. of 250 KSWader Fantasy Series No 1"
Unicorn: Printed in gold "Wade Special Edition of 25 KSWader Fantasy Series No 1"
Dragon: Printed "Dragon Regular Edition KSWader Fantasy Series No 2 Ltd Edt. of 250" and "Wade est 1810 England"
Dragon: Printed "Dragon Special Edition KSWader Fantasy Series No 2 Ltd Edt. of 25" and "Wade est 1810 England"
Gargoyle: Printed "Gargoyle Regular Edition KSWader Fantasy Series No 3 Ltd Edt. of 250" and "Wade est 1810 England"
Gargoyle: Printed "Gargoyle Special Edition KSWader Fantasy Series No 3 Ltd Edt. of 25" and "Wade est 1810 England"

Date	Name	Description	Issue	Price	Size	U.S. $	Can. $	U.K. £
2002	Dragon	Grey-blue; beige; pink tongue; honey rock	250	$38 US	110	60.	65.	35.
2002	Dragon	Black; gold spines; grey rock	25	Prizes	110	130.	145.	75.
2002	Gargoyle	Grey; pink tongue, inner ears	250	$38 US	85	50.	55.	30.
2002	Gargoyle	White; pink tongue; gold base	25	Prizes	85	130.	145.	75.
2002	Unicorn	White; gold horn	250	$35 US	77 x 70	60.	65.	35.
2002	Unicorn	Black; gold horn, hooves	25	Prizes	77 x 70	130.	145.	75.

RABBIT WHIMSIES

2005

These whimsical rabbits are from the same mould as the *English Whimsies* rabbit

Backstamp: Embossed: "Wade England"

Date	Name	Description	Issue	Price	Size	U.S. $	Can. $	U.K. £
2005	Rabbit (Calico)	Black, brown, white	250	Set of	30	10.	11.	6.
2005	Rabbit	Lavender	250	Three	30	10.	11.	6.
2005	Rabbit	Pink	250	$28 US	30	10.	11.	6.
2005	Rabbit (Dutch)	Black, white	300	$12 US	30	15.	16.	8.
2005	Rabbit (PA WADE FEST)	White; red Wade logo	100	$15 US	30	18.	20.	10.
2005	Rabbit	White, gold ears, face, nose, rump	10	Prizes	30	—	—	—

UNICORN BLOW-UP

2003

The Blow-up Unicorn is a larger version of the KS Waders Fantasy Series Unicorn. It was modelled by Cyril Roberts. The white and gold colourway was issued in a limited edition of 100, and issued at the 2003 Wade Fest.

Backstamp: **A.** Printed "Made in England Unicorn Blow-Up KS Wader
Special Limited Edition of 100" and red "Wade" logo
B. Printed "Made in England Unicorn Blow-Up KS Wader
Special Limited Edition of 20" and red "Wade" logo

Date	Name	Description	Issue	Price	Size	U.S. $	Can. $	U.K. £
2003	Unicorn Blow-up	Black; gold horn, hooves	100	$79 US	90	75.	85.	45.
2003	Unicorn Blow-up	Cobalt blue; silver horn, hooves	20	Prizes	90	—	—	—
2003	Unicorn Blow-up	White; gold horn, hooves	100	$79 US	90	75.	85.	45.

UNICORN WHIMSIES

2006

The Unicorn Whimsies were produced using a new plaster mould the Wade Pottery had been experimenting with that does not have the ribbed base which so easily identifies the Wade Whimsies. The set was produced in a limited edition of 150

Backstamp: Embossed: "Wade England"

Date	Name	Description	Issue	Price	Size	U.S. $	Can. $	U.K. £
2006	Unicorn Whimsie	Black; gold horn, hooves	150	Set of	45	20.	22.	12.
2006	Unicorn Whimsie	Brown; honey mane, tale; copper horn, hooves	150	Three	45	20.	22.	12.
2006	Unicorn Whimsie	White; gold horn, base; green base	150	$52 US	45	20.	22.	12.
2006	Unicorn Whimsie	Green gold horn, hooves	100	$25 US	45	20.	22.	12.
2006	Unicorn Whimsie	Red; gold horn, hooves	100	$25 US	45	20.	22.	12.
2006	Unicorn Whimsie	Gold; black base	25	Prizes	45	—	—	—

WIZARD OF OZ

2001-2005

| Tin Woodman | Scarecrow | Jack Pumpkinhead |

Backstamp: **Scarecrow:** Printed "SCARECROW SPECIAL EDITION KS WADER OZ BY WADE NO. 5 LIMITED EDITION 250" and "Wade est 1810 England" logo
Tin Woodman: Hand written "Oz No 4" with printed "Wade Est 1810 England"
Jack Pumpkinhead: Printed "Oz by Wade No. 7, Limited Edition of 250, www.kswade.com" with Wade logo

Date	Name	Description	Issue	Price	Size	U.S. $	Can. $	U.K. £
2001	Tin Woodman	Grey; brown, green	500	$28 US	85	30.	33.	18.
2001	Tin Woodman	White	25	Prizes	85	—	—	—
2002	Scarecrow	Blue suit, hat; black boots, crow; yellow base; black lettering	250	$39 US	27 x 30	50.	55.	28.
2002	Scarecrow	White	25	Prizes	27 x 30	—	—	—
2005	Jack Pumpkinhead and the Sawhorse	Mottled blue, orange, beige, black	250	$40 US	82	50.	55.	28.
2005	Jack Pumpkinhead and the Sawhorse	White	25	Unk.	82	—	—	—

Note: For the other models in the Wizard of Oz series see the Kansas City Wade Show 2001, page 165.

PATTY KEENAN
CHRISTMAS ORNAMENTS
1994-1997

Both Wade Ceramics and Keenan Antiques sold "Santa's Train," only 500 models have a Keenan Antiques backstamp.

Backstamp: **A.** Red ink stamped "Wade made in England"
B. Printed "Wade Ceramics"
C. Printed "Keenan Antiques Wade England Christmas No 4" (on 500 Santa's Train models)

Date	Name	Description	Issue	Price	Size	U.S. $	Can. $	U.K. £
1994	Santa's Sleigh	White/red	2,000	—	40	28.	30.	16.
1995	Rocking Horse	Grey horse; dark grey mane	2,000	—	38	28.	30.	16.
1996	Rocking Horse	Honey horse; dark brown mane	600	—	38	28.	30.	16.
1997	Santa's Train	Grey; multicoloured prints	500	£10.50 $17 US	35	28.	30.	16.

KEY KOLLECTABLES LTD
BESIDE THE SEASIDE
2004

The *Beside the Seaside* figures were introduced at the following shows: Bathing Beauty — Wade Show, Stoke, April 2004; Seaside Donkey — Dunstable Wade Show, 2004; Sun, Sea and Sid — Arundel Collectors Meet, July 2004.

| Bathing Beauty | Seaside Donkey | Sun, Sea and Sid |

Backstamp: Printed "Key Kollectables Ltd Beside the Seaside Limited or Special Edition of [number] Wade [Date] [name of model]"

Date	Name	Description	Issue	Price	Size	U.S. $	Can. $	U.K. £
2004	Bathing Beauty	Blue swimsuit with orange band	100	£35	107	60.	65.	35.
2004	Bathing Beauty	Blue polka dot swimsuit	20	£35	107	—	—	—
2004	Seaside Donkey	Pale yellow donkey; dark brown halter and saddle; orange blanket	100	£35	80	60.	65.	35.
2004	Seaside Donkey	Grey donkey; gold halter and saddle; pink blanket	20	£35	80	—	—	—
2004	Sun, Sea and Sid	Red trousers; red spotted kercheif; red deck chair	100	£35	80	60.	65.	35.
2004	Sun, Sea and Sid	Rose pink trousers; blue spotted kerchief; gold deck chair	20	£35	80	—	—	—

Note: 1. A dash in any of the technical data columns of the table indicates that we do not have the required information, if you do, we would be pleased to hear from you.

2. Dashes in the pricing columns indicate one of two things: firstly, there was insufficient market pricing available, and secondly, pieces issued in small quantities of 10 or 20 pieces will be subject to wide pricing swings.

HOMEPRIDE FRED
ANNUAL FIGURINES
2004-2006

Happy Birthday Fred (2004)

Happy New Year Fred (2006)

Backstamp: Key Kollectables Ltd, Happy Birthday Fred, with Signed Certificate of Authenticity, Wade, This is not a Toy, © 2004 & TM Campbell Grocery Products Limited. Annual Figurine 2004

Date	Name	Description	Issue	Price	Size	U.S. $	Can. $	U.K. £
2004	Happy Birthday Fred	Black suit/hat; pink cake, blue, gold candles	Time Ltd.	£40	100	70.	75	40.
2006	Happy New Year Fred	Black suit/hat; tan clock, multicoloured balloons	200	£58	115	90.	100.	50.

HALLOWEEN FRED
2004

Backstamp: Homepride Fred © 2004 & TM Campbell Grocery Products Limited

Date	Name	Description	Issue	Price	Size	U.S. $	Can. $	U.K. £
2004	Halloween Fred	Black suit, hat; orange/black pumpkin	500	£35	100	60.	65.	35.

HOMEPRIDE FRED
2001-2003

Fred At Your Service

Fred's Tasting Time

Fred's Christmas Surprise

Fred's Little Blue Book

Fred's Christmas Pudding

Fred's Easter Egg

Backstamp: Printed "Key Kollectables [name of model] With Signed Certificate of Authenticity This is not a Toy. © &TM Campbell Grocery Products Limited. Limited edition [edition number]" and "Wade" logo

Date	Name	Description	Issue	Price	Size	U.S. $	Can. $	U.K. £
2001	Fred at Your Service	Black suit, hat; blue/white cloth	500	£27.50	100	80.	90.	45.
2001	Fred's Tasting Time	Black suit, hat; silver ladle	500	£27.50	100	80.	90.	45.
2002	Fred's Christmas Surprise	Black suit, hat; yellow gift box; red ribbon	763	£32.50	100	80.	90.	45.
2002	Fred's Little Blue Book	Black suit, hat; blue book	750	£30.00	100	80.	90.	45.
2002	Fred's Christmas Pudding	Black suit, hat; brown/white pudding	557	£37.50	100	80.	90.	45.
2003	Fred's Easter Egg	Black suit, hat; blue/red egg	500	£35.00	100	80.	90.	45.

HOMEPRIDE FRED BLOW-UPS

2002-2003

Backstamp: Printed "Key Kollectables,
[name of model] This is not a Toy,
With signed Certificate of
Authenticity, Limited Edition of
[number] pieces. WADE © &TM
Campbell Grocery Products Limited

Hungry Fred

Souper Fred

Date	Name	Description	Issue	Price	Size	U.S. $	Can. $	U.K. £
2002	Hungry Fred	Black suit, hat; silver knife and fork	300	£55	190	190.	210.	110.
2003	Souper Fred	Black suit, hat; blue/white bowl	450	£60	185	115.	125.	55.
2003	Souper Fred	Black suit, hat; silver/white bowl	50	£60	185	175.	195.	100.

HOMEPRIDE FRED MINIATURES

2004

Backstamp: Printed "Homepride Fred © 2004 TM CGPL Wade logo"

Date	Name	Description	Issue	Price	Size	U.S. $	Can. $	U.K. £
2004	Fred holding a Carrot	Black suit, hat; orange carrot	500	£18.99	53	35.	40.	20.
2004	Fred Holding a Leek	Black suit, hat; green, white leek	500	£18.99	53	35.	40.	20.
2004	Fred Holding a Mushroom	Black suit, hat; light brown musrhroom	500	£18.99	53	35.	40.	20.
2004	Fred Holding an Onion	Black suit, hat; yellow onion	500	£18.99	53	35.	40.	20.
2004	Fred Holding a Pepper	Black suit, hat; green pepper	500	£18.99	53	35.	40.	20.
2004	Fred Holding a Tomato	Black suit, hat; red tomato	500	£18.99	53	35.	40.	20.

HOMEPRIDE FRED WHIMSIES

2004

This set of four whimsies shows Homepride Fred with a variety of expressions on his face.

Backstamp: Wade CPGL (on side of base)
Homepride Fred © 2004 & TM Campbell
Grocery Products Limited

Date	Name	Description	Issue	Price	Size	U.S. $	Can. $	U.K. £
2004	Both eyes closed	Black suit, hat; white base	750	Set	40	14.	16.	8.
2004	Both eyes open	Black suit, hat; white base	750	of	40	14.	16.	8.
2004	Left eye closed	Black suit, hat; white base	750	Four	40	14.	16.	8.
2004	Right eye closed	Black suit, hat; white base	750	£30	40	14.	16.	8.

HOMEPRIDE FRED'S BIG BAND

2004-2005

Fred Playing the Tuba

Fred Playing the Violin

Backstamp: Printed: Homepride Fred © 2004 / TM CGPL. Fred's Big Band [name of instrument], Wade

Date	Name	Description	Issue	Price	Size	U.S. $	Can. $	U.K. £
2004	Fred the Conductor	Black suit, hat; silver baton	500	£25	Unk.	70.	80.	40.
2004	Fred Playing the Double Base	Black suit, hat; brown double base	500	£25	Unk.	70.	80.	40.
2004	Fred Playing the Drums	Black suit, hat; blue drums	500	£25	Unk.	70.	80.	40.
2004	Fred Playing the Keyboard	Black suit, hat; brown, white keyboard	500	£25	Unk.	70.	80.	40.
2004	Fred Playing the Saxophone	Black suit, hat; silver saxophone	500	£25	Unk.	70.	80.	40.
2004	Fred Playing the Tuba	Black suit, hat; copper tuba	500	£25	Unk.	70.	80.	40.
2004	Fred Playing the Violin	Black suit, hat; brown violin	500	£25	Unk.	70.	80.	40.
2005	Fred's Big Bandstand	White bandstand; black lettering	500	Unk.	Unk.	—	—	—

HOMEPRIDE FRED'S FORTIETH BIRTHDAY
2004

Backstamp: Printed Wade, Fred at Forty, © 2004 & TM Campbell Grocery Products Limited. This is not a Toy, Key Kollectables Ltd. Limited Edition of 500 or Special Edition of 25

Fred at Forty

Date	Name	Description	Issue	Price	Size	U.S. $	Can. $	U.K. £
2004	Fred at Forty	Black suit, hat; red numerals	500	£55.00	120	75.	85.	45.
2004	Fred at Forty	Black suit, hat; gold numerals	25	Unk.	120	—	—	—

WORLD CUP FRED
2006

Referee Fred

Training Fred

Backstamp: Homepride Fred © 2006 & TM Campbell Gocery Products Limited

Date	Name	Description	Issue	Price	Size	U.S. $	Can. $	U.K. £
2006	Champion Fred	Black suit, hat; gold trophy	250	£45	100	75.	85.	45.
2006	Linesman Fred	Black suit, hat; red flag	250	£45	100	75.	85.	45.
2006	Referee Fred	Black suit, hat; red book; gold whistle	250	£45	100	75.	85.	45.
2006	Training Fred	Black suit, hat; blue vest; black, white ball	250	£45	100	75.	85.	45.

COLOUR AND MOULD VARIATIONS

RHINO

WHELK

Grey/Green (EW)   Grey (TS)

Honey brown (King Aquariums Ltd.)   Blue (TS)

POODLE

White (RRC)   Apricot (TS)   Black (Patty Keenan)

SEAL ON ROCK

PANDA

Beige/Blue (RRC)   Blue (TS)   Dark Brown (TS)

First Whimsies
Large   Small

COLOUR VARIATIONS

GRIZZLY CUB

Light Brown (First Whimsies)   White (First Whimsies)   Brown (First Whimsies)

HIPPO

Mother Hippo, Happy Families — First Issue (left), Second Issue (centre), Wade Pocket Pal "Paddles" (right)

RABBIT

Mother Rabbit, Happy Families, First Issue (left),
Second Issue (centre), Wade Pocket Pal "Bounce" (right)

MONGREL

Dark/Light Brown (EW)   Grey/Blue (TS)

COLOUR VARIATIONS

GIRAFFE

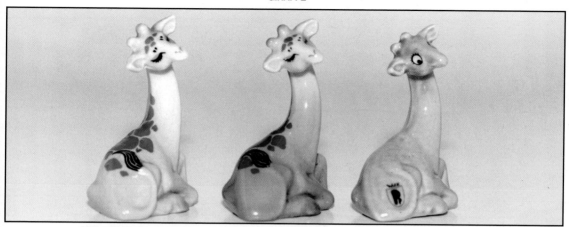

Mother Giraffe, Happy Families — First Issue (left), Second Issue (cente), Wade Pocket Pal "Stretch" (right)

POLAR BEAR

Beige/Blue-grey (TS)   White/Blue (EW)   White (TS)

ZEBRA

Black (EW)   Beige/Green (EW)   Grey (TS)   Light Grey (RRU)

COLOUR VARIATIONS

MINIKINS

Cat, Standing

Dog

Pelican (left), Fawn (right)

Cat Walking

Narrow-Eared Rabbit

COLOUR VARIATIONS

MINIKINS

Mouse (front view)

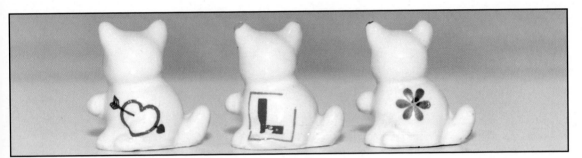

Mouse (rear view)

Mouse (front view)

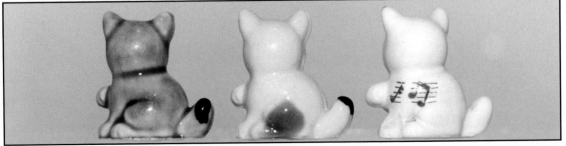

Mouse (rear view)

COLOUR VARIATIONS

MINIKINS

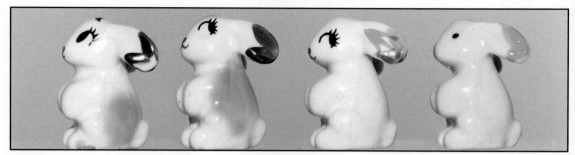

Rabbit Sitting (left view)

Rabbit Sitting (right view)

Wide-Eared Rabbit (front view)

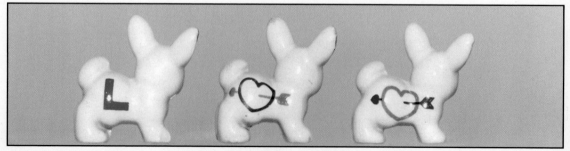

Wide-Eared Rabbit (rear view)

COLOUR VARIATIONS

MINIKINS

Cow (front view)

Cow (rear view)

Bull (front view)

Bull (rear view)

COLOUR VARIATIONS

FROG

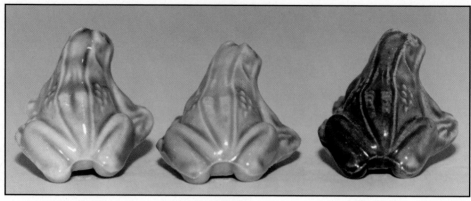

Green (RRC)   Yellow (RRC)   Brown (EW)

FROG

Mother Frog, Happy Families (left), Wade Pocket Pal "Hip Hop" (centre), Collect It! Pocket Pal "Hopper" (right)

CAT

Variations of Mother Cat, Happy Families
Wade Pocket Pal "Slinky" (left), C&S pocket Pal "Tango" (right)

DOG

Variations of Mother Dog, Happy Families
Wade Pocket Pal "Waggs" Left, Collect It! Pocket Pal "Woofit" (right)

WHIMSEY-ON-WHY

CHRISTMAS IN WHIMSEY-ON-WHY

2003

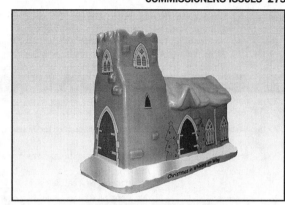

Backstamp: Printed Key Kollectables Ltd Limited Edition of [number] Wade Christmas in Whimsey-on-Why 2003 St. Sebatian's Church

Date	Name	Description	Issue	Price	Size	U.S. $	Can. $	U.K. £
2003	St. Sebatian's Church	Grey; white roof; brown doors, white snow	125	£49.95	110 x 140	120.	130.	70.
2003	St. Sebatian's Church	Grey; white roof; brown doors, gold snow	25	Un k.	110 x 140	175.	200.	100.

PEOPLE FROM WHIMSEY-ON-WHY

2003-2006

Collectors purchasing all models produced in 2004 were eligible to purchase the special Whimsey-on-Why model "Lord Whimsie".

Butcher, Vicar and Doctor

Blacksmith

Fishmonger

Backstamp: **Blacksmith:** Printed "Wade Whimsey-On-Why Blacksmith" red, gold or silver "Wade" logo;
Butcher / Doctor: Red or gold "Wade" logo
Fishmonger, Landlord, Postman: Printed "Wade"
Miller: Printed "Wade Key Kollectables Ltd Miller"
Vicar: Printed "Key Kollectables Limited or Special Edition Vicar Whimsey-On-Why"; red or gold "Wade" logo

Date	Name	Description	Issue	Price	Size	U.S. $	Can. $	U.K. £
2003	Blacksmith	Blue hat; honey apron; green trousers; grey anvil	250	£29.95	70	45.	50.	25
2003	Blacksmith	Blue hat; honey apron; green trousers; silver anvil	20	£29.95	70	—	—	—
2003	Blacksmith	Honey apron; green trousers; gold anvil	10	Prizes	70	—	—	—
2003	Butcher	Yellow hat, blue band; white shirt; blue/white striped apron; pink sausages	250	£29.95	65	45.	50.	25
2003	Butcher	Yellow hat, blue band; white shirt; blue/white striped apron; gold sausages	20	£29.95	65	—	—	—
2003	Dr Healer	White coat; blue trousers	250	£29.95	65	45.	50.	25.
2003	Dr Healer	White coat; blue trousers; silver stethoscope	20	£29.95	65	—	—	—
2003	Dr Healer	White coat; green trousers	10	Prizes	65	—	—	—
2003	Vicar	Black cassock; white cup/saucer	250	£29.95	65	50.	55.	30.
2003	Vicar	Black cassock; gold cup/saucer	20	£29.95	65	—	—	—
2003	Vicar	Burgundy cassock; gold cup/saucer	10	Prizes	65	—	—	—
2004	Fishmonger	White, green, black; grey fish	200	£29.95	65	110.	120.	65.
2004	Fishmonger	White, green, black; silver fish	20	£29.95	65	—	—	—
2004	Fishmonger	White, green, black; gold fish	10	Prizes	65	—	—	—
2004	Lord Whimsie	Brown jacket, yellow trousers, black shoes	Unk.	Unk.	Unk.	50.	55.	30.
2004	The Miller	White smock; orange necktie	200	£29.95	70	50.	55.	30.
2004	The Miller	White smock; silver necktie	20	£29.95	70	—	—	—
2004	The Miller	White smock; gold necktie	10	Prizes	70	—	—	—
2004	Landlord Barley Mow	Beige, brown, black; brown tankard	200	£29.95	60	50.	55.	30.
2004	Landlord Barley Mow	Beige, brown, black; silver tankard	20	£29.95	60	—	—	—
2004	Landlord Barley Mow	Beige, brown, black; gold tankard	10	Prizes	60	—	—	—
2004	Postman	Blue uniform; yellow buttons and hat badge	200	£29.95	60	50.	55.	30.
2004	Postman	Blue uniform; silver buttons and hat badge	20	£29.95	60	—	—	—
2004	Postman	Blue uniform; gold buttons and hat badge	10	Prizes	60	—	—	—
2006	Usherette	Royal blue jacket	100	£35.00	60	45.	50.	25.
2006	Usherette	Royal Blue jacket; silver buttons, epaulettes	20	£35.00	60	—	—	—
2006	Usherette	Royal blue jacket; gold buttons, epaulettes	10	Prizes	60	—	—	—

Note: **1.** A dash in any of the technical data columns of the table indicates that we do not have the required information, if you do, we would be pleased to hear from you.

2. Dashes in the pricing columns indicate one of two things: firstly, there was insufficient market pricing available, and secondly, pieces issued in small quantities of 10 or 20 pieces will be subject to wide pricing swings.

THE STRAW FAMILY

1999-2000

Backstamp: Printed "Key Kollectables - Limited Edition of 2,000 with Certificate of Authenticity - Wade England" [name of model]

Date	Name	Description	Issue	Price	Size	U.S. $	Can. $	U.K. £
1999	Pa Straw	Red/grey/black/yellow	2,000	£27	140	60.	65.	35.
1999	Ma Straw	Blue/white/brown	2,000	£27	134	50.	55.	30.
1999	Teen Straw	White/brown/blue vest/yellow	2,000	£27	120	50.	55.	30.
2000	Baby Straw	Pink/white bib/blue/yellow	2,000	£27	85	50.	55.	30.

TRAIN SETS

2001-2003

The letters on top of the carriages spell either Spring (blue) or Summer (yellow). The carriage size is 26 x 46 mm, and the engine 34 x 55 mm. The Autumn Train set was issued in June 2002, and the Winter Train set in spring 2003. Each set has an engine with the "Wade" logo on the roof, and six carriages with lettering spelling 'autumn' or 'winter' on the roofs, and various autumn and winter theme decals on the carriages. They were produced in a limited edition of 200 each with standard lettering, and 100 sets with gold lettering.

The Christmas Train set was issued in winter 2002, and was packaged in a specially designed gift box, which included a postcard certificate.

Spring Train

Autumn Train

Winter Train

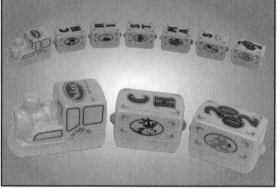

ChristmasTrain

Backstamp: **A.** Embossed "Wade England Key"
B. Embossed "Wade England Key"

Date	Name	Description	Issue	Price	Size	U.S. $	Can. $	U.K. £
2001	Spring Train Set	Blue; multicoloured lettering	400	£35.00	55 x 34	85.	95.	50.
2001	Spring Train Set	Blue; gold lettering	100	Unk.	55 x 34	125.	135.	70.
2001	Summer Train Set	Yellow; multicoloured lettering	400	£35.00	55 x 34	85.	95.	50.
2001	Autumn Train Set	Beige; multicoloured decals	200	£35.00	55 x 34	85.	95.	50.
2002	Autumn Train Set	Beige; multicoloured decals; gold lettering	100	£40.00	55 x 34	85.	95.	50.
2002	Christmas Train Set	White; multicoloured decals	100	£49.50	55 x 34	85.	95.	50.
2003	Winter Train Set	Cream; multicoloured decals	200	£35.00	55 x 34	85.	95.	50.
2003	Winter Train Set	Cream; multicoloured decals; gold lettering	100	£40.00	55 x 34	85.	95.	50.

KING AQUARIUMS LTD.

AQUARIUM SET

1976-1980

The *Aquarium Set* was produced for King Aquariums Ltd., a British company that supplied aquarium products to pet stores, and were not on sale in gift stores. The "Bridge" is marked with "Wade England" embossed at the base of each span, whereas the other figures are marked on the back rims. For the blue colourway of the water snail / whelk see Tom Smith Crackers Sealife page 322.

Backstamp: Embossed "Wade England"

No.	Name	Description	Size	U.S. $	Can. $	U.K. £
1	Bridge	Beige; light brown base	45 x 80	95.	105.	55.
2	Diver	Honey; brown base	70 x 28	35.	40.	20.
3a	Lighthouse	Beige/honey; grey-green base	75 x 45	60.	65.	35.
3b	Lighthouse	Honey; grey-green base	75 x 45	60.	65.	35.
4	Mermaid	Beige; yellow hair; grey-green base	60 x 58	60.	65.	35.
5	Seahorse	Blue/beige pattern	70 x 30	175.	190.	100.
6	Water Snail/Whelk	Honey; green-grey shell	30 x 35	95.	105.	55.

KEITH LANGFORD
ABSOLUTELY CRACKERS

BIRDS

November 2001

This set of Christmas crackers contains previously issued *English Whimsies, Tom Smith* or *Red Rose Tea Whimsies*, and *Whimsie-land* bird models. There are eight figures in the set, but only six crackers in a box. The issue price of the boxed crackers was £14.99.

Backstamp: Embossed "Wade England"

No.	Name	Description	Size	U.S. $	Can. $	U.K. £
1	Cockerel (WL)	Grey	50 x 35	9.	10.	5.
2	Duck (WL)	Beige	45 x 35	9.	10.	5.
3	Eagle (TS)	Tan	50 x 35	9.	10.	5.
4	Goose (RR)	Brown	30 x 35	9.	10.	5.
5	Owl (WL)	Beige	35 x 25	9.	10.	5.
6	Partridge (WL)	Blue	35 x 25	9.	10.	5.
7	Pelican (EW)	White	45 x 40	9.	10.	5.
8	Wren (TS)	Green	33 x 24	9.	10.	5.

MISCELLANEOUS CHRISTMAS CRACKER BOXES

2004

In 2004 Absolutely Crackers offered old stock of Wade Tom Smith models in their new *Party Cracker Boxes* at the prices shown in the table below.

Backstamp: Embossed "Wade England"

No.	Description	Issue	Size	U.S. $	Can. $	U.K. £
1	Tales From the Nursery [8 crackers] (Tom Smith 1994-96)	£14.99	50 x 35	25.	28.	15.
2	Bear Ambitions Crackers [6 crackers] (Tom Smith 1996-97)	£14.99	45 x 35	25.	28.	15.
3	Hedgerow Crackers [6 crackers] (Tom Smith 19998)	£13.99	50 x 35	25.	28.	15.
4	Sealife Crackers [6 crackers] (Tom Smith 1998)	£13.99	30 x 35	25.	28.	15.
5	Nursery Crackers [6 crackers] (Wade 2001 Ltd. Ed.)	£19.99	35 x 25	35.	40.	20.
6	Bird Set [6 crackers] (Absolutely Crackers 2001)	£14.99	35 x 25	25.	28.	15.

Note: The following initials indicate the origin of the models:
   EW: *English Whimsies*
   RW: Red Rose Tea
   TS: Tom Smith
   WL: Whimsie-land

SHARON LATKA

BLACK TERRIER DOG

2000

Commissioned by Sharon Latka of Clarence, New York, this model which was originally the West Highland Terrier from the *Tom Smith Animate Crackers* set "World of Dogs," see page 332.

Backstamp: Embossed "Wade England"

Date	Name	Description	Issue	Price	Size	U.S. $	Can. $	U.K. £
2000	Terrier Dog (TS)	Black	2,000	$10 US	30	12.	13.	7.

LEVER REXONA
New Zealand
NURSERY RHYME MODELS

Early 1970s

Lever Rexona, makers of Signal toothpaste, offered 24 miniature *Nursery Rhyme* models as a promotion, one model per box. The same models were used in the 1972-1979 Canadian Red Rose Tea promotion.

Backstamp: Unknown

No.	Name	Description	Size	U.S. $	Can. $	U.K. £
1	Baa Baa Black Sheep	Black	25 x 30	16.	18.	10.
2	Cat and the Fiddle	Beige cat; yellow fiddle	47 x 33	20.	22.	12.
3	Dr. Foster	Light brown; yellow tie; blue puddle	43 x 26	8.	9.	5.
4	Gingerbread Man	Red-brown; grey-green base	43 x 30	40.	45.	25.
5	Goosey Gander	Honey head, neck; dark brown wings; pink beak	33 x 36	8.	9.	5.
6	Hickory Dickory Dock	Red-brown/honey clock; brown mouse	44 x 20	16.	18.	10.
7	House that Jack Built	Honey; red-brown roof	32 x 35	12.	15.	8.
8	Humpty Dumpty	Honey; pink cheeks; blue bow tie; brown wall	36 x 23	7.	8.	4.
9	Jack	Light brown; blue shirt, bucket	34 x 33	10.	11.	6.
10	Jill	Yellow hair; beige dress; blue bucket	28 x 39	20.	22.	12.
11	Little Bo-Peep	Light brown; blue apron; green base	44 x 24	8.	9.	5.
12	Little Boy Blue	Blue hat, coat; honey trousers	41 x 25	10.	11.	6.
13	Little Jack Horner	Beige; blue plum; pink cushion	37 x 21	7.	8.	4.
14	Little Miss Muffett	Honey/grey dress; red-brown spider	39 x 35	10.	11.	6.
15	Mother Goose	Blue hat, bodice; honey dress, goose	41 x 31	16.	18.	10.
16	Old King Cole (Gap)	Beige; blue hat, hem; pink sleeves	37 x 32	10.	11.	6.
17	Old Woman Who Lived in a Shoe	Honey; red-brown roof	35 x 40	10.	11.	6.
18	Pied Piper	Light brown coat; green bush	46 x 28	8.	9.	5.
19	Puss in Boots	Brown; blue boots; green base	43 x 20	20.	22.	12.
20	Queen of Hearts	Pink hat; beige dress; two red hearts	42 x 25	12.	15.	8.
21	Red Riding Hood	Beige dress; red/pink hood, cape; green base	44 x 24	8.	9.	5.
22	Three Bears	Dark brown; honey base	36 x 38	28.	30.	16.
23	Tom Tom the Piper's Son	Honey; blue hat, kilt; brown jacket	39 x 33	12.	13.	7.
24	Wee Willie Winkie	Yellow hair, candle; beige nightshirt	44 x 24	8.	9.	5.

LUX SOAP

FREE WADE MINIATURES

c.1970

This English Whimsie Mongrel was distributed free with packets of Lux with Dermasil. Lux is a brand name of Unilever, U.K. The value given is for the packaged model.

Backstamp: Embossed "Wade England"

No.	Name	Description	Size	U.S. $	Can. $	U.K. £
1	Mongrel	Dark brown; light brown	35 x 35	25.	28.	15.

MEMORY JARS

YEAR OF THE RABBIT

1999

Memory Jars commissioned a new colourway of the *English Whimsie Rabbit* to mark the last year of the Millennium (the Chinese Year of the Rabbit). Obtainable with the purchase of a limited edition Memory Jar, they were made available June 1999.

Backstamp: Embossed "Wade England" on rim

Date	Name	Description	Issue	Price	Size	U.S. $	Can. $	U.K. £
1999	Rabbit	Blue	450	—	30 x 30	40.	45.	25.
1999	Rabbit	Gold	50	—	30 x 30	—	—	—

NEW VICTORIA THEATRE

TOAD OF TOAD HALL

2000

This model is a scaled-down version of the original O.I.W.C.C. "Toad of Toad Hall," and was complimentary with admission to the theatre's production of the *Wind in the Willows*.

Backstamp: Printed "New Vic Theatre Wade England"

Date	Name	Description	Issue	Price	Size	U.S. $	Can. $	U.K. £
2000	Toad of Toad Hall	Honey coat, cap; dark brown trousers	—	Free	80	40.	45.	25.

OUT OF THE BLUE CERAMICS
(Collectables Magazine)

COLLECT 99 BEAR

1999

Backstamp: Black printed "Produced by Wade Ceramics England in Collaboration with Collectables Magazine"

Date	Name	Description	Issue	Price	Size	U.S. $	Can. $	U.K. £
1999	Bear	Honey; blue/white lettering	500	£25	1105	50.	55.	30.

TINY TREASURES

SET ONE: BATMAN and SUPERMAN

1999

Backstamp: Red printed "Wade Made in England" and black printed "DC Comics 1999 Wade [name of model]"

Alfred, Batman, Lois Lane, Supergirl

Date	Name	Description	Issue	Price	Size	U.S. $	Can. $	U.K. £
1999	Alfred	Black suit; white shirt	1939	£5.90	58	18.	20.	10.
1999	Batman	Honey; black cloak, gloves, boots	1939	£5.90	58	25.	28.	15.
1999	Lois Lane	Maroon jacket; brown skirt	1939	£5.90	58	18.	20.	10.
1999	Supergirl	Red cloak; blue suit	1939	£5.90	58	20.	22.	12.

SET TWO: PETER PAN

1999

Backstamp: Embossed "TT 2 Wade" on the back of base

Mermaid, Pirate, Peter Pan, Mrs. Darling

Date	Name	Description	Issue	Price	Size	U.S. $	Can. $	U.K. £
1999	Mermaid	Grey-green mermaid; honey base	500	£9.50	60	20.	22.	12.
1999	Mrs. Darling	Grey-green dress; brown trim	500	£9.50	67	20.	22.	12.
1999	Peter Pan	Honey; olive suite; brown shoes	500	£9.50	62	20.	22.	12.
1999	Pirate	Honey; grey-green trousers	500	£9.50	64	20.	22.	12.

SET THREE: SANTA AND SNOWMAN

2000

Backstamp: Black printed "Wade England T.T.3 [name of model]"

Date	Name	Description	Issue	Price	Size	U.S. $	Can. $	U.K. £
2000	Santa Claus	Red/white suit; black belt, boots	500	£15	60	40.	45.	25.
2000	Snowman	White; blue scarf; black hat	500	£15	60	40.	45.	25.

POS-NER ASSOCIATES

SHERWOOD FOREST

1989-1998

A new colourway of Friar Tuck was issued in 1998, although it still carried the original embossed 1994 date in the backstamp. The box lid lists five figures, but the last two, Little John (as a beggar) and the Sheriff of Nottingham, have to date not been produced.

Backstamp:
   A. Embossed "Mianco 89 Wade England"
   B. Embossed "Mianco 90 Wade England"
   C. Embossed "Wade Mianco 94"

Robin Hood, Maid Marian, Friar Tuck

Date	Name	Description	Issue	Price	Size	U.S. $	Can. $	U.K. £
1989	Robin Hood	Green/honey brown	5,000	—	70 x 30	30.	33.	17.
1989	Maid Marian	Grey-blue/brown	5,000	—	65 x 25	30.	33.	17.
1994	Friar Tuck	Honey brown robes	5,000	—	45 x 30	30.	33.	17.
1998	Friar Tuck	Green-blue robes	500	—	45 x 30	50.	55.	30.

R & M COLLECTABLES

BRITANNIA

2000

Backstamp: Printed "Wade England Britannia Produced exclusively for R & M Collectables in a Limited edition of 250 to commemorate the Millennium"

Date	Name	Description	Issue	Price	Size	U.S. $	Can. $	U.K. £
2000	Britannia	White robes; gold helmet, trident	250	£45	165	85.	95.	50.

RED ROSE TEA (CANADA) LTD.
MINIATURE ANIMALS

FIRST ISSUE
1967-1973

In early 1967, when the sales of Red Rose Tea were in decline and the company was falling behind its competitors, it decided to start a promotional campaign to win back customers. In its campaign Wade miniature animals were used as free premiums in packages of Red Rose Tea Bags.

The first 12 promotional models were released in early 1967 and used in a trial run in Quebec, Canada, to test the public's reaction. The idea proved so successful that the series was quickly increased to 32 models in autumn 1967. The models were then offered nationally, region by region across Canada. Their popularity was so great that the promotional area and period (originally intended for two to three years) was extended to cover all of Canada for six years (from 1967 to 1973).

The models marked with "Wade England" in a recessed base were the first of this series to be produced. When the dies on five of these — the "Beaver," "Bushbaby," "Kitten," "Owl" and "Squirrel" — were retooled in 1967, the marks were placed on the back rim of the models; however the "Bear Cub," had "Wade" between the front feet and "England" on the back rim.

The "Bison" and "Hippo" are found in two sizes because, when the original dies broke, the new dies produced smaller models. In fact, there can be slight size variations in all the models listed below.

A second "Rabbit" was made with open ears because the closed ears on the first version were too difficult to fettle. The first issue "Trout" was unmarked, and the back of the base differs slightly from the second issue, which is marked "Wade England" on the back rim.

This first issue was later produced as English Whimsies, except for the "Fantail Goldfish," "Butterfly," "Frog," "Poodle," "Crocodile," "Terrapin," "Seal on Rock" and "Rabbit" with closed ears. The "Butterfly," "Frog" and "Fantail Goldfish" were also used for a Brooke Bond Tea, UK (Sister Company to Red Rose Tea) promotion and the "Crocodile" and "Terrapin" were previously used in the Balding and Mansell Flintstones Christmas Cracker set.

Due to the replacement of worn dies the hedgehog model has been found with two different types of base: Type 1 has three pads; Type 2 has two pads. The Crocodile model is found with two base variations: a recessed base and a disc base. It is not known which was produced first.

A 'Trout' with a recessed base has been found in North America. A late 1960s advertisement has been seen that shows the Crocodile named as 'Alligator.' A variation in the "Bushbaby" exists where the whole of the top arm is in front of the knee, and there is no gap under the base.

The following list is in alphabetical order.

Backstamp: A. Embossed "Wade England" on rim (1, 2a, 3a, 4a, 4b, 6a, 8, 9, 11, 12, 13, 14, 16, 18a, 18b, 19a, 19b, 20, 21, 22, 23a, 24, 25a, 25b, 26, 27, 28, 29a, 31a, 32)
B. Embossed "Wade England" in recessed base (2b, 3b, 5, 6b, 7a, 7b, 10a, 10b, 15a, 15b, 17a, 17b, 19b, 23b, 29b, 30a, 30b, 30c)
C. Embossed "Wade England" on disk (10a)
D. Unmarked (31b)

No.	Name	Description	Size	U.S. $	Can. $	U.K. £
1	Alsatian	Grey; tan face	30 x 40	4.	5.	2.
2a	Bear Cub	Grey; beige face	30 x 40	4.	5.	2.
2b	Bear Cub (recessed base)	Grey; beige face	30 x 40	9.	10.	5.
3a	Beaver	Grey-brown; honey-brown face	35 x 45	3.	4.	2.
3b	Beaver (recessed base)	Grey-brown; honey-brown face	35 x 45	9.	10.	5.
4a	Bison, large	Honey; dark brown head, mane	32 x 45	9.	10.	5.
4b	Bison, small	Honey; dark brown head, mane	28 x 40	4.	5.	3.
5	Bluebird	Beige; blue wings, head	15 x 35	10.	11.	6.
6a	Bushbaby, Type 1	Brown; blue ears; black nose	30 x 30	3.	4.	2.
6b	Bushbaby, Type 1 (recessed base)	Brown; blue ears; black nose	30 x 30	4.	5.	3.
6c	Bushbaby, Type 2	Brown; blue ears; black nose	30 x 30	4.	5.	3.
7a	Butterfly	Honey; grey tips; raised circles	10 x 45	10.	11.	6.
7b	Butterfly	Olive/brown; green tips; raised circles	10 x 45	10.	11.	6.
7c	Butterfly	Honey	10 x 45	10.	11.	6.
8	Chimpanzee	Dark brown; light brown face, patches	35 x 35	7.	8.	4.

No.	Name	Description	Size	U.S. $	Can. $	U.K. £
9	Corgi	Honey-brown; black nose	30 x 35	7.	8.	4.
10a	Crocodile/Alligator	Brownish green	14 x 40	9.	10.	5.
10b	Crocodile/Alligator	Brownish green	14 x 40	9.	10.	5.
11	Duck	Blue/brown; yellow beak	30 x 40	9.	10.	5.
12	Fantail Goldfish	Green/yellow; blue rock	30 x 35	9.	10.	5.
13	Fawn	Brown; blue ears; black nose	30 x 30	9.	10.	5.
14	Fox	Dark brown; fawn face, chest	30 x 30	9.	10.	5.
15a	Frog	Green	15 x 30	18.	20.	11.
15b	Frog	Yellow	15 x 30	18.	20.	11.
16	Giraffe	Beige	35 x 35	9.	10.	5.

Note: The above pricing tables are listed in photograph order from bottom left to upper right.

No.	Name	Description	Size	U.S. $	Can. $	U.K. £
17a	Hedgehog, Type 1	Light brown; honey face; black nose	23 x 40	5.	6.	3.
17b	Hedgehog, Type 2	Dark red brown; honey face; black nose	23 x 40	5.	6.	3.
18a	Hippo, large	Honey brown	25 x 45	14.	15.	8.
18b	Hippo, small	Honey brown	20 x 40	5.	6.	3.
19a	Kitten, seated	Dark/light brown; pink wool	30 x 30	5.	6.	3.
19b	Kitten, seated	Dark/light brown; red wool	30 x 30	5.	6.	3.
20	Lion	Light brown; dark brown head, mane	35 x 45	5.	6.	3.
21	Mongrel	Dark brown/light brown	35 x 35	5.	6.	3.
22	Otter	Beige; blue base	30 x 35	5.	6.	3.
23a	Owl	Dark/light brown	35 x 20	5.	6.	3.
23b	Owl	Dark/light brown	35 x 20	5.	6.	3.
24	Poodle	White; green base	40 x 45	7.	8.	4.

Note: The above pricing table is listed in photograph order from bottom left to upper right.

Rabbit, closed ears (left); Rabbit, open ears (right)

Embossed backstamp in recessed base of Trout

No.	Name	Description	Size	U.S. $	Can. $	U.K. £
25a	Rabbit	Beige; closed ears	30 x 30	22.	25.	14.
25b	Rabbit	Beige; ears open	30 x 30	3.	4.	2.
26	Seal on Rock	Brown; blue rock	35 x 35	9.	10.	5.
27	Setter	Brown; grey-green base	35 x 50	3.	4.	2.
28	Spaniel	Honey brown; green on base	35 x 35	6.	7.	4.
29a	Squirrel	Grey; beige; yellow acorn	35 x 30	3.	4.	2.
29b	Squirrel (Recessed)	Grey; beige; yellow acorn	35 x 30	10.	11.	6.
30a	Terrapin	Beige; brown markings	10 x 40	12.	13.	7.
30b	Terrapin	Beige; grey markings	10 x 40	12.	13.	7.
30c	Terrapin	Beige; purple-blue markings	10 x 40	12.	13.	7.
31a	Trout	Brown; red tail; grey-green base	30 x 30	3.	4.	2.
31b	Trout	Brown; red tail; grey-green base	30 x 30	3.	4.	2.
31c	Trout (recessed base)	Brown; red tail; grey-green base	30 x 30	14.	15.	8.
32a	Wild Boar	Brown; green on base	30 x 40	3.	4.	2.
32b	Wild Boar	Brown	30 x 40	6.	7.	4.

Note: The above pricing table is listed in photograph order from bottom left to upper right.

MINIATURE NURSERY RHYMES

SECOND ISSUE

1972-1979

A series of 24 miniature nursery rhyme characters was given away free in the second Red Rose Tea promotion. For the first two years, these models were only distributed in selected areas; it was not until 1973 that they were distributed throughout Canada.

When a new die replaces a worn one, variations in models sometimes occur, as in "The Queen of Hearts" and "Old King Cole." Models with colour variations may indicate a painters whim or that a particular glaze was temporarily out of stock. All the models are marked "Wade England" around the rim of the base.

Because over 20 million of these models are reported to have been made; only the undamaged models are worth keeping. Thin, more breakable models in mint condition are worth more than the solid, heavier models, which stand up to rough handling better. Lever Rexona of New Zealand used the same 24 models in an early 1970s promotion for Signal Toothpaste. Five of the models were released in England as a boxed set.

As the 'Queen of Hearts" with eight hearts on her dress is so rarely found, it is now believed that this model was a prototype and not put into full production.

Backstamp: Embossed "Wade England"

No.	Name	Description	Size	U.S. $	Can. $	U.K. £
1	Baa Baa Black Sheep	Black all over	23 x 30	14.	15.	8.
2	Cat and the Fiddle	Beige front; grey back; yellow fiddle	47 x 33	20.	22.	12.
3a	Dr. Foster	Light brown all over	43 x 26	12.	13.	7.
3b	Dr. Foster	Light brown; blue puddle	43 x 26	12.	13.	7.
3c	Dr. Foster	Light brown; yellow tie; blue puddle	43 x 26	15.	16.	9.
3d	Dr. Foster	Brown; grey puddle	43 x 26	15.	16.	9.
4	Gingerbread Man	Red-brown; grey-green base	43 x 30	35.	40.	20.
5	Goosey Goosey Gander	Honey; brown wings; pink beak	33 x 36	8.	9.	5.
6	Hickory Dickory Dock	Red-brown/honey brown	44 x 20	7.	8.	4.
7	House that Jack Built	Honey brown; red-brown roof	32 x 35	10.	11.	6.
8a	Humpty Dumpty	Honey brown; blue tie; brown wall	36 x 23	7.	8.	4.
8b	Humpty Dumpty	Honey brown; brown wall	36 x 23	7.	8.	4.

Note: The above pricing table is listed in photograph order from upper left to lower right.

Backstamp: Embossed "Wade England"

No.	Name	Description	Size	U.S. $	Can. $	U.K. £
9a	Jack	Brown; blue shirt; brown bucket	34 x 33	10.	11.	6.
9b	Jack	Brown; blue shirt; blue bucket	34 x 33	10.	11.	6.
10	Jill	Yellow hair; beige dress; blue bucket	28 x 39	10.	11.	6.
11	Little Bo-Peep	Brown; blue apron; green base	44 x 24	4.	5.	3.
12	Little Boy Blue	Blue hat, coat; brown trousers	41 x 25	12.	13.	7.
13	Little Jack Horner	Beige; pink cushion; blue plum	37 x 21	5.	6.	3.
14	Little Miss Muffett	Honey/grey dress; red-brown spider	39 x 35	10.	11.	6.
15	Little Red Riding Hood	Beige dress; red cape; green base	44 x 24	10.	11.	6.
16a	Mother Goose	Brown hat; honey brown dress	41 x 31	14.	15.	9.
16b	Mother Goose	Blue hat; honey brown dress	41 x 31	14.	15.	9.

Note: The above pricing table is listed in photograph order from upper left to lower right.

Backstamp: Embossed "Wade England"

No.	Name	Description	Size	U.S. $	Can. $	U.K. £
17a	Old King Cole, Type 1	Gap; brown body, shoes, pot; blue hat, cloak	40 x 35	8.	9.	5.
17b	Old King Cole, Type 1	Gap; brown body, pot; blue hat, cloak, shoes	40 x 35	8.	9.	5.
17c	Old King Cole, Type 2	No gap; brown body shoes, pot; blue hat	40 x 35	8.	9.	5.
17d	Old King Cole, Type 2	No gap; brown body; blue hat, cloak, shoes, pot	40 x 35	8.	9.	5.
18a	Old Woman Who Lived in a Shoe	Honey brown; red-brown roof	35 x 40	7.	8.	4.
18b	Old Woman Who Lived in a Shoe	Honey brown	35 x 40	7.	8.	4.
19a	Pied Piper	Light brown coat; green bush	46 x 28	7.	8.	4.
19b	Pied Piper	Pink/brown coat; green bush	46 x 28	7.	8.	4.
20	Puss in Boots	Brown; blue boots; green base	43 x 20	12.	13.	7.
21a	Queen of Hearts	2 small hearts; beige dress; pink hat	42 x 25	14.	15.	8.
21b	Queen of Hearts	2 large hearts; beige dress; pink hat	42 x 25	14.	15.	8.
21c	Queen of Hearts	8 small hearts; beige dress; pink hat	42 x 25	26.	28.	15.
22a	The Three Bears	Dark brown; honey base	36 x 38	26.	28.	15.
22b	The Three Bears	Light brown; honey base	36 x 38	12.	13.	7.
23a	Tom Tom the Piper's Son	Honey brown; blue tam, kilt	36 x 38	12.	13.	7.
23b	Tom Tom the Piper's Son	Honey brown; brown tam, kilt	39 x 33	12.	13.	7.
23c	Tom Tom the Piper's Son	Honey brown; grey tam, kilt	39 x 33	8.	9.	5.
24	Wee Willie Winkie	Yellow hair; beige nightshirt	44 x 24	8.	9.	5.

Note: The above pricing table is listed in photograph order from upper left to lower right.

WHOPPAS
THIRD ISSUE
1981

In 1981 the English series of *Whoppas* came to an end, and the surplus stock was used for Red Rose Tea Canada premiums. To obtain a model, Canadian collectors had to mail in the tab from a box of Red Rose Tea, plus $1.00 for postage. The models in these sets were issued in numbered boxes, and all are marked "Wade England" around the rim of the base.

Numbers 1 through 5 are from Wade's *Whoppas*, Set One; 6 to 10 are from *Whoppas*, Set Two; 11 to 15 are from *Whoppas*, Set Three.

SET ONE

Backstamp: Embossed "Wade England"

No.	Name	Description	Size	U.S. $	Can. $	U.K. £
1	Polar Bear	White; grey-blue base	35 x 55	24.	26.	14.
2	Hippo	Grey; green base	35 x 50	24.	26.	14.
3	Brown Bear	Red-brown; brown base	35 x 45	24.	26.	14.
4	Tiger	Honey brown; green base	30 x 60	24.	26.	14.
5	Elephant	Grey	55 x 50	24.	26.	14.

SET TWO

Backstamp: Embossed "Wade England"

No.	Name	Description	Size	U.S. $	Can. $	U.K. £
6	Bison	Brown; green base	40 x 50	25.	28.	15.
7	Wolf	Grey; green base	60 x 45	25.	28.	15.
8	Bobcat	Light brown; dark brown spots; green base	55 x 50	25.	28.	15.
9	Chipmunk	Brown; dark brown base	55 x 40	25.	28.	15.
10	Raccoon	Brown; black stripes, eye patches; green base	40 x 50	25.	28.	15.

Note: The above pricing tables are listed in photograph order from bottom left to upper right.

SET THREE

Backstamp: Embossed "Wade England"

No.	Name	Description	Size	U.S. $	Can. $	U.K. £
11	Fox	Red-brown; green on base	30 x 60	27.	30.	16.
12	Badger	Brown; cream stripe; green base	35 x 45	27.	30.	16.
13	Otter	Brown; blue base	30 x 55	27.	30.	16.
14	Stoat	Brown; green base	35 x 55	27.	30.	16.
15	Hedgehog	Brown; green base	30 x 50	27.	30.	16.

MINIATURE ANIMALS
FOURTH ISSUE
1982-1984

Six animal models from the first Red Rose Tea Canada Promotion, marked RRC, were reissued some with slight colour variations, and 17 models from the 1971-1984 English *Whimsies* series were added to make this fourth promotion of 23 animals. New dies resulted in three sizes of pig..

Backstamp: Embossed "Wade England"

No.	Name	Description	Size	U.S. $	Can. $	U.K. £
1	Angelfish	Grey; dark grey stripes; blue base	35 x 30	10.	11.	6.
2	Beaver (RRC)	Brown; honey brown face	35 x 45	3.	4.	2.
3a	Bushbaby, Type 1 (RRC)	Beige	30 x 30	3.	4.	2.
3b	Bushbaby, Type 2 (RRC)	Beige	30 x 30	3.	4.	2.
4	Camel	Dark grey; green base	35 x 35	8.	9.	5.
5	Collie	Honey; green base	35 x 35	8.	9.	5.
6	Corgi (RRC)	Honey; black nose	30 x 35	8.	9.	5.
7	Cow	Honey; green base	35 x 35	8.	9.	5.
8	Fox (RRC)	Dark brown; fawn face	30 x 30	5.	6.	3.

Note: The above pricing tables are listed in photograph order from bottom left to upper right.

Backstamp: Embossed "Wade England"

No.	Name	Description	Size	U.S. $	Can. $	U.K. £
9	Giraffe (RRC)	Beige	35 x 35	3.	4.	2.
10	Gorilla, standing	Dark grey; green on base	35 x 25	5.	6.	3.
11	Horse	Dark grey; green base	35 x 35	18.	20.	10.
12	Lamb	Light beige; green base	30 x 25	8.	9.	5.
13	Langur, Type 1	Beige; brown stump	35 x 30	5.	6.	3.
14	Leopard	Honey; green base	17 x 45	8.	9.	5.
15	Orang-outan	Dark brown	30 x 30	5.	6.	3.

Backstamp: Embossed "Wade England"

No.	Name	Description	Size	U.S. $	Can. $	U.K. £
16	Pelican	Honey/brown; green base	45 x 40	18.	20.	11.
17a	Pig, large	Beige	27 x 44	20.	22.	12.
17b	Pig, medium	Beige; green base	25 x 40	17.	19.	10.
17c	Pig, small	Beige; green base	25 x 35	17.	19.	10.
18	Pine Marten	Honey	30 x 30	3.	4.	2.
19	Rabbit, ears open (RRC)	Beige	30 x 30	3.	4.	2.
20	Rhino	Dark grey; green base	17 x 45	5.	6.	3.
21	Seahorse	Honey-yellow; grey-blue base	50 x 17	18.	20.	11.
22a	Turtle	Dark grey	15 x 50	10.	11.	6.
22b	Turtle	Greenish-grey	15 x 50	10.	11.	6.
23	Zebra	Beige	40 x 35	8.	9.	5.

Note: The above pricing tables are listed in photograph order from bottom left to upper right.

RED ROSE TEA U.S.A. LTD. (REDCO FOODS LTD.)

1983-2002

The Canadian Red Rose Tea promotion was so successful that it was extended to the United States in 1983. Red Rose estimates that over two hundred million Wade models have been distributed in packets of Red Rose Tea in the U.S.A. and in Canada during its promotions. In many states figurine promotions overlap, with some model series still being offered in one area whilst a new series is offered in another.

A variation in the "Bushbaby" exists where the whole of the top arm is in front of the knee, and there is no gap under the base.

MINIATURE ANIMALS

FIRST ISSUE

1983-1985

In this first American series, two of the models, the "Hare" and "Squirrel," were not original *English Whimsies*, but models from the 1980-1981 Tom Smith *British Wildlife* set. All figures are in all-over, one-colour glazes, and they may vary slightly from the measurements indicated below. They are listed in alphabetical order.

Backstamp: **A.** Embossed "Wade England"
B. Embossed "Wade" between front feet and "England" on back of model

No.	Name	Description	Size	U.S. $	Can. $	U.K. £
1	Bear Cub (RR/EW)	Beige	30 x 40	7.	8.	4.
2	Bison (RR/EW)	Dark brown	30 x 40	8.	9.	5.
3	Bluebird (RR/EW)	Beige	15 x 35	8.	9.	5.
4a	Bushbaby, Type 1 (RR/EW)	Beige	30 x 30	8.	9.	5.
4b	Bushbaby, Type 2	Beige	30 x 30	3.	4.	2.
5	Chimpanzee (RR/EW)	Honey brown	35 x 35	10.	11.	6.
6	Elephant (EW)	Blue; no eyes	35 x 45	20.	22.	12.
7	Hare (TS)	Dark brown	50 x 30	8.	9.	5.
8	Hippo (RR/EW)	Honey	23 x 40	3.	4.	2.
9	Lion, standing (RR/EW)	Honey	35 x 45	8.	9.	5.
10	Otter (RR/EW)	Beige	30 x 35	7.	8.	4.
11	Owl (RR/EW)	Dark brown	35 x 20	13.	14.	8.
12	Seal on Rock (RR/TS)	Blue	35 x 35	7.	8.	4.
13a	Squirrel (TS)	Dark blue	40 x 40	8.	9.	5.
13b	Squirrel (TS)	Grey-blue/light blue	40 x 40	8.	9.	5.
14	Turtle (EW)	Light grey	15 x 50	13.	14.	8.
15	Wild Boar (RR/EW)	Beige	30 x 40	8.	9.	5.

Note: **1.** The following initials indicate the origin of the models.
EW: *English Whimsies;* RR: *Red Rose Tea;* TS: *Tom Smith British Wildlife* set
2. The above pricing table is listed in photograph order from upper left to lower right.

SECOND ISSUE

1985-1990

All the models in this series are in all-over, one-colour glazes. Some of these figures are in the same colours used in the 1982-1984 Canada Red Rose Tea promotion. In Washington State, in early 1992 the same models were offered with Red Rose Decaffeinated tea.

Backstamp: Embossed "Wade England"

No.	Name	Description	Size	U.S. $	Can. $	U.K. £
1	Beaver (EW/RRC)	Light brown	35 x 45	8.	9.	5.
2	Camel (EW/RRC)	Beige	35 x 35	5.	6.	3.
3	Giraffe (EW/RRC)	Beige	35 x 35	3.	4.	2.
4	Gorilla, standing (EW/RRC)	Dark brown	35 x 25	5.	6.	3.
5	Kangaroo (EW)	Honey brown	45 x 25	7.	8.	4.
6a	Koala (EW)	Beige	35 x 25	7.	8.	4.
6b	Koala (EW)	Brown	35 x 25	7.	8.	4.
7	Langur, Type 1 (EW/RRC)	Dark brown	35 x 30	7.	8.	4.
8	Leopard (EW/RRC)	Honey brown	17 x 45	3.	4.	2.
9	Orang-outan (EW/RRC)	Dark brown	30 x 30	5.	6.	3.
10	Pine Marten (EW/RRC)	Honey brown	30 x 30	3.	4.	2.
11	Polar Bear, head forward (EW/TS)	White	30 x 30	3.	4.	2.
12	Raccoon (EW)	Dark brown	25 x 35	5.	6.	3.
13	Rhino (EW/RRC)	Blue-grey	17 x 45	5.	6.	3.
14	Tiger, (EW)	Honey brown	35 x 25	3.	4.	2.
15	Zebra (EW/RRC)	Grey	40 x 35	3.	4.	2.

Notes: 1. The following initials indicate the origin of the models.
> EW: *English Whimsies*
> RRC: Red Rose Tea Canada
> TS: Tom Smith

2. The above pricing table is listed in photograph order from upper left to lower right.

THIRD ISSUE

1990-1996

The 15 models offered in the 1985-1990 Red Rose Tea promotion were increased to 20 in late 1990, with the addition of five Tom Smith 1988-1989 models (indicated below by TS). By late 1993 in New York State, Philadelphia, Florida and in Portland, Maine, the models were no longer included free in boxes of teabags, but could be obtained by sending in the UPC code and a small shipping and handling charge. In other areas of the U.S., the 20 animal figurines were available until mid 1995.

Backstamp: Embossed "Wade England"

No.	Name	Description	Size	U.S. $	Can. $	U.K. £
1	Cock-a-teel (Cockatoo) (TS)	Green	35 x 30	5.	6.	3.
2	Kitten (TS)	Grey	25 x 33	5.	6.	3.
3	Pony (Shetland) (TS)	Beige	25 x 30	5.	6.	3.
4	Rabbit (TS)	Dark brown	30 x 25	5.	6.	3.
5	Puppy (Spaniel) (TS)	Honey brown	25 x 30	5.	6.	3.

FOURTH ISSUE

1992

Red Rose U.S.A. offered these models as a mail-in offer with their packages of decaffeinated tea in early 1992. The models were obtained by mail order as the packaging method for decaffeinated tea did not allow for the inclusion of a model in the box of tea.

New dies resulted in three types of Langur: Type One (as seen on the Red Rose Tea packet) has no gap between the neck and stump; Type Two has a gap between the neck and stump, and under the left arm; Type Three has the gap between the neck and stump, but not under the left arm. The Koala has been reported in two colourways for this series, surplus models from other series may have been used to complete the order. The beige colourway of the Koala is illustrated on the Red Rose Tea packet.

Tiger, Type 1, Tiger Type 2

Backstamp: Embossed "Wade England"

No.	Name	Description	Size	U.S. $	Can. $	U.K. £
1	Beaver (EW/RRC/RRU)	Dark brown	35 x 45	8.	9.	5.
2	Camel (EW/RRC)	Dark grey	35 x 35	5.	6.	3.
3	Cock-a-teel (TS)	Green	35 x 30	5.	6.	3.
4	Giraffe (EW/RRC)	Beige	35 x 35	3.	4.	2.
5a	Gorilla, standing (EW/RRC)	Dark brown	35 x 25	5.	6.	3.
5b	Gorilla, standing (EW/RRC)	Black	35 x 25	17.	19.	10.
6	Kangaroo (EW/RRU)	Honey brown	45 x 25	7.	8.	4.
7	Persian kitten (TS)	Grey	25 x 33	5.	6.	3.
8a	Koala (EW/RRU)	Beige	35 x 25	7.	8.	4.
8b	Koala (EW/RRU)	Dark grey; beige stump	35 x 25	15.	16.	9.
9a	Langur, Type 1 (EW/RRC)	Light brown; brown stump	35 x 30	7.	8.	4.
9b	Langur, Type 1 (EW/RRC)	Dark brown	35 x 30	7.	8.	4.
9c	Langur, Type 2 (EW/RRC)	Dark brown	35 x 30	10.	11.	6.
9d	Langur, Type 3 (EW/RRC)	Brown	35 x 30	10.	11.	6.
10	Leopard (EW/RRC/RRU)	Mottled olive brown	17 x 45	14.	15.	18.
11	Orang-outan (EW/RRC)	Brown	30 x 30	8.	9.	5.
12	Pine Marten (EW/RRC)	Honey	30 x 30	3.	4.	2.
13	Polar Bear, head forward (EW/TS/RRU)	White	30 x 30	3.	4.	2.
14	Pony (Shetland) (TS)	Beige	25 x 30	7.	8.	4.
15	Rabbit (TS)	Dark brown	30 x 25	5.	6.	3.
16	Raccoon (EW/RRU)	Brown	25 x 35	5.	6.	3.
17	Rhino (EW/RRC/RRU)	Blue-grey/light grey	17 x 45	5.	6.	3.
18	Puppy (Spaniel) (TS)	Honey	25 x 30	7.	8.	4.
19a	Tiger, Type 1, (EW/RRU)	Mottled olive brown	35 x 25	14.	15.	18.
19b	Tiger, Type 2, Thick Tail	Mottled Olive Brown	35 x 25	17.	19.	10.
20	Zebra (EW/RRC/RRU)	Light grey	40 x 35	5.	6.	3.

Note:
1. For an illustration of model numbers 3, 7, 14, 15 and 18 please see previous page.
2. The following initials indicate the origin of the models:
   EW: *English Whimsies*; RRC: Red Rose Tea Canada; RRU: Red Rose Tea U.S.A.; TS: Tom Smith

FIFTH ISSUE: CIRCUS ANIMALS

1993-1999

In late 1993, Red Rose offered a reissue of the most popular of the Tom Smith cracker models, *The Circus* set, originally issued in England for Tom Smith from 1978 to 1979 (indicated by the initials TS). The original moulds were used and with only a slight variation in colour from the older models. Two variations have been found in the *Circus* Tiger due to a new mould being made: the mouth of the second variation appears to be more open and there is more detailing in the fur of the throat and chest which gives it the appearance of a beard.

FIFTH ISSUE: CIRCUS ANIMALS (cont.)
1993-1998

Backstamp: **A.** Embossed "Wade England" on back rim of base
B. Embossed "Wade Eng" on back rim of base

No.	Name	Description	Size	U.S. $	Can. $	U.K. £
1	Brown Bear (TS)	Dark brown	32 x 32	8.	9.	5.
2	Chimpanzee Boy (TS)	Brown	42 x 18	8.	9.	5.
3	Chimpanzee Girl (TS)	Brown	40 x 18	8.	9.	5.
4	Elephant, seated (TS)	Pale blue	30 x 30	8.	9.	5.
5	Elephant, standing (TS)	Pale blue	30 x 30	8.	9.	5.
6	Pony (TS)	Beige	43 x 20	8.	9.	5.
7	Lion (TS)	Honey brown	37 x 22	8.	9.	5.
8	Poodle (TS)	White; blue skirt	43 x 17	8.	9.	5.
9	Sea Lion (TS)	Light grey	43 x 30	8.	9.	5.
10a	Tiger, Type 1 (TS)	Honey brown; without beard	42 x 20	8.	9.	5.
10b	Tiger, Type 2 (RRU)	Honey brown; with beard	42 x 20	8.	9.	5.

SIXTH ISSUE
1996-1998

Five new *Circus* models were produced for Redco Foods (Red Rose Tea U.S.A.) and were available in all U.S.A. states where Red Rose Tea is sold from July of 1996. The five new models were added to the *Circus* set which was first introduced in 1993, making a total of 15 models for this series. A brown glazed version of the "Human Cannon-ball" has been reported, the reason for the colour variation is unknown.

Backstamp: Embossed "Wade England"

Large Custard Pie (left), Small Custard Pie (right)

No.	Name	Description	Size	U.S. $	Can. $	U.K. £
11a	Clown, large custard pie, Type 1	Dark blue	40	8.	9.	5.
11b	Clown, large custard pie, Type 1	Pale blue	40	8.	9.	5.
11c	Clown, small custard pie, Type 2	Blue	40	8.	9.	5.
12	Clown, water bucket	Light green	44	8.	9.	5.
13a	Human Cannonball	Light grey	30	8.	9.	5.
13b	Human Cannonball	Brown	30	8.	9.	5.
14	Ringmaster	Light grey	44	8.	9.	5.
15	Strongman	Honey brown	40	8.	9.	5.

SEVENTH ISSUE: ENDANGERED NORTH AMERICAN ANIMALS
1998-2002

In late 1998, Red Rose Tea U.S.A. started to phase out the *Circus* models in preparation for their new *Endangered North American Animals* which was a set of 10 models included in Red Rose Tea boxes from December 1998. Also in the boxes was a leaflet offering collectors the opportunity of purchasing the last of the *Circus* models that they needed to complete their sets at $1.00 per model.

There are seven new designs in the *Endangered Animals* set. Three models have been used in previous promotions, but were recoloured and renamed i.e. "Spotted Owl" (previously the *English Whimsies* Barn Owl) "Bald Eagle" (previously the *Whimsie-land* British Wildlife Golden Eagle), "Polar Bear" (previously the Tom Smith Survival Polar Bear). Please note that the "Polar Bear" has a thicker white glaze applied over the original white glaze.

Backstamp:
   A. Embossed "Wade Eng" on Peregrine Falcon
   B. Embossed "Wade England" on other models

No.	Name	Description	Size	U.S. $	Can. $	U.K. £
1	Bald Eagle / Golden Eagle (WL)	Honey brown	35 x 40	5.	6.	3.
2	Florida Panther	Honey brown	35 x 40	5.	6.	3.
3	Green Sea Turtle	Light green	30 x 44	5.	6.	3.
4	Humpback Whale	Grey	20 x 53	5.	6.	3.
5	Manatee	Blue-grey	25 x 53	5.	6.	3.
6	Peregrine Falcon	Beige	25 x 45	5.	6.	3.
7	Polar Bear (TS)	White	27 x 45	5.	6.	3.
8	Spotted Owl / Barn Owl (EW)	Beige	35 x 20	5.	6.	3.
9	Sturgeon	Blue	27 x 47	5.	6.	3.
10	Timber Wolf	Grey	45 x 28	5.	6.	3.

Note: The following initials indicate the origin of the models.
   EW: *English Whimsies*
   TS: Tom Smith
   WL: Whimsie-Land

EIGHTH ISSUE: NOAH'S ARK
2002-2006

In June 2002, Red Rose Tea U.S.A. issued a new series named "Noah's Ark," a set of 15 models, which was available in packages of Red Rose Regular, Decaffeinated and English Breakfast teas. The set includes Noah/Wife, a double-sided model, and a selection of animals. Also available via mail order was the opportunity to purchase a Wade Ceramics porcelain model of the Ark on which to display the complete set.

A variation exists in the shape of the base of "Noah and Wife." In Type 1 the base is oval, and in Type 2 the base is peanut shaped. There are also slight variations in the green glaze colours. Some models have a "Wade England" backstamp whilst others have "Wade Eng." Although an ongoing promotion, Red Rose Teas is not available in a large number of USA states.

Backstamp: **A.** Embossed "Wade England"
B. Embossed "Wade Eng"

Noah / Wife (oval base)

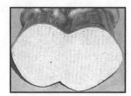

Noah / Wife
(peanut-shaped base)

No.	Name	Description	Size	U.S. $	Can. $	U.K. £
1	Ark	Dark brown	120 x 280	45.	50.	25.
2	Chicken, female, on nest	Green	30 x 30	7.	8.	4.
3	Chicken, male, standing	Green	36 x 25	7.	8.	4.
4	Elephant, female, trunk down	Grey	25 x 36	7.	8.	4.
5	Elephant, male, trunk up	Grey	33 x 36	7.	8.	4.
6	Goose, female, preening	Blue	33 x 38	7.	8.	4.
7	Goose, male, feeding	Blue	30 x 35	7.	8.	4.
8	Lion, female, lying	Honey	23 x 36	7.	8.	4.
9	Lion, male, with mane	Honey	30 x 36	7.	8.	4.
10a	Noah / Wife, Type 1	Green	41 x 25	7.	8.	4.
10b	Noah / Wife, Type 2	Green	41 x 25	7.	8.	4.
11	Rhinoceros, female, head down	Beige	28 x 35	7.	8.	4.
12	Rhinoceros, male, head up	Beige	28 x 43	7.	8.	4.
13	Sheep, female, head down	White	20 x 30	7.	8.	4.
14	Sheep, male, head up	White	25 x 28	7.	8.	4.
15	Zebra, female, lying	White	25 x 33	7.	8.	4.
16	Zebra, male, standing	White	25 x 33	7.	8.	4.
—	Complete set		—	85.	95.	50.

NINTH ISSUE: PET SHOP FRIENDS
2006

Backstamp: Unknown

No.	Name	Description	Size	U.S. $	Can. $	U.K. £
1	Budgie	Light green	45 x 20	5.	6.	3.
2	Cat	Brown	40 x 20	5.	6.	3.
3	Duck	Light brown	40 x 20	5.	6.	3.
4	Kittens	Light blue	35 x 28	5.	6.	3.
5	Labrador	Chocolate	40 x 35	5.	6.	3.
6	Pet Shop	Grey pet shop; creamy-white base	254 x 112	5.	6.	3.
7	Pony	Grey	35 x 35	5.	6.	3.
8	Puppies	Honey	30 x 38	5.	6.	3.
9	Rabbit	White	20 x 30	5.	6.	3.
10	Tropical Fish	Orange	35 x 32	5.	6.	3.
11	Turtle	Light green	25 x 30	5.	6.	3.
12	Pet Shop	Grey, cream, red lettering	254 x 114	45.	50.	25.

Note: The Pet Shop was purchased separately from Red Rose Tea.

ROBELL MEDIA PROMOTIONS LTD.

MR. MEN COLLECTION

1997-1999

The characters in this series are from storybooks by Roger Hargreaves. They were produced for the Mr. Men and Little Miss Club, and were marketed by Robell Media Promotions.

Mr. Happy   Mr. Bump   Little Miss Giggles

Mr. Snow

Backstamp: Black printed "Genuine Wade Porcelain Robell Produced exclusively for the Mr. Men & Little Miss Club Mr. Men and Little Miss TM & © 1997 Mrs. Roger Hargreaves" with "Mr. Happy and Little Miss" logo

Date	Name	Description	Issue	Price	Size	U.S. $	Can. $	U.K. £
1997	Mr. Happy	Yellow; black eyes/mouth	2,000	£15.99	100	35.	40.	20.
1998	Little Miss Giggles	Blue; red hair; yellow bows, nose	2,000	£15.99	95	35.	40.	20.
1998	Mr. Bump	Blue; white bandages; green base	2,000	£15.99	95	35.	40.	20.
1999	Mr. Snow	White; black hat; red/white scarf	2,000	£15.99	120	35.	40.	20.

ST. JOHN AMBULANCE BRIGADE (U.K.)

BERTIE BADGER

1989-2002

In 1987 the St. John Ambulance Brigade formed a section for children aged five to ten years, they are known as "Badgers" because of the black and white uniform. "Bertie Badger" was produced in a limited edition of 5,000 as a promotional item for the British St. John Ambulance Brigade in late 1989. It was given as a reward to child members of the brigade after they completed three years of service and training. Those models that are unmarked were produced from 1989 to 1994; those embossed with the Wade mark were produce from 1994 to 2001.

For the *Bertie Badge Money Box* see Wade Collectables, 4th edition.

Backstamp: Embossed "Wade"

Date	Name	Description	Issue	Price	Size	U.S. $	Can. $	U.K. £
1989	Bertie Badger	Black/white; white coveralls	5,000	—	100	130.	145.	75.

SALADA TEA CANADA

WHIMSEY-ON-WHY

1984

Six models from the *Whimsey-on-Why* sets 1, 2 and 3 were introduced as a short promotional offer by Salada Tea Canada between September and December 1984.

Backstamp: Embossed "Wade England"

No.	Name	Description	Size	U.S. $	Can. $	U.K. £
1	Pump Cottage	Brown thatch; white walls; yellow doors	28 x 39	17.	20.	10.
2	Tobacconist's Shop	Brown roof; red doors	33 x 39	17.	20.	10.
3	The Greengrocer's Shop	Grey roof; green windows, doors	35 x 35	17.	20.	10.
4	The Antique Shop	Purple-brown roof; blue/yellow windows	35 x 37	17.	20.	10.
5	The Post Office	Beige roof; yellow/blue windows	40 x 38	17.	20.	10.
6	Whimsey Station	Red-brown; brown roof	35 x 39	17.	20.	10.

SHARPS CHOCOLATE

HONEY-BROWN SMILING RABBIT

1970

The *Honey Brown Smiling Rabbit* was produced in 1970 as a premium with Sharps Chocolate Easter eggs. The box was shaped like a hollow log, and the rabbit was fixed beside an egg containing milk chocolate buttons. The original price was 7/9d.

Backstamp: Unmarked

No.	Name	Description	Size	U.S. $	Can. $	U.K. £
1a	Honey-brown Smiling Rabbit	Honey-brown; large dark brown eyes	65 x 43	40.	45.	25.
1b	Honey-brown Smiling Rabbit	Honey-brown; small brown eyes	65 x 43	40.	45.	25.

HONEY-BROWN BO-PEEP

1971

The following year Wade produced the *Honey Brown Bo-Peep*, also as a premium with Sharps Chocolate Easter eggs. The model was fixed beside an egg containing milk chocolate buttons, and was packaged in a box decorated with a design of sheep and trees. The original price was 8/-.

Backstamp: Embossed "Wade England"

No.	Name	Description	Size	U.S. $	Can. $	U.K. £
1a	Honey-brown Bo-Peep	Honey-brown	70 x 28	28.	30.	16.
1b	Honey-brown Bo-Peep	Honey-brown; dark blue hair, apron, flowers	70 x 28	28.	30.	16.

SIMONS ASSOCIATES, INC.

CIRCA 1975

Some time in the mid 1970s, Wade exported a set of 24 *English Whimsies* to Simons Associates, Inc., of Los Angeles, California. The models were packaged in a plastic bubble on a blue card. The front of the card has a colourful design of a tree, smiling sun, baby birds in a nest, butterfly, snail and toadstools. Also printed there is "Whimsies Miniatures Collection Solid English Porcelain," and each package is numbered in the top left corner. On the back is printed: "Collect all these Whimsies miniatures / little creatures from the farm, forest and jungle of solid porcelain," and on the top right hand corner, "Whimsies Wade of England Est. 1810," along with the Union Jack and the American flag.

The values are given for models intact on their cards as they are indistinguishable from Red Rose Tea or English Whimsies models outside the packet. Note that these models were not given the same issue numbers as *English Whimsies*, although they are identical to the originals.

Backstamp: **A.** Embossed "Wade England" (1-3, 5-8)
B. Embossed "Wade England" in a recessed base (4)

No.	Name	Description	Size	U.S. $	Can. $	U.K. £
1	Rabbit, open ears	Beige	30 x 30	7.	8.	4.
2	Fawn	Brown; blue ears	30 x 30	7.	8.	4.
3	Mongrel	Dark brown/light brown front	35 x 35	7.	8.	4.
4	Squirrel	Grey; beige; yellow acorn	35 x 30	7.	8.	4.
5	Elephant	Grey; with or without black eyes	55 x 50	7.	8.	4.
6	Setter	Brown; grey-green base	35 x 50	7.	8.	4.
7	Cat	Beige	40 x 17	7.	8.	4.
8	Collie	Brown; grey-green base	35 x 35	7.	8.	4.

Note: The above pricing table is listed in photograph order from lower left to upper right.

Backstamp:
- **A.** Embossed "Wade England" (9-11, 14-16)
- **B.** Embossed "Wade England" in a recessed base (12, 13)
- **C.** Embossed "Wade" between front feet and "England" on back of model (10)

No.	Name	Description	Size	U.S. $	Can. $	U.K. £
9	Zebra	Light brown; green base	40 x 35	8.	9.	5.
10	Bear Cub	Grey; beige face	30 x 40	5.	6.	3.
11	Field Mouse	Honey; yellow corn; green on base	35 x 25	12.	13	7.
12	Owl	Dark brown; light brown chest, face	35 x 20	7.	8.	4.
13	Kitten, seated	Dark/light brown; pink or red wool	30 x 30	7.	8.	4.
14	Chimpanzee	Dark brown; light brown face, patches	35 x 35	7.	8.	4.
15	Horse	Dark grey; green base	35 x 35	20.	22.	12.
16	Duck	Blue/brown; yellow beak	30 x 40	10.	12.	6.

Backstamp:
- **A.** Embossed "Wade England" (17-23)
- **B.** Embossed "Wade England" in a recessed base (24)

No.	Name	Description	Size	U.S. $	Can. $	U.K. £
17	Spaniel	Honey; green on base	35 x 35	7.	8.	4.
18	Giraffe	Beige	35 x 35	7.	8.	4.
19	Lion	Light brown; dark brown head, mane	35 x 45	7.	8.	4.
20	German Shepherd	Grey; tan face (formerly Alsatian)	30 x 40	7.	8.	4.
21	Lamb	Light beige; green base	30 x 25	7.	8.	4.
22	Pine Marten	Honey brown	30 x 30	7.	8.	4.
23	Corgi	Honey; black nose	30 x 35	7.	8.	4.
24	Hedgehog, Type 2	Dark brown; light brown face	23 x 40	7.	8.	4.

Note: The above pricing tables are listed in photograph order from lower left to upper right.

SPILLERS DOG FOODS LTD.

RETRIEVER

1991

Commissioned by Spillers Dog Foods, this model could be obtained by sending in a certain number of tokens from packets of the dog food.

Backstamp: Embossed "Wade England"

Datae	Name	Description	Size	U.S. $	Can. $	U.K. £
1991	Retriever	Honey; green base	26 x 53	25.	27.	15.

STAFFORDSHIRE HOUSE GIFTS

FIRST WHIMSIES ENGLISH ANIMALS

SET TWO

CIRCA 1954-1958

These models were produced for "Staffordshire House" and were sold in a gift shop in Niagara Falls, Ontario, Canada. Each model is marked with a black, hand written "Made in England" on the base and has "Niagara Falls Canada" on the body of the model. The box for this set is different from the normal Whimsies boxed sets issued, the box has "Whimsies Porcelain Miniatures" on the front with a picture of "Dora the Donkey Soprano" from the *Drum Box* set. The inside of the box is a plain buff brown with silver lettering "Whimsies Porcelain Miniatures by Wade of England" there is also a black and gold label, which reads "A Staffordshire House Gift."

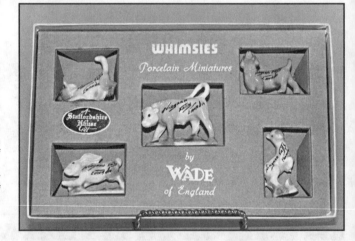

Backstamp: Black ink hand written "Made in England with Niagara Falls Canada"

No.	Name	Description	Size	U.S. $	Can. $	U.K. £
1	Bull	White with brown markings; green base; black lettering	45 x 55	95.	105.	55.
2	Dachshund	Beige; black lettering	35 x 45	110.	120.	65.
3	Hare	White with grey markings; green base; black lettering	30 x 45	50.	55.	28.
4	Kitten	White with grey markings; blue bow; black lettering	30 x 40	110.	120.	65.
5	Lamb	White with brown markings; green base; black lettering	42 x 25	70.	80.	40.
—	5 pce set	Boxed	—	475.	525.	275.

THOMAS WAIDE & SONS LTD

1978

The Wade English Whimsies Horse (#29) was used in this packaging to mark the centenary of Thomas Waide & Sons Limited (1878-1978), printers and carton manufacturers, of Kirkstall Hill, Lees, U.K. The price given is for the model in the package.

Backstamp: Embossed "Wade England"

Front

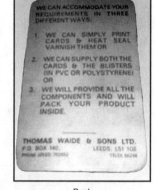

Back

Date	Name	Description	Size	U.S. $	Can. $	U.K. £
1978	Horse in Packet	Dark grey; green/beige base	38 x 30	35.	40.	20.

TOM SMITH AND COMPANY LTD.

1973-1999

The world famous Christmas cracker manufacturer, Tom Smith and Company Ltd., collaborated with George Wade and Son Ltd. over a number of years to produce a series of miniature animals exclusively for the Christmas and party cracker market. Each series of animals was used exclusively by Tom Smith for two years, after which time the design rights reverted back to Wade, then they could be reused for other premiums or included in the *English Whimsies* series. In August 1998 Tom Smith Crackers was sold to Napier Industries of Rickmansworth, Herts., UK and the factory closed in 1999.

The first models issued for Tom Smith and Company were eight figures previously used in the 1967-1973 Red Rose Tea Canada series. Next came a set of ten *Safari Park* models. All but two of the models —the "Lion" and the "Musk Ox"— were from either Red Rose Tea Canada or the *English Whimsies* series. The Polar Bear and Koala differ in colour from the *English Whimsies* models. Each is marked with "Wade England" embossed on the rim of the base.

Only the five models in the *Safari Park* series Nos 2, 3, 4, 5, and 7 can be distinguished from those in the *English Whimsies* series; therefore, they have a higher collectors value. All models are listed in alphabetical order for ease of reference.

ANIMATE CRACKERS

1973-1975

Although a blue terrapin is illustrated on the outer box of the Tom Smith Animate Crackers, this colourway has not been seen.

Backstamp: Embossed "Wade England" on the rim or in a recessed base

No.	Name	Description	Size	U.S. $	Can. $	U.K. £
1	Alsatian	Dark grey/honey	30 x 40	3.	4.	2.
2	Bluebird (recessed)	Light brown; blue wings	15 x 35	8.	9.	5.
3	Bullfrog (recessed)	Light green	15 x 30	14.	16.	8.
4	Butterfly (recessed)	Honey; grey tips; raised circles	10 x 45	10.	12.	6.
5	Fantail Goldfish	Light green/yellow; blue base	30 x 35	8.	9.	5.
6	Pine Marten	Honey	30 x 30	3.	4.	2.
7	Terrapin (recessed)	Dark greenish-grey	10 x 40	10.	12.	6.
8	Wild Boar	Beige; green base	30 x 40	3.	4.	2.

BIRDLIFE SERIES

1992-1993

All the models in the *Birdlife* series, except for the "Wren," had been previously issued, either as *English Whimsies*, as other Tom Smith cracker models or as *Whimsie-land* figures. The "Eagle" and the "Goose" were former Tom Smith models, but this time were produced in different coloured glazes than the originals.

Backstamp: Embossed "Wade England"

No.	Name	Description	Size	U.S. $	Can. $	U.K. £
1	Barn Owl (EW)	Grey-blue	35 x 25	14.	16.	8.
2	Cockerel (WL)	Green	50 x 35	14.	16.	8.
3	Duck (WL)	White	45 x 35	14.	16.	8.
4	Goose (RRT/TS)	Honey	35 x 40	14.	16.	8.
5	Eagle (TS *Survival*)	Beige	35 x 23	14.	16.	8.
6	Partridge (WL)	Beige	35 x 35	14.	16.	8.
7	Pelican (EW)	Brown	45 x 40	14.	16.	8.
8	Wren	Beige	33 x 24	14.	16.	8.

Note: The following initials indicate the origin of the models:
    EW: *English Whimsies*
    RRT: Red Rose Tea Canada *Miniature Nurseries*
    TS: Tom Smith
    WL: *Whimsie-land*

BRITISH WILDLIFE

1980-1981

Backstamp: Embossed "Wade England"

No.	Name	Description	Size	U.S. $	Can. $	U.K. £
1	Badger	Dark grey	25 x 40	8.	9.	5.
2	Dormouse	Honey; green base	30 x 35	8.	9.	5.
3	Fox	Brown	35 x 40	8.	9.	5.
4	Hare	Honey	50 x 30	8.	9.	5.
5	Mole	Dark grey	25 x 40	8.	9.	5.
6	Partridge	Beige; green base	30 x 20	8.	9.	5.
7	Squirrel	Red-brown	40 x 40	8.	9.	5.
8	Weasel	Beige; green base	35 x 40	8.	9.	5.

CAT COLLECTION
1996-1997

Eight of these cats are reissued from *English Whimsies*, the *Whimsie-land Series* and from Red Rose Tea's *Miniature Nurseries*. Some are in new colours, but others are similar to the Red Rose Tea U.S.A. issues. Two new cat models — one stalking and the other standing — were produced for this series. Although there are only eight crackers in a box, there are ten models in the set.

Collectors in the U.K. have reported a colour variation in two of the Tom Smith cat models: "Cat and the Fiddle" in a grey colourway, and "Puss in Boots" in a dark grey colourway.

Backstamp: Embossed "Wade England"

No.	Name	Description	Size	U.S. $	Can. $	U.K. £
1	Cat (EW)	Light brown/beige	40 x 17	8.	9.	5.
2a	Cat and the Fiddle (RR)	Dark brown	46 x 33	8.	9.	5.
2b	Cat and the Fiddle (RR)	Light grey	46 x 33	8.	9.	5.
3	Cat, stalking	Apricot	23 x 43	8.	9.	5.
4	Cat, standing	Light brown	35 x 34	8.	9.	5.
5a	Kitten, lying (WL)	Dark blue	20 x 42	8.	9.	5.
5b	Kitten, lying (WL)	Pale blue	20 x 42	8.	9.	5.
6	Kitten, seated (EW)	Apricot	30 x 30	8.	9.	5.
7	Leopard (EW)	Honey	17 x 45	8.	9.	5.
8	Lion, standing (EW)	Honey	35 x 45	8.	9.	5.
9a	Puss in Boots (RR)	Light grey	45 x 20	8.	9.	5.
9b	Puss in Boots (RR)	Dark grey	45 x 20	8.	9.	5.
10	Tiger (EW)	Honey	35 x 25	8.	9.	5.

Note: The initials after the model indicates its origin.
EW: *English Whimsies*
RR: Red Rose *Miniature Nurseries*
WL: *Whimsie-land Series*

CHRISTMAS TIME CRACKERS

BEAR AMBITIONS

1996-1997

Tom Smith used the *Bear Ambitions* set, which was originally produced as a Wade giftware line, in its Christmas crackers. Four of the models are glazed in different colours from the originals, which were all honey brown. See also Bear Ambitions page 102 and Ripley Village Fete and Teddy Bears' Picninc page 154.

Backstamp: **A.** Embossed "Wade England" (3)
　　　　　　　B. Embossed "Wade Eng" (1, 2, 4, 5, 6)

No.	Name	Description	Size	U.S. $	Can. $	U.K. £
1	Admiral Sam	Dark brown	50	8.	9.	5.
2	Alex the Aviator	Light brown	45	8.	9.	5.
3	Artistic Edward	Light brown	40	8.	9.	5.
4	Beatrice Ballerina	Honey	50	8.	9.	5.
5	Locomotive Joe	Dark brown	50	8.	9.	5.
6	Musical Marco	Honey	45	8.	9.	5.

CIRCUS ANIMATES CRACKERS
1978-1979

These ten models were set on drum bases, which are marked on their rims. These figures were reissued for Red Rose Tea U.S.A., with only a very slight variation in colour on some models. The "Lion," "Pony" and "Tiger," Type 1 are in the same glaze colour and are particularly hard to differentiate.

During the Red Rose Tea promotion a new mould was produced which resulted in two variations of the Tiger. Type 1 has a larger mouth; Type 2 has a smaller mouth, and added detail to the throat and chest resulting in a 'beard' effect. For Type 2 see Redco Foods U.S.A..

Backstamp: Embossed "Wade England" on front and back rims

Circus Animates Crackers Box (1978-79)

No.	Name	Description	Size	U.S. $	Can. $	U.K. £
1	Brown Bear	Red-brown	35 x 32	8.	9.	5.
2	Chimpanzee Boy	Beige; blue teapot	43 x 18	8.	9.	5.
3	Chimpanzee Girl	Beige; blue skirt	40 x 18	8.	9.	5.
4	Elephant, Seated	Blue	30 x 30	8.	9.	5.
5	Elephant, standing	Blue	30 x 30	8.	9.	5.
6	Lion	Honey brown	37 x 22	8.	9.	5.
7	Pony	Beige	43 x 20	8.	9.	5.
8	Poodle	White; blue skirt	43 x 17	8.	9.	5.
9	Sea Lion	Dark grey	43 x 30	8.	9.	5.
10	Tiger, Type 1	Honey brown	42 x 20	8.	9.	5.

ELEPHANT AND PIG

c.1975

The elephant has a hole in the end of the trunk and the pig has a hole in the rump; these were intended holders for miniature sparkler fireworks.

Elephant

Pig

Backstamp: Unmarked

No.	Name	Description	Size	U.S. $	Can. $	U.K. £
1	Elephant	Charcoal grey (biscuit glaze)	27 x 35	50	55.	30.
2	Pig	White (gloss)	25 x 50	50.	55.	30.

FAMILY PETS

1988-1989

Backstamp: Embossed "Wade England"

No.	Name	Description	Size	U.S. $	Can. $	U.K. £
1	Cockatoo	Green	35 x 30	5.	6.	3.
2	Guinea Pig	Honey brown	20 x 30	15.	16.	9.
3	Mouse, sleeping	White	15 x 25	18.	20.	10.
4	Persian Kitten	Blue	25 x 33	5.	6.	3.
5	Rabbit	Brown	30 x 25	5.	6.	3.
6	Shetland Pony	Beige	25 x 30	5.	6.	3.
7	Spaniel Puppy	Honey	25 x 30	5.	6.	3.
8	Tropical Fish	Green	20 x 30	18.	20.	10.

FARMYARD ANIMALS

1982-1983

The "Goose" was previously used in the 1971-1979 Red Rose *Miniature Nurseries* series (the earlier model has a pink beak.)

Backstamp: Embossed "Wade England"

No.	Name	Description	Size	U.S. $	Can. $	U.K. £
1	Bull	Dark brown	30 x 50	8.	9.	5.
2	Collie	Honey; brown base	25 x 50	8.	9.	5.
3	Cow	Orange-brown	30 x 40	8.	9.	5.
4	Duck, swimming	White; blue base	25 x 30	8.	9.	5.
5a	Goat	Beige	40 x 40	8.	9.	5.
5b	Goat	White; green base	40 x 40	8.	9.	5.
6	Goose	Honey/brown; brown beak	35 x 40	8.	9.	5.
7	Horse, cropped mane	Brown; green base	40 x 30	8.	9.	5.
8	Pig	Pale pink	25 x 40	8.	9.	5.

HEDGEROW and SEALIFE PARTY TIME CRACKERS

1998

There were two new Tom Smith Party Cracker Animal series produced for 1998-1999, *Hedgerow* and *Sealife*. Each set contained eight models, but the Tom Smith boxes contained only six crackers, which meant collectors would have to buy more than one box of crackers to complete a full set.

All the models had been used in previous promotions (some as many as four times). The models were produced in new all-over one-colour glazes except for the "Mole" and the "Badger," which are lighter colours than the originals. These two sets were the last models produced for Tom Smith Crackers. The Tom Smith Company closed its doors for the last time in 1999.

Hedgerow

Sealife

Backstamp: Embossed "Wade England"

HEDGEROW - 1998

Although all the hedgerow animals are all previously issued models, they are all in new colours.

No.	Name	Description	Size	U.S. $	Can. $	U.K. £
1	Badger (TS)	Pale grey	25 x 40	7.	8.	4.
2	Butterfly (RRC)	Blue	10 x 45	12.	13.	7.
3	Hare (TS)	Light brown	50 x 30	5.	6.	3.
4	Mole (TS)	Pale grey	25 x 40	5.	6.	3.
5	Mouse (EW)	Apricot	40 x 25	8.	9.	5.
6	Otter (RRC)	Dark brown	30 x 35	7.	8.	4.
7	Rabbit (RRC)	Honey	30 x 30	8.	9.	5.
8	Squirrel (RRC)	Apricot	35 x 30	7.	8.	4.

SEALIFE - 1998

The "Whale" in this series is a brighter blue than the original 1984 "Survival Whale." For the honey colourway Whelk/Water Snail see King Aquarium, page 279.

No.	Name	Description	Size	U.S. $	Can. $	U.K. £
1	Angel Fish (EW)	Light green	35 x 40	7.	8.	4.
2	Dolphin (EW)	Light grey	30 X 40	7.	8.	4.
3	Seahorse (EW)	Apricot	50 x 17	7.	8.	4.
4	Seal on Rock (RRC)	Dark brown	35 x 35	7.	8.	4.
5	Turtle (EW)	Light green	15 x 50	7.	8.	4.
6	Walrus (EW)	Honey	30 X 30	7.	8.	4.
7	Whale (Baleen TS)	Bright blue	22 x 52	9.	10.	6.
8	Whelk (Water Snail KA)	Bright blue	30 X 35	9.	10.	6.

MISCELLANEOUS MODELS
1987-1996

Wade re-coloured surplus models from the *English Whimsies*, Red Rose Tea Whimsies, Whimsie-lands and former Tom Smith Crackers for the Tom Smith Group, who included them with other small gifts in their Bric-a-Brac, Catering, De Luxe, Luxury, Gallerie Noel, Table Decoration and Victorian Crackers. Only one or two models were used in each box of crackers and there is no reference to Wade on the outer box. Tom Smith do not keep records of these odd Wade models, and the only way to find them is to look closely at Tom Smith advertising leaflets and packaging where they can be seen amongst plastic toys and paper hats.

1987 ISSUE

Backstamp: Embossed "Wade England"

No.	Name	Description	Size	U.S. $	Can. $	U.K. £
1	Gorilla, seated (TSS)	Dark brown	40 x 40	5.	6.	3.
2	Hare (TSB)	Beige	50 x 30	5.	6.	3.
3	Hickory Dickory Dock (RRC)	Beige	44 x 20	5.	6.	3.
4	Humpty Dumpty (RRC)	Brown	36 x 23	5.	6.	3.
5	Little Bo-Peep (RRC)	Brown	44 x 24	12.	13.	7.
6	Old King Cole (RRC)	Blue	37 x 32	18.	20.	10.
7	Old Woman Who Lived in a Shoe (RRC)	Blue	35 x 40	18.	20.	10.
8	Wee Willie Winkie (RRC)	Blue	44 x 24	18.	20.	10.

Note: The following initials indicate the origin of the figures:
> EW: *English Whimsies*
> RR: Red Rose
> RRC: Red Rose Canada
> RRU: Red Rose U.S.A.
> TSB: Tom Smith *British Wildlife* set
> TSD: Tom Smith *Dogs* set
> TSS: Tom Smith *Survival* set

1989 ISSUE

Backstamp: Embossed "Wade England"

No.	Name	Description	Size	U.S. $	Can. $	U.K. £
1	Hickory Dickory Dock (RR, RRC)	Honey/dark brown	44 x 20	7.	8.	4.
2	Kangaroo (EW, RRU)	Honey brown	45 x 25	7.	8.	4.
3	Koala (EW)	Beige	35 x 25	7.	8.	4.
4	Little Bo-Peep (RR)	Brown; blue apron	44 x 24	5.	6.	3.
5	Wee Willie Winkie (RR)	Beige; yellow hair	44 x 24	9.	10.	6.

1990 ISSUE

Backstamp: Embossed "Wade England"

No.	Name	Description	Size	U.S. $	Can. $	U.K. £
1	Hare (TSB)	Dark brown	50 x 30	8.	9.	5.
2	Old King Cole (RR)	Brown; blue hat	37 x 32	9.	10.	6.
3	Squirrel (TSB)	Blue	40 x 40	8.	9.	5.

1991 ISSUE

Backstamp: Embossed "Wade England"

No.	Name	Description	Size	U.S. $	Can. $	U.K. £
1	Koala (EW)	Honey brown	35 x 25	10.	12.	6.
2	Poodle (RR/TSD)	Dark orange/apricot	40 x 45	10.	12.	6.

1992 ISSUE

Backstamp: Embossed "Wade England"

No.	Name	Description	Size	U.S. $	Can. $	U.K. £
1	Bluebird (RR/EW)	Blue	15 x 35	20.	22.	12.
2	Bulldog (TSD)	Beige	35 x 35	8.	9.	5.
3	Mongrel (RR/EW)	Blue	35 x 35	8.	9.	5.

1996 ISSUE

Three *English Whimsies* models were used in assorted Tom Smith crackers. The "Duck" can be found in Tom Smith Catering, De Luxe and Luxury crackers, the "Camel" was used in the Gallerie Noel crackers, and the "Fieldmouse" was in Catering, De Luxe, Luxury and Table Decoration crackers.

Photograph not available
at press time

Backstamp: Unknown

No.	Name	Description	Size	U.S. $	Can. $	U.K. £
1	Camel (EW)	Light brown	35 x 35	5.	6.	3.
2	Duck (EW)	Green	30 x 40	18.	20.	10.
3	Duck, swimming (TS)	Beige	25 x 30	9.	10.	6.
4	Field Mouse (EW)	Honey; yellow corn	35 x 25	8.	9.	5.
5	Horse, cropped mane (TS)	Beige	40 x 30	9.	10.	6.

NURSERY RHYME CRACKERS

Circa Mid-1980s

At some time in the mid-1980s, Tom Smith issued a box of "Nursery Rhyme" crackers. The box contained a set of six miniature nursery rhymes, the same models used in the Red Rose Tea Canada promotion of 1972-1979.

Backstamp: Embossed "Wade England" on rim

No.	Name	Description	Size	U.S. $	Can. $	U.K. £
1	Hickory Dickory	Red brown/honey brown	44 x 20	8.	9.	5.
2	Humpty Dumpty	Honey; blue bow tie; brown wall	36 x 23	8.	9.	5.
3	Little Bo-Peep	Beige; blue apron; green base	44 x 24	8.	9.	5.
4	Old King Cole, Type 1	Gap; brown; blue hat, cloak	37 x 32	8.	9.	5.
5	Old Woman Who Lived ina Shoe	Honey; red-brown roof	35 x 40	8.	9.	5.
6	Wee Willie Winkie	Yellow hair; beige nightshirt	44 x 24	8.	9.	5.

SAFARI PARK

1976-1977

Backstamp: Embossed "Wade England"

No.	Name	Description	Size	U.S. $	Can. $	U.K. £
1	Kangaroo	Dark brown; light brown base	45 x 25	18.	20.	10.
2	Koala	Black; brown stump	35 x 25	20.	22.	12.
3	Langur, Type 1	Light brown; dark brown stump	35 x 30	5.	6.	3.
4a	Lion, lying	Honey brown	30 x 45	15.	16.	9.
4b	Lion, lying	Honey brown; green base	30 x 45	15.	16.	9.
5	Musk Ox	Grey; brown horns	27 x 30	20.	22.	12.
6	Orang-outan	Ginger	30 x 30	5.	6.	3.
7	Polar Bear	Brown; black nose; grey/blue base	30 x 30	15.	16.	9.
8	Raccoon	Brown; grey-green base	25 x 35	12.	13.	7.
9	Tiger	Honey; green on base	35 x 25	12.	13.	7.
10	Walrus	Brown; grey-base	30 x 30	8.	9.	5.

SNOWLIFE ANIMALS

1992-1994

All the models in this set, except the "Reindeer," had been previously issued as *English Whimsies*, Tom Smith cracker figures or in the *Whimsie-land* series. The models are produced in a different all-over, one-colour glaze from the originals. Due to a new mould being made, two types of Reindeer exist: Type 1 has a gap between the legs; Type 2 has no gap between the legs.

Reindeer Type 1
Gap between legs

Reindeer, Type 2
No gap between legs

Backstamp: **A.** Embossed "Wade Eng" (4a, 4b)
B. Embossed "Wade England" (1-3, 5-10)

No.	Name	Description	Size	U.S. $	Can. $	U.K. £
1	Fox (WL)	Red-brown	35 x 35	18.	20.	10.
2	Penguin (EW)	Grey-blue	45 x 17	12.	13.	7.
3	Polar Bear, head forward (EW)	White	27 x 45	12.	13.	7.
4a	Reindeer, Type 1 (TS)	Gap between legs; beige	30 x 35	15.	16.	9.
4b	Reindeer, Type 2 (TS)	No gap; beige	30 x 35	15.	16.	9.
5	Seal Pup (EW)	Grey	17 x 30	15.	16.	9.
6	Snow Goose (RR)	White	33 x 37	15.	16.	9.
7	Snowshoe Hare (TS "Hare")	White	50 x 30	15.	16.	9.
8	Snowy Owl (WL "Owl")	White	35 x 25	15.	16.	9.
9	Walrus (EW)	Beige	30 x 30	15.	16.	9.
10	Whale (Baleen TS)	Grey	22 x 52	15.	16.	9.

Note: The following initials indicate the origin of the models:
  EW: *English Whimsies*
  RR: Red Rose
  TS: Tom Smith
  WL: *Whimsie-land*

SURVIVAL ANIMALS

1984-1985

From 1984 onwards, all Tom Smith crackers models were produced in a one-colour glaze. The "Sea Lion" was previously used as the "Seal on Rock" in the 1967-1973 Red Rose *Miniature Animals* series; the earlier model is brown on a blue base. The "Bison" had been number 51 of the *English Whimsies* series, where it is honey brown and dark brown.

Backstamp: Embossed "Wade England"

No.	Name	Description	Size	U.S. $	Can. $	U.K. £
1	Armadillo (TS)	Dark grey	25 x 45	8.	9.	5.
2	Bison (RRC, EW)	Dark brown	28 x 40	8.	9.	5.
3	Eagle (TS)	Honey	35 x 23	8.	9.	5.
4	Gorilla, seated (TS)	Brown	40 x 40	8.	9.	5.
5	Polar Bear (TS)	White	27 x 45	8.	9.	5.
6	Sea Lion (RRC)	Blue	38 x 30	8.	9.	5.
7	Sea Turtle (TS)	Green-grey	25 x 45	8.	9.	5.
8	Whale (Baleen) (TS)	Blue	25 x 50	8.	9.	5.

Note: The following initials indicate the origin of the models.
        EW: *English Whimsies*
        RRC: Red Rose Canada
        TS: Tom Smith

TALES FROM THE NURSERY
1994-1996

Some of the models from the Red Rose Tea *Miniature Nurseries* were reissued for this set. Two new figures were added in 1994, "Ride a Cock Horse" and a newly modeled "Little Boy Blue." All the models are in an all-over, one-colour glaze. Although there are ten models in this set, the box contains only eight crackers, making some models more difficult to find than others.

Backstamp: Embossed "Wade England"

No.	Name	Description	Size	U.S. $	Can. $	U.K. £
1	Cat and the Fiddle	Light grey	47 x 33	5.	6.	3.
2	Dr. Foster	Dark brown	43 x 26	5.	6.	3.
3	Hickory Dickory Dock	Light brown	44 x 20	5.	6.	3.
4	Humpty Dumpty	Pale blue	36 x 23	5.	6.	3.
5	Little Bo-Peep	Wine	44 x 24	5.	6.	3.
6	Little Boy Blue	Blue	41 x 25	5.	6.	3.
7	Little Jack Horner	Honey	37 x 21	5.	6.	3.
8	Queen of Hearts	Apricot	42 x 25	5.	6.	3.
9	Ride a Cock Horse	Green	45 x 35	5.	6.	3.
10	Tom Tom the Piper's Son	Honey	39 x 33	5.	6.	3.

VILLAGE OF BROADLANDS

1988

Due to high production costs, only five of these models were produced for Tom Smith and Company. A further set of five figures was planned, but never issued.

They come from the same moulds as the following *Whimsey-on-Why* models, but are in different colours:

Whimsey-on-Why Models became	Village of Broadlands Models
Whimsy School	The Chapel
Whimsey Station	The Coach House Garage
Pump Cottage	The Thatched Cottage
The Sweet Shop	The Pink House
The Greengrocers Shop	The Village Store

Backstamp: Embossed "Wade England"

No.	Name	Description	Size	U.S. $	Can. $	U.K. £
1	The Chapel	Grey; green roof; brown door	38 x 51	60.	65.	35.
2	The Coach House Garage	White; grey roof; black beams	35 x 39	60.	65.	35.
3	The Pink House	Pink; grey roof	40 x 40	70.	75.	40.
4	The Thatched Cottage	White; brown roof	28 x 39	60.	65.	35.
5	The Village Store	Brown; brown roof	35 x 35	60.	65.	35.

WILDLIFE
1986-1987

These models are reissued *English Whimsies* in all-over, one-colour glazes. Listed below are all the models that have been found in this series, although a number of British collectors have reported finding different figures in their crackers than were illustrated on the outer box (models 9 through 15). It is believed that surplus models from previous Red Rose Tea and Tom Smith promotions were used to fill the orders in time for Christmas sales.

Backstamp: Embossed "Wade England"

No.	Name	Description	Size	U.S. $	Can. $	U.K. £
1	Dolphin (EW)	Dark blue	30 x 40	12.	13.	7.
2	Kangaroo (EW)	Beige	45 x 25	8.	9.	5.
3	Koala (EW)	Honey	35 x 25	12.	13.	7.
4	Leopard (EW)	Honey	17 x 45	3.	4.	2.
5	Orang-outan (EW)	Dark brown	30 x 30	3.	4.	2.
6	Penguin (EW)	White	45 x 17	12.	13.	7.
7	Rhino (EW)	Grey	25 x 35	5.	6.	3.
8	Wild Boar (RR/EW)	Beige	30 x 40	8.	9.	5.

No.	Name	Description	Size	U.S. $	Can. $	U.K. £
9	Bison (RR/EW)	Brown	30 x 40	8.	9.	5.
10	Collie (TSF)	Dark brown	25 x 50	14.	15.	8.
11	Duck, swimming (TSF)	Dark blue	25 x 30	14.	15.	8.
12a	Goat (TSF)	Beige	40 x 40	14.	15.	8.
12b	Goat (TSF)	White; green base	40 x 40	8.	9.	5.
13	Hare (TSB)	Brown	50 x 30	8.	9.	5.
14	Squirrel (TSB)	Dark brown	40 x 40	8.	9.	5.
15	Zebra (EW)	Blue-grey	40 x 35	3.	4.	2.

Note: The following initials indicate the origin of the models:
EW: *English Whimsies*; RR: *Red Rose Canada*; TSB: Tom Smith *British Wildlife* set; TSF: Tom Smith *Farmyard* set

WORLD OF DOGS

1990-1991

Only two of these figures were new issues. The others were reissued *English Whimsies* and the first issue of Red Rose Tea Canada models in a new all-over, one-colour glaze.

Backstamp: Embossed "Wade England"

No.	Name	Description	Size	U.S. $	Can. $	U.K. £
1	Alsatian (RR/EW)	Dark brown	30 x 40	14.	15.	8.
2	Bulldog	Beige	35 x 35	10.	11.	6.
3	Corgi (RR/EW)	Honey	30 x 35	7.	8.	4.
4	Husky (EW)	White	35 x 30	10.	11.	6.
5	Mongrel (RR/EW)	Blue-grey	35 x 35	10.	11.	6.
6	Poodle (RR)	Apricot	40 x 45	12.	13.	7.
7	Spaniel (RR/EW)	Black	35 x 35	10.	11.	6.
8	West Highland Terrier	White	30 x 30	10.	11.	6.

Note: The following initials indicate the origin of the models:
　　　　EW: *English Whimsies*
　　　　RRT: Red Rose Tea Canada *Miniature Nurseries* 1989 ISSUE

TRAUFLER
1992

A slip-cast Sheep in two colours and sizes and the Cockerel Salt Pot and the Hen Pepper Pot were produced by Wade for Traufler, a tableware manufacturer, to compliment its imported table wares, which featured sheep, shepherds and farmyard scenes. These models were also produced by another manufacturer and are also unmarked. Those figures not made by Wade have darker faces, more eyelashes and ears that are closer to their faces.

SHEEP

Backstamp: Unmarked

No.	Name	Description	Size	U.S. $	Can. $	U.K. £
1a	Sheep, large	Cream; pink face	85 x 145	30.	35.	17.
1b	Sheep, large	Black	85 x 145	30.	35.	17.
2a	Sheep, small	Cream; pink face	65 x 45	20.	22.	12.
2b	Sheep, small	Black	65 x 45	20.	22.	12.

COCKEREL SALT POT AND HEN PEPPER POT

Backstamp: Unmarked

No.	Name	Description	Size	U.S. $	Can. $	U.K. £
1a	Cockerel Salt	White; red/black markings	110 x 55	20.	22.	12.
1b	Cockerel Salt	Yellow; pink comb; black markings	110 x 55	20.	22.	12.
2a	Hen Pepper	White; red/black markings	90 x 70	20.	22.	12.
2b	Hen Pepper	Yellow; pink comb; black markings	90 x 70	20.	22.	12.

21ST CENTURY COLLECTABLES

MICHELIN MAN
2005-2007

Backstamp: Unknown

Date	Name	Description	Issue	Price	Size	U.S. $	Can. $	U.K. £
2005	Bibendum Cowboy	White; black waistcoat; brown boots	750	£48	112	90.	100.	50.
2005	Bibendum Indian	White; red, blue, black tipped feathers	750	£48	112	90.	100.	50.
2006	Bibendum Santa	White; red, white Santa suit; black boots	750	£52	112	90.	100.	50.
2006	Bibendum Sailor	White; blue hat; orange life jacket	750	£52	112	90.	100.	50.
2007	Bibendum Rugby	White; yellow, blue jersey; black shorts	750	£55	112	90.	100.	50.

21ST CENTURY KEEPSAKES

MEMORIES COLLECTION

1998-1999

These models were based on string puppets in two 1950s BBC children's television programs; *Andy Pandy* and *Bill and Ben the Flowerpot Men*.

Andy Pandy (left) Looby Loo and Ted (right)

Bill and Ben and Little Weed

Backstamp: **A.** Printed "Limited Edition 1500 Wade England" with name of model and "21ST Century" logo (1, 2)
B. Printed "Bill & Ben Little Weed Limited Edition of 500 With Gold Edged Petals Wade England" with "21ST Century" logo (3)

Date	Name	Description	Issue	Price	Size	U.S. $	Can. $	U.K. £
1998	Andy Pandy	Blue/white striped suit	1,500	£39	123	70.	75.	40.
1999	Looby Loo and Ted	Ted: Brown; red bow; Looby Loo: White blouse; blue skirt	1,500	£39	100	70.	75.	40.
1999	Bill and Ben / Little Weed	Bill/Ben: Red-brown flowerpots; Weed: Yellow	1,500	£39	115	70.	75.	40.
1999	Bill and Ben / Little Weed	Bill/Ben: Red-brown flowerpots; Weed: Yellow, gold edged petal	500	£39	115	70.	75.	40.

UK INTERNATIONAL CERAMICS LTD.
1996-2001

THE CATKINS COLLECTION
1999-2001

The *Catkins* models were first displayed at UK Fairs in 1998-1999. In April 1999, UKI Ceramics introduced their new series of catkin models.

Clown Catkins (left) Out For A Duck (right) [1999]

Old Father Time (2000)

Policeman Catkins (2000)

England Olympic Catkins (2000)

Town Crier Catkins (2000)

Witch Catkins (2000)

Backstamp: Printed "Exclusive Limited Edition of [number of pieces] Wade ©UKI Ceramics LTD ©Wade Ceramics LTD"

Date	Name	Description	Issue	Price	Size	U.S. $	Can. $	U.K. £
1999	Clown	Yellow tunic; white hat, trousers; black collar, pompons	750	£28.00	120	60.	65.	35.
1999	Out For a Duck	White cricketing clothes	750	£28.00	120	60.	65.	35.
2000	England Olympic	Blue jersey, white trousers	100	£50.00	130	85.	95.	50.
2000	Father Christmas	Red/white suite	250	£49.50	110	85.	95.	50.
2000	Old Father Time	White robes; gold watch chain	250	£32.50	110	60.	65.	35.
2000	Old Father Time	Grey robes; gold watch chain	100	£50.00	110	85.	95.	50.
2000	Policeman	Dark blue uniform	200	£45.00	120	85.	95.	50.
2000	Town Crier	Red coat, hat; yellow trim	250	£49.50	120	85.	95.	50.
2000	Witch	Black cloak, hat; purple skirt	250	£46.50	120	85.	95.	50.

THE CATKINS COLLECTION (cont.)
CLOWN and GYPSY CATKINS
2001

Clown Catkins

Gypsy Catkins

Backstamp: Unknown

Date	Name	Description	Issue	Price	Size	U.S. $	Can. $	U.K. £
2001	Clown	Yellow tunic; white trousers, hat; black ruff, bobbles	22	£45	120	60.	65.	35.
2001	Clown	Yellow tunic; red trousers; grey hat; black ruff, bobbles	22	£45	120	60.	65.	35.
2001	Clown	Yellow tunic; white trousers; gold hat; black ruff, bobbles	22	£45	120	60.	65.	35.
2001	Clown	Yellow tunic; white trousers; gold hat; black ruffle, pewter bobbles	22	£45	120	60.	65.	35.
2001	Clown	Blue tunic; white trousers; gold hat; black ruffle, pewter bobbles	22	£45	120	60.		35.
2001	Clown	Yellow tunic; grey trousers, hat; black ruffle, bobbles	22	£45	120	60.	65.	35.
2001	Clown	Pink tunic; trousers, grey hat; black ruffle, bobbles	22	£45	120	60.	65.	35.
2001	Clown	Yellow tunic; white trousers; blue hat; black ruffle, bobbles	22	£45	120	60.	65.	35.
2001	Clown	Yellow tunic; white trousers; red hat; black ruffle, bobbles	22	£45	120	60.	65.	35.
2001	Gypsy	Grey shirt, maroon waistcoat; light blue trousers	22	£45	120	60.	65.	35.
2001	Gypsy	Pearl shirt; maroon waistcoat; bright blue trousers	22	£45	120	60.	65.	35.
2001	Gypsy	Pearl shirt; maroon waistcoat; dark blue trousers; black belt	22	£45	120	60.	65.	35.
2001	Gypsy	Pearl shirt; maroon waistcoat; dark blue trousers; gold belt	22	£45	120	60.	65.	35.
2001	Gypsy	Pearl shirt; maroon waistcoat; blue trousers	22	£45	120	60.	65.	35.
2001	Gypsy	Pearl shirt; dark blue waistcoat; purple trousers	22	£45	120	60.	65.	35.
2001	Gypsy	Silver shirt; maroon waistcoat; bright blue trousers	22	£45	120	60.	65.	35.
2001	Gypsy	Silver shirt; grey waistcoat; blue trousers	22	£45	120	60.	65.	35.
2001	Gypsy	Orange shirt; maroon waistcoat; bright blue trousers	22	£45	120	60.	65.	35.

FELIX THE CAT

1997

Backstamp: Black printed "WADE TM™ 1997 FTC PROD. INC.
Limited edition of 1500 ™ UKI CERAMICS LTD
Licensed by El Euro lizenzen, Munchen"

Date	Name	Description	Issue	Price	Size	U.S. $	Can. $	U.K. £
1997	Felix	Black cat	1,500	£38	135	100.	110.	60.

THE FLINTSTONES COLLECTION

1996-1998

Backstamp: Printed "™The Flintstones™ Limited Edition of 1500 © 1996 H-B Prod. Inc © UKI Ceramics Ltd
Licensed by CPL [name of model]"

Date	Name	Description	Issue	Price	Size	U.S. $	Can. $	U.K. £
1996	Fred	Orange/black coat; blue scarf	1,500	£34	120	75.	80.	45.
1996	Wilma	White dress;	1,500	£34	125	75.	80.	45.
1997	Barney	Brown coat	1,500	£34	105	75.	80.	45.
1997	Betty	Pale blue dress	1,500	£34	115	75.	80.	45.
1998	Bamm Bamm	Orange/black shorts	1,000	£34	100	75.	80.	45.
1998	Pebbles	Green dress; blue pants	1,000	£34	100	75.	80.	45.

THE NODDY SET
STYLE TWO

1997-1999

"Noddy" and "Big Ears," were the first two models in this series. Unlike their 1950s predecessors, they are slip cast (hollow) and much larger. For Noddy and Big Ears, Style One, see page 33.

Backstamp: **A.** Black printed "Wade © UKI Cer. Ltd 1997 © D.W. 1949/90 Licenced by BBC WL Ltd [name of model] Limited Edition 1500"
B. Printed "Wade Limited Edition 1,500 © 1998 EBL Ltd - A.R.R. © UKI Ceramics Ltd, 1998 [name of model]"

Date	Name	Description	Issue	Price	Size	U.S. $	Can. $	U.K. £
1997	Big Ears	Dark blue coat; yellow/red sweater	1,500	£34.00	138	100.	110.	60.
1997	Noddy	Red shirt; light blue shorts	1,500	£34.00	110	90.	100.	50.
1999	Mr. Plod	Dark blue uniform	1,500	£42.50	140	90.	100.	50.
1999	Tessie Bear	Pink/blue dress	1,500	£42.50	110	90.	100.	50.

TOM AND JERRY

Style Two

1998

The large size versions of *Tom and Jerry* standing on round bases were commissioned by UK International Ceramics in a limited edition of 1,500. The cost direct from UKI was £75.00 for the pair. For Tom and Jerry, Style One, see page 42.

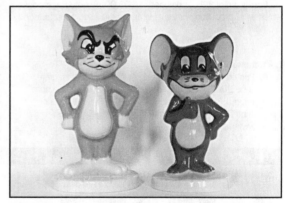

Backstamp: **A.** Printed "Wade Tom from Tom & Jerry ❑ © 1997 Turner ENT. Co. A.R.R. Limited Edition of 1500 © UKI Ceramics LTD Licensed by CPL"
B. Printed "Wade Jerry from Tom & Jerry ❑ © 1997 Turner ENT. Co. A.R.R. Limited Edition of 1500 © UKI Ceramics LTD Licensed by CPL"

Date	Name	Description	Issue	Price	Size	U.S. $	Can. $	U.K. £
1998	Tom	Grey/white; pink inside ears; black eyebrows, eyes, nose, whiskers; white base	1,500	£37.50	135	70.	80.	45.
1998	Jerry	Brown/beige; black eyebrows, eyes, nose, whiskers; white base	1,500	£37.50	110	70.	80.	45.

WADE WATCH USA

Pretty-in-Pink Budgie

2003

The "Pretty-in-Pink Budgerigar" Whimsie is from the C&S Direct Whimsie Budgie mould. Wade Watch in collaboration with C&S, produced a limited edition pink colourway of the budgie, the issue price was $10.50. See also C&S Collectables page 224.

Backstamp: Embossed "Wade C/S"

Date	Name	Description	Issue	Price	Size	U.S. $	Can. $	U.K. £
2003	Pretty-in-Pink Budgie	Pink	50	$10.50 US	50	10.	11.	6.

WADEUSA.COM 2003

CHILDREN'S SONG FIGURINES

2003

This new Wade series named "Children's Song Figurines" was produced for Michael and Reva Matthew of wadeusa.com. The first model was named "When Elephants Fly," which is based on a song from the Walt Disney film *Dumbo*. It was produced in a limited edition of 225, and priced at $60.00. Twenty-five models, which were produced with gold wings, were used for prizes and promotions.

Backstamp:
A. Printed "When Elephants Fly Children's Song Figurines June 2003 Limited Edition of 225 www.wadeusa.com"
B. Printed "When Elephants Fly Children's Song Figurines June 2003 Special Limited Edition of 25 www.wadeusa.com"

Date	Name	Description	Issue	Price	Size	U.S. $	Can. $	U.K. £
2003	When Elephants Fly	Grey; pink mouth; white wings, toe nails, base	225	$60 US	80	60.	65.	35.
2003	When Elephants Fly	Grey; pink mouth; gold wings; white toe nails, base	25	Prizes	80	—	—	—

Note:
1. A dash in any of the technical data columns of the table indicates that we do not have the required information, if you do, we would be pleased to hear from you.
2. Dashes in the pricing columns indicate one of two things: firstly, there was insufficient market pricing available, and secondly, pieces issued in small quantities of 10 or 20 pieces will be subject to wide pricing swings.

WARNER BROTHERS

MY DOG SKIP

2001

A solid Whimsie model of a Jack Russell terrier was produced for Warner Brothers, and was attached to their video film *My Dog Skip*. Fifty thousand models were produced and were available on the videos sold only in the U.K. Excess models were available from Wade at the Pennsylvania Wade Fest.

Backstamp: Embossed "Wade"

No.	Name	Description	Size	U.S. $	Can. $	U.K. £
2001	My Dog Skip	White; brown ears, patches	40	15.	16.	8.

WHIMSICAL WADERS

FLYING FLOWERS

2004

In 2004 the organisers of the West Coast Wade Collectors Fair, Michael and Reva Matthew joined with Robert and Suzie Coleman of Ameriwade to form the partnership Whimsical Waders. They intend to specialise in miniature Whimsie models. Their first venture was "Flying Flowers" which was a set of re-issued Red Rose Canada butterflies, in difference colourways.

Backstamp: Embossed "Wade England"

Date	Name	Description	Issue	Price	Size	U.S. $	Can. $	U.K. £
2004	Butterfly	Black; white spots	125	—	10 x 45	9.	10.	5.
2004	Butterfly	Blue	220	—	10 x 45	9.	10.	5.
2004	Butterfly	Gold	10	—	10 x 45	—	—	—
2004	Butterfly	Maroon	220	—	10 x 45	9.	10.	5.
2004	Butterfly	Orange; black spots	125	—	10 x 45	9.	10.	5.
2004	Butterfly	White	220	—	10 x 45	9.	10.	5.
2004	Butterfly	White/blue; red spots	100	—	10 x 45	9.	10.	5.

ROBERT WILLIAMSON AND PETER ELSON

GINGERBREAD MAN AND GINGERBREAD CHILDREN

1995-1996

A hollow model of a giant gingerbread man was commissioned by Robert Williamson and Peter Elson. It was available for sale at the 2nd U.K. Fairs Wade Show in Birmingham. Following the success of the "Giant Gingerbread Man," a hollow model of the "Gingerbread Children" (a waving girl and boy) was produced in a limited edition of 2,000, (they were sold at the Dunstable Wade show in September 1996). The original cost of both models was £15.00 each.

Please note, the "Gingerbread Children" with a gold base were not produced by Wade.

Backstamp: Embossed "Wade"

Date	Name	Description	Issue	Price	Size	U.S. $	Can. $	U.K. £
1995	Gingerbread Children	Ginger brown	2,000	£15	84 x 84	50.	55.	30.
1996	Gingerbread Man	Brown; dark green base	—	£15	105 x 80	50.	55.	30.

UNKNOWN COMPANY
3 FOR 49¢ WHIMSIES
CIRCA 1972

A number of red carded Whimsies have been discovered in Canada and the U.S.A. There has been no further information found as to who for or why these models were produced. It is probable that they were for a chain of North American Dime Stores. A Field Mouse on one of the red card models has a recessed base, as did some of the early 1967-1973 Canadian Red Rose Tea models. Others are from the 1971-1984 *English Whimsies* series, which would suggest that surplus stock was distributed to this company. A date of early 1970s is estimated for these models. The values given are for models intact on their cards, as some models are indistinguishable from Red Rose Tea or *English Whimsie* models outside the packet.

Backstamp: **A.** Embossed "Wade England" in recessed base
B. Embossed "Wade England" on rim
C. Embossed "Wade" between front feet and "England" on back of model (2)

No.	Name	Description	Size	U.S. $	Can. $	U.K. £
1	Alsatian	Grey; brown face	30 x 40	7.	8.	4.
2	Bear Cub	Honey brown	34 x 20	7.	8.	4.
3	Bison, large	Honey brown	34 x 46	28.	30.	16.
4	Duck	Blue/brown; yellow beak	30 x 40	10.	11.	6.
5	Field Mouse	Honey brown; yellow corn; green on base	35 x 25	12.	13.	7.
6	Fox	Dark brown; fawn face	30 x 30	8.	9.	5.
7	Giraffe	Beige	35 x 35	7.	8.	4.
8	Kitten, seated	Dark/light brown; pink wool	30 x 30	7.	8.	4.
9	Lion, standing	Light brown; dark brown mane	35 x 45	8.	9.	5.
10	Mongrel	Dark brown back; light brown front	35 x 35	7.	8.	4.
11	Setter	Brown; grey-green base	35 x 50	7.	8.	4.
12	Terrapin	Beige; brown markings	10 x 40	13.	14.	8.
13	Trout	Brown; red tail; grey-green base	30 x 30	7.	8.	4.
14	Zebra	Black	40 x 35	70.	75.	40.

UNKNOWN COMPANY

Sometimes models are found in North America, the United Kingdom or even as far away as Australia which cannot be attributed to any company promotion, due to the fact that they were not found in their original packaging, or seen listed in company promotional advertising. Collectors from the U.K. could have transported models to North America, and models found in the U.K. could have been transported from North America.

KODIAK BEAR

Circa 1965

No one seems to be able to identify the series for which the "Kodiak Bear" was produced or why it was made. It may have been a prototype model produced for the first Red Rose Tea premiums, then rejected due to high production costs (its open arms required more fettling). As a result, the "Kodiak Bear" was not put into full production, and any models produced may have been used up in miscellaneous premiums. A second variation of the bear is slightly smaller in size and has a small gap between his legs.

Backstamp: **A.** Embossed "Wade England"
B. Unmarked

No.	Name	Description	Size	U.S. $	Can. $	U.K. £
1a	Kodiak Bear	Beige brown; green base	35 x 25	60.	65.	35.
1b	Kodiak Bear	Brown; honey-brown face, chest, stomach	40 x 25	60.	65.	35.
1c	Kodiak Bear	Light brown; black nose; green base	40 x 25	60.	65.	35.
1d	Kodiak Bear	Red-brown	38 x 25	60.	65.	35.

UNKNOWN COMPANIES
MISCELLANEOUS WHIMSIE MODELS

These models, in all-over one colour glazes, are promotional models and most likely Redco Foods (Red Rose Tea U.S.A.) or Tom Smith (Miscellaneous) Cracker Models.

Backstamp: Embossed "Wade England" on rim

No.	Name	Description	Size	U.S. $	Can. $	U.K. £
1	Collie (TS)	Beige	25 x 50	12.	13.	7.
2	Duck, standing (EW)	Beige	30 x 40	12.	13.	7.
3	Duck, swimming (TS)	White	25 x 30	12.	13.	7.
4a	Elephant (EW)	Dark grey	35 x 28	12.	13.	7.
4b	Elephant (EW)	Pale grey	35 x 28	12.	13.	7.
5	Little Jack Horner (RRC/TS)	Blue	40 x 20	12.	13.	7.
6	Old Woman Who Lived in a Shoe	Honey	40 x 40	12.	13.	7.
7a	Persian Kitten (TS)	Apricot	25 x 33	12.	13.	7.
7b	Persian Kitten (TS)	Dark brown	25 x 33	12.	13.	7.
7c	Persian Kitten (TS)	Honey	25 x 33	12.	13.	7.
8	Rabbit, open ears (RR/EW)	Grey body; white face; black eyes; pink nose	30 x 30	12.	13.	7.

Note: The black kitten is suspect, as Wade rarely reglaze models black. In the known black models that were reglazed by Wade, the original design (fur/stripes) on the model can still be seen beneath the black glaze, as in the *English Whimsie* black "Zebra" and black "Poodle" models. Some models have been deliberately painted black by persons unknown to mislead collectors; these suspect models have a heavy coat of paint applied over the original Wade glaze.

The following initials indicate the origin of the model.
EW: *English Whimsies*
RRC: Red Rose Tea Canada
TS: Tom Smith

UNKNOWN COMPANIES (cont)
MISCELLANEOUS WHIMSIES MODELS
COLOUR VARIATIONS

The reason for these colour variations is unknown. They may have been sample colourways not accepted by the commissioner and used in miscellaneous promotions in the U.K. and U.S.A. to fill orders.

Elephant (RRC)

Hedgehog (RRC)

Rabbit, Type 2, Ears open (EW)

Cat (EW), Humpty Dumpty (RRC), Persian Kitten (TS), Kitten (EW)

Backstamp: Embossed "Wade England"

No.	Name	Description	Size	U.S. $	Can. $	U.K. £
1	Bo Peep (RRC)	Olive green	44 x 24	12.	13.	7.
2	Cat (EW)	Light blue	40 x 17	12.	13.	7.
3	Duck (WL)	Dark brown	45 x 35	12.	13.	7.
4a	Eagle (TS)	Olive green	35 x 23	12.	13.	7.
4b	Eagle (TS)	Tan	25 x 23	12.	13.	7.
5	Elephant (EW)	Cream	35 x 28	12.	13.	7.
6	Hedgehog (EW)	Grey	23 x 40	12.	13.	7.
7	Humpty Dumpty (RRC)	Dark brown	36 x 23	12.	13.	7.
8	Kitten (EW)	Grey	30 x 30	12.	13.	7.
9a	Persian Kitten (TS)	Apricot	25 x 33	12.	13.	7.
9b	Persian Kitten (TS)	Dark brown	25 x 33	12.	13.	7.
9c	Persian Kitten (TS)	Honey	25 x 33	12.	13.	7.
10	Pine Martin (EW)	Grey	30 x 30	12.	13.	7.
11	Rabbit, Type 2 (EW)	White	25 x 30	12.	13.	7.
12	Trout (EW)	Grey	30 x 30	12.	13.	7.

INDEX

A

Absolutely Crackers, 280
Accordion Golliwog, 261
Admiral Sam, 102, 153, 154, 318
African Lion, 197
Alex the Aviator, 102, 154, 318
Alexandra Palace, Teddy Bear Show, 1998, 136
Alfred, 285
Alf's Corner Shop, 256
Alice (Mabel Lucie Attwell). 230
Alice in Wonderland, 177, 184, 189
Alice and the Dodo, 28
Alice in Wonderland Series, 189
Alligator, 133, 171, 177, 289
Alphabet Train, 98
Alsatians:
    Alsatian, 50, 52, 56, 67, 71, 74, 205, 289,
        314, 332, 343
    Alsatian Candle Holder, 74
    Alsatian Pipe Stand, 52
    Alsatian Puppy, Lying, Dish, 53
    Alsatian Puppy, Seated, Dish, 53
    Alsatian Tray, 71
    Mother, 50
    Puppy, Lying, 50
    Puppy, Seated, 50
Alton Towers Fair, 1998-2000, 137
Amelia Teddy Bear, 177, 187
American Bald Eagle, 174
American Bear Cub, 172
American Eagle, 169
American Patriotic Eagle, 175
Ameriwade, 203
Andy Capp, 177, 211
Andy Capp and Flo, 211
    Andy Capp Cigarette, 211
Andy Pandy, 335
Anchor, The, 251
Angel Fish, 59, 185, 296, 322
Angels, 99-101
    Angel, 78, 99,
    Kneeling Angel, 99
    Kneeling Angel Candle Holder, 100
    Kneeling Angel Dish, 101
    Sitting Angel, 99
    Sitting Angel Candle Holder, 100
    Sitting Angel Dish, 101
    Standing Angel, 99
    Standing Angel Candle Holder, 100

    Standing Angel Dish, 101
Angus Calf, 264
Animal Families, 243
Animaland, 212
Annabel Waiting for Christmas, 177, 199
Antique Bully, 152
Antique Shop, 89, 91, 308
Ape, 79
Aqualand, 213
Aquarium Set, 279
Ark, 305
Armadillo, 165, 328
Arnie (pig), 159
Art Deco Ashtray, 113
Arthur Hare:
    Arthur Hare, 214
    Arthur Hare Teenies, 215
    Arthur Hare Wizhared Whimsie, 168, 215
    Collecthare Collection, The, 216
    Travelhare Collection, The, 216
    Village People Collection, The, 217
Art Deco ashtray, 12
Arthur Price of England, 204
Artistic Edward, 102, 154, 318
Arun Bear Town Crier, 218
Arundel Bear, 147
Arundel Bunny, 143, 177
Arundel Castle, 223
Arundel Cat, 144, 177
Arundel Chick, 144, 177
Arundel Christmas Bonanza, 1999-2006,
    138-142
Arundel Collectors/Swap Meets, 1997-2006,
    143-147
Arundel Duck, 143, 177
Arundel Fox, 146
Arundel Lamb, 146
Arundel Pig, 147
Arundel Pony, 145
Arundel Puppy, 145
Arundel Salmon, 144
Arndel SWap Meet, 216
Arundel Town Mouse, 145
Arundel Travelhare, 216
Ash Bowl, 130
Australia Olympic Catkins, 158

B

Baa Baa Black Sheep, 38, 282, 292
Baby Badger, 146
Baby Bear, 32, 140, 186
Baby Bear Cub, 55, 163. 210, 212, 240,
    250, 289, 298, 311, 343
Baby Bear in Pyjamas, 149, 177
Baby Bird, 22
Baby Bodzilla, 123
Baby Elephant, 15, 65
Baby Frog, 15
Baby Giraffe, 16, 245
Baby Hedgehog, 146
Baby Hippo, 16, 245
Baby Mice, 17, 245
Baby Owl, 18
Baby Pigs, 18
Baby Rabbit, 19
Baby Seal, 66
    Candle Holder, 74
    Tray, 71
Baby Straw, 277
Baby Tiger, 20
Baby Turtle, 246
Bactrian Camel, 68
    Candle Holder, 74
    Tray, 71
Badger, 64, 74, 87, 88, 96, 190, 255, 296,
    316, 322
    Baby, 146
    Bertram, 242
    Bertie Badger, 309
    Candle Holder, 74
    Key Ring, 88
    Mother, 146, 181,
    Traveling, 155, 182
    Whimsie, 146
Bahamas Tortoise, 130
Baker, 30
Bald Eagle, 304
Balding and Mansell, 206
Bamm Bamm, 338
Bandstand, 261, 274
Barber Shop, 93
Barley Mow, 91
Barn Owl, 58, 304. 315
Barney, 338
Barnyard Cat Whimsie, 263

Barrister, 249
Bass Golliwog, 261
Basset Hound, 29, 62
Bathing Beauty, 269
Batman, 285
Batman and Superman, 285
Beagle, 65, 121
Beano Collection, The, 208
Bear Ambitions, 102, 153, 154, 281, 318
    Crackers, 280, 318
Bear Whimsie, 147
Bears:
    Admiral Sam, 102, 153, 154, 318
    Alex the Aviator, 102, 154, 318
    Amelia Teddy Bear, 177, 187
    American Bear Cub, 172
    Annabel Waiting for Christmas, 177, 199
    Antique Bully, 152
    Artistic Edward, 102, 154, 318
    Arun Bear Town Crier, 201
    Arundel Bear, 147
    Baby Bear, 32, 140, 186
    Baby Bear Cub, 55, 163, 210, 212,
        240, 250, 289, 298, 311, 343
    Baby Bear in Pyjamas, 149, 177
    Bear Ambitions, 102, 153, 154, 281,
        318
    Bear (Circus), 105
    Bears Just Want to Have Fun, 137
    Bear Whimsie, 147
    Bears with Flags, 218
    Beary Christmas, 203
    Beatrice Ballerina, 102, 154, 318
    Bee on Face, 165, 243
    Best Friends Bears. 185
    Boo Boo, 252
    Bookend Bear, 177
    Brown Bear, 95, 295, 303, 319
    Bug Hunt Bear, 196
    Camping Bear, 154, 177
    Christmas Gingie Bear, 142, 229
    Christmas Ging"E", 229
    Christmas Teddy Bear, 164, 177, 181,
        199
    Chintz Bear, 177
    Clever Bear, 110
    Cross-eyed Bear, 110, 149
    Collect It! Honey Bear Cub, 240
    Collect 99 Bear, 285

Cub, 55, 163. 210, 212, 240, 250,
    289, 298, 311, 343
Daddy Bear, 179, 186
Firm Friends, 185
Football Bear, 152
For You (Gingie Bear), 229
Giant Panda Bear, 68
Giant Panda Candleholder, 75
Giant Panda Whimtray, 71, 72
Gingy the Bear, 127
Ging"E" Trick or Treat, 229
Gold Book Ted "E" Bear, 226
Golly Gosh Bear, 110, 149, 179
Gone Fishin' Bear, 196
Grizzly Bear, 68
Grizzly Bear Candle Holder, 75
Grizzly Bear Tray, 72
Grizzly Cub, 68
Grizzly Cub Tray, 72
Halloween (Gingie Bear), 229
Honey Bear, 110, 149, 179
Honey Bunch Bears, 110, 149, 179
Hugging Bear Cubs, 141
Internet Guide, Ted "E" Bear, 226
Jet Set (Gingie Bear), 229
Jonno Bear, 161
King Velveteen, 125, 179
Koala Bear, 59, 151, 204, 259, 299,
    301, 324, 325, 326, 331
Kodiak Bear, 344
Li'Bear'ty, 203
Library Bear, 136, 179
Lil' American Footballer, 171, 179
Lil' Cricketer, 151
Lil' Easter Bear, 159
Lil' Footballer Bear, 160
Lil' Uncle Sam, 169, 175
Lil' Witch, 151
Locomotive Joe, 102, 154, 318
Lucky the Bear, 140
Mama Bear, 32
Maple the Canadian Bear, 218
Millennium Teddy, 157, 181
Money Box, 243
Mother and Baby Bear, 140
Mother Polar Bear and Cub on Ice, 233
Mummy Bear, 181, 186
Musical Marco, 102, 154, 318

Nanny Fluffins and Baby Velveteena,
    125, 181
North American Bear, 171
Oops! the Bear, 138, 149, 181
Oscar the Christmas Teddy Bear, 164,
    177, 181, 199
Paddington Bear, 235
Paddington's Snowy Day, 235
Panda Bear, 46, 86, 212, 255
    Blow Up, 212
    Candleholder, 75
    Keyring, 88
    Plaque, 137
    Tray, 71-72
    Whimsie, 212
Polar Bear, 61, 66, 72, 79, 95, 151,
    204, 258, 259, 295, 299, 301,
    304, 326, 327
Polar Bear Tray, 72
Polar Bear Cub, 66, 73, 75, 139, 140,
    141, 233
    Blow Up, 83
    Candleholder, 75
    Seated, 140
    Standing, 140
    Tray, 73
Polar Bearcubs on Ice, 233
Polar Bear Mother Blow Up, 83
Polar Bear Mother and Cub on Ice, 233
Poppa Bear, 32
Prince George Tedward, 125, 181
Princess Elizabeth Tedwina, 125, 179
Princess Plushette, 125, 181
Queen Beatrice, 125, 181
Queen Mum, 125
Royal Guard, 125, 181
Rupert Bear, 235
Rupert and the Snowman, 235
Ruffles the Bear, 185
Seated, 165, 202, 243
Sleeping, 165, 202
Sleepy Bear, 110, 149
Sooty, 235
Standing Bear Cub, 141
Sunny Bear, 110
Ted "E" Bear, 182, 226
Teddy Bear Plaque, 143, 154, 164
Tessie Bear, 340

Three Bears, 35, 38, 244, 282, 294
    Whimble, 260
Traveller (Gingie Bear), 229
Tubby the Bear, 163, 182
Uncle Sam (Gingie Bear), 229
Union Bear, 151, 218
Victor"E" Bear, 218, 226
Wade Book Ted "E" Bear, 226
Wakey, Wakey! Bears, 196
We're Hungrey Bears, 196
Whimsie (Gingie Bear), 229
Yogi Bear, 44, 252
Yum-Yum Bear, 196
Bears Just Want to Have Fun, 137
Beary Christmas, 203
Beast, 193
Beatrice Ballerina, 102, 154, 318
Beau the Greyhound, 160
Beauty, 184, 193
Beauty and the Beast, 193
Beauty and the Beast Dancing, 193
Beauty's Father, 193
Beaver, 55, 79, 210, 257, 289, 296, 299, 301
Beggar Man, 41
Bengo, 29
Benny, 6
Bermuda Tortoise, 130
Bermuda Triangle Tortoise, 130
Bermuda, Devil's Hole, Tortoise, 130
Bernie and Poo, 132
Bertie Badger, 308
Bertram Badger, 242
Best Friends (Madel Lucie Attwell), 230
Best Friends Bears. 185
Betty, 338
Betty Boop:
    Air Hostess, 221
    Beach Belle Bikini, 177, 219
    Beach Belle, 177, 219
    Betty Boop, 219
    Betty in Black, 221
    Betty in Red, 221
    Cheerleader, 221
    Cheers, 147
    Cheers Ten Years, 221
    Christmas Morning, 219
    Christmas Present, 142, 221
    Christmas Surprise, 219
    Christmas Time, 141, 221
    Classic Plaque, 177, 239

Cool Breeze, 147, 221
Elegance, 219
Elegant, 221
Graduate, U.K., 219
Graduate, U.S.A., 219
Halloween, 219, 221
Halloween Trick or Treat, 221
Hubble Bubble, 221
I Love You, 221
Jubilee, 219
Juke Box, 221
Ladies Day, 221
Lazy Daze, 219
Liberty (figure), 219
Liberty (plaque), 219, 239
Material Girl, 221
Movie Queen, 219
Nurse, 221
Party Time, 221
Plaque, 219
Queen of Hearts, 219
Rainy Days, 221
Ringmaster, 177, 219
Ringmaster and Pudgy, 219
Rose, 219
St. Patrick's Day, 219
Satin and Lace, 221
Seasons Greetings, 221
Showtime, 221
Snow Queen, 221
Southern Belle, 219
Springtime, 219
Superstar, 219
Sweetheart, 221
Swinging 60s, 221
Top of the World, 102
Toy Box, 221
Trick or Treat, 221
Uptown Girl, 221
Valentine, 219
Viva Las Vegas, 221
Wall Plaque, 219
Whimsies, 141, 223
World Cup Betty, 221
Bibendum
    Cowboy, 334
    Indian, 334
    Rugby, 334
    Santa, 334

    Sailor, 334
Big Bad Wolf, 177, 185, 253
Big Bad Wolf and the Three Little Pigs Series, 185
Big Chief Bravehare, 217
Big Ears, 33, 339
Bill and Ben and Little Weed, 335
Billingsgate Porter, 103
Billy the Bottle Oven, 173, 238
Birds:
    American Bald Eagle, 174
    American Eagle, 169
    American Patriotic Eagle, 175
    Arundel Chick, 144, 177
    Baby Bird, 22
    Baby Owl, 18
    Barn Owl, 58, 304, 315
    Bird Set Crackers, 280
    Blackbird, 152
    Bluebird, 60, 162, 206, 289, 298, 314, 325
    Bluebird Whimsie, 162
    Blue Tit (on milk churn), 146
    Budg"E", 226
    Budgie, 160, 306
    Budgie, Pretty-in-Pink, 341
    Budgie Whimsies, 224
    Christmas Robin, 139
    Cock-a-teel, 300, 301
    Cockatoo, 68, 197, 259, 320
    Cockatoo Candle Holder, 75
    Cockatoo Tray, 71
    Cockerel, 62, 81, 86, 280, 315
    Cockerel Salt Pot, 333
    Eagle, 280, 315, 328, 346
    Eagle, American, 169
    Eagle, Americsn Bald, 174
    Eagle, Bald, 304
    Eagle, Golden, 87, 304
    Eagle, American Patriotic, 175
    Eagle Whimsie, 174
    Flying Birds, 108
    Hector the Owl, 158
    Hen Pepper Pot, 333
    Kingfisher, 161
    Oswald Owl, 242
    Owl, 55, 87, 88, 158, 210, 250, 255, 280, 290, 298, 311
    Owl Family, 18

Owl Mother, 18
Owl Specs, 122
Owl Tray, 88
Palm Cockatoo, 197
Partridge, 87, 140, 280, 315, 316
Pelican, 59, 118, 280, 297, 315
Peregrine Falcon, 304
Pheasant, 87
Robin Whimsie, 142
Snowy Owl, 68, 197, 212, 258, 327
Snowy Owl Tray, 73
Spotted Owl, 304
Swallows, 108
Swan, 69, 77, 145
Swan Tray, 73
Swifts, 108
Toco Toucan, 197
Toots the Owl, 109
Woodstock, 225
Wren, 172, 280, 315
Birmingham Fairs, 148
Bison, 60, 96, 210, 289, 295, 298, 328, 331, 343
BJ Promotions, 208
Black Terrier Dog, 281
Blackbird, 152
Blacksmith, 276
Bloodshott Hall, 91
Blow Up Lamb, 184
Blow Up Spaniel With Ball, 77
Blue Boy, 244
Blue Lady, 237
Bluebell the Pony, 160
Bluebird, 60, 162, 206, 289, 298, 314, 325
Blue Tit (On milk churn), 146
Blyth Ceramics, 209
Blynken, 43, 44
Boar's Head Pub, 90
Bobcat, 96, 295
Boo Boo (bear), 252
Bo-Peep, 35, 36, 38, 80, 244, 248, 255, 260, 282, 293, 310, 323, 326, 329, 346
Bookend Bear, 177
Boots the Rabbit, 163, 177
Border Collie, 121
Boris, 82
Born Free (lions), 290

Born to be a Big Brother, 134
Born to be Cool, 134
Born to be a Daydreamer, 134
Born to be Friends, 134
Born to be Loved, 134
Born to be Naughty, 134
Born to be Sleepy, 134
Born to Slide, 134
Born to be Wild, 134
Bossy, Miss, 119
Both Eyes Closed (Homepride Fred), 273
Both Eyes Open (Homepride Fred), 273
Bounce, (Rabbit) 122, 240
Boy Frog, 5
Boy Pig, 8
Boxer, 62, 67
    Candle Holder, 74
    Tray, 71
Brand"E" the St. Bernard, 226
Brandy the St. Bernard, 160
Bravehare, 215
Briar Row, 92
Brick House Pig, 177, 185
Bridge, 279
Brighton Corporation, 209
Brighton Pavilion, 209
Britannia, 287
British Bulldog, 161
British Character Set, 103
British Heritage Collection, 223
British Lion, 151
British Myths and Legends Series, 188
British Wildlife, 316
Bronti, 206
Brooke Bond Oxo Ltd., England, 210
Broomyshaw Cottage, 92
Brontosaurus, 207
Brother Angelo, 262
Brother Benjamin, 262
Brother Crispin, 262
Brother Francis, 262
Brother Peter, 262
Brown Bear, 95, 295, 303, 319
Brown Hare, 197
Brown Lady, 237
Bruno Junior, 29
Brutus, 247
Budg"E", 226
Budgie, 160, 306

Budgie, Pretty-in-Pink, 341
Budgie Whimsies, 224
Buffalo Travelhare, 216
Bug Hunt Bear, 196
Buildings:
    Alf's Corner Shop, 256
    Antique Shop, 89, 91, 308
    Barber Shop, 93
    Barley Mow, 91
    Bloodshott Hall, 91
    Blue Lady, 237
    Boar's Head Pub, 90
    Briar Row, 92
    Brighton Pavilion, 209
    Broomyshaw Cottage, 92
    Brown Lady, 237
    Butcher Shop, 93
    Chapel, 330
    Circular Pavilion, 209
    Coach House Garage, 330
    District Bank, 93
    Dr. Healer's House, 91
    Duckworths, No. 9, 256
    Fire Station, 93
    Fishmonger's Shop, 94
    Florist Shop, 89
    Greengrocer's Shop, 91, 308
    Healer's House, Dr., 91
    House that Jack Built, 38, 282, 292
    Jubilee Terrace, 89
    Library, 94
    Lighthouse, 280
    Manor, 92
    Market Hall, 93
    Merryweather Farm, 92
    Miss Prune's House, 93
    Morgan's the Chemist, 91
    No. 9 The Duckworths, 256
    Oblong Pavilion, 209
    Old Smithy, 93
    Picture Palace, 93
    Pink House, 330
    Pink Lady, 237
    Police Station, 94
    Post Office, 90, 91, 308
    Prune's House, Miss, 93
    Pump Cottage, 91, 308
    Rose Cottage, 90
    Rovers Return, 256

St. John's School, 89
St. Lawrence Church, 89
St. Sebastian's Church, 91, 275
School Teacher's House, 94
Stag Hotel, 91
Sweet Shop, 92
Thatched Cottage, 330
Tinker's Nook, 92
Tobacconist's Shop, 91, 308
Town Garage, 90
Vale Farm, 90
Vicarage, 92
Village Store, 330
Watermill, 91
Whimsey School, 91
Whimsey Service Station, 91
Whimsey Station, 92, 308
White Lady, 237
Why Knott Inn, 91
Windmill, 91
Yellow Lady, 237
Bulgie the Frog, 171, 177
Bull, 64, 116, 312, 321
Bull (The), 251
Bulldog, 174, 325, 332
 Key Chain, 146
 Whimsie, 174
Bullfrog, 60, 314
Bump, Mr., 119, 308
Bunn "E", 226
Burglar, 249
Bushbaby, 55, 204, 210, 250, 289, 296, 298
Butcher, 30, 276
Butcher Shop, 93
Buttercup (horse), 151
Butterfly, 210, 289, 314, 322, 341

C

C&S Collectables Direct, 211
C&S Crackers, 224
Cable Car, 237
Cadbury World, 234
Cairns:
 Cairn Pipe Stand, 52
 Cairn Puppy, Lying, Dish, 53
 Cairn Puppy, Standing, Dish, 53
 Cairn Terrier, sitting, 246
Cairn Terrier, standing, 246
Mother, 50, 243
Puppy, Lying, 50, 243
Puppy, Standing,, 50, 243
Calves, 264
 Angus, 264
 Holstein, 264
Camarasaurus, 49
Camel, 58, 257, 296, 299, 301, 325
 (See also Bactrian Camel)
Camelot Collection, 187
Camtrak, 235
Camping Bear, 154, 177
Candle holders (see listing under name of model)
Candlestick Maker, 30
Captain Hook and Crocodile, 192
Carpet Bag, Felix the Cat, 106
Carryer Craft of California, 237
Cat and Fiddle, 244, 248
Cat and the Fiddle, 35, 36, 38, 80, 244, 248, 260, 282, 292, 317, 329
Cat and Kitten, 48
Cats:
 Arundel Cat, 144, 177
 Australia Olympic Catkins, 158
 Barnyard Cat, 263
 Cat, 48, 58, 205, 306, 310, 317, 346
 Cat and Kitten, 48
 Cat and Puppy Dishes, 53
 Cat and the Fiddle, 35, 36, 38, 80, 244, 248, 261, 283, 293, 318, 330
 Cat Sitting, 48
 Cat Standing, 48, 115, 317
 Cat Walking, 115, 318
 Christmas Cat, 264
 City Gent Catkins, 155
 Cheshire Cat, 177, 189
 Clown Catkins, 158, 337, 338
 Cook Catkins, 151
 Dick Whittington's Cat, 38, 179, 186
 Dustbin Cat, 132
 England Catkins, 336
 Family, 14
 Father Christmas Catkins, 336
 Felix, 106, 152, 162, 184, 199, 241, 338
 Fireman Catkins, 157
 Fluffy Cat, Miss, 33
 Garfield, 229
 Goldie, 168
Gypsy Catkins, 158, 337
Jerry, 42, 340
Jinks, Mr., 44, 252
Kitten, 54, 64, 141, 300, 311, 346
Kitten Key Ring, 88
Kitten, Lying, 14, 85, 88, 317
Kitten on the Keys, 132
Kitten, Seated, 14, 79, 205, 250, 290, 300, 311, 317, 343
Kitten Whimsie, 141
Kittens, 306
Lightning, 168
Lil' Bit Cat, 174
Long-neck Cat, 181
Millennium Catkins, 157
Miss Fluffy Cat, 33
Mitzi, 29
Mother, 14
Mr. Jinks, 44, 252
Old Father Time Catkins, 336
Out For A Duck Catkins, 336
Persian Kitten, 301, 320, 345, 346
Policeman Catkins, 336
Puss in Boots, 35, 80, 244, 283, 295, 318
Rosie the Kitten, 109, 182
Slinky, 122
Spook "E" (cat), 226
Tabby Cat Dish, 53
Tango, 231
Thunder, 168
Tom, 42, 339
Town Crier Catkins, 336
Witch Catkins, 336
Work's Cat "Burslem," 184
Catkins Collection, 336
Ceasar (pig), 159
Ceramica, 238
Champion Fred, 274
Chapel, 330
Charlie Brown, 225
Charlie Brown and Linus, 225
Characters from Charlie Brown, 225
Chee-Chee, 29
Cheeky Duckling, 22
Cheerful Charlie, 2
 Salt Pot, 3
 Posy Bow, 3
Cheesy (Mouse), 122, 240

Cheshire Cat, 177, 189
Chicken, female, on nest, 305
Chicken, male, standing, 305
Child Studies, 104
Childhood Favourites Display Plaque, 235
Childhood Favourites Series, 235
Chill Flake, Mr., 120
Chimp, 204
Chimpanzee, 56, 255, 289, 298, 311
    Boy, 303, 319
    Girl, 303, 319
    Mischief the Chimp, 169, 175, 181
Chintz Bear, 177
Chipmunk, 96, 295
Christmas Bonanza, 138
Christmas Bonanza Collecthare, 216
Christmas Cat, 264
Christmas Cheer, 199
Christmas Crackers, 46, 206, 207, 224,
    281
Christmas Crackers, Tap Cap, 209
Christmas Flake, Mr., 120
Christmas Gingie Bear, 142
Christmas Ging, "E", 226, 229
Christmas in Whimsie-on-Why, 275
Christmas Models, 198-199
Christmas Mouse, 141
Christmas Ornaments, 268
Christmas Puppy, 139, 177, 184
Christmas Rabbit, 141
Christmas Robin, 139
Christmas Snoopy, 142
Christmas Teddy Bear, 164, 177
Christmas Time Betty Boop, 141
Chucklebean, 234
Chucklenut Keyring, 234
Chuckles the Clown, 177, 179, 187
Ciba Geigy, 238
Cinderella in Rags 184, 191
Cinderella, Ready for the Ball, 191
Cinderella Series, 191
Circular Pavilion, 209
Circus Animals, 303, 304
Circus Animates Crackers, 320
Circus Bear, 105
Circus Display Stand, 105
Circus Set:
    Clown, 105
    Elephant, 105

Lion, 105, 258
Pony, 105
Poodle, 137
Ringmaster, 105
Strongman, 105
City Gent Catkins, 155
Clara, 105
Clarence the Cow, 145
Clarinet Golliwog, 261
Clever Bear, 110
Clorinda (Ugly Sister), 179, 191
Clown, 105
Clown, banjo, 144, 179
Clown Catkins, 158, 336, 337
Clown Custard Pie, 303
Clown, singing, 144, 179
Clown Water Bucket, 303
Coach House Garage, 330
Cock-a-teel, 300, 301
Cockatoo, 68, 259, 320
    Candle Holder, 75
    Palm, 197
    Tray, 71
Cockerel, 62, 81, 86, 280, 315
    Salt Pot, 333
Cold Flake, Mr., 120
Cocktail Felix, 106, 162
Collect It! Fairies, 239
Collect It! Fairs, 1998, 216
Collect It! Honey Bear Cub, 240
Collect It! Magazine, 239
Collect 99 Bear, 285
Collectable Limited Edition Crackers, 47
Collectania, 239
Collecteenie, 239
Collecthare Collection, 216
Collector, The , 242
Collectus, 239
Collie, 57, 205, 296, 310, 321, 331, 345
Colt, 65
Comic Animals and Birds, 2-12
Comical Whimsies, 48
Cook Catkins, 151
Coco the Monkey, 194
Cool Cats, 48
Corgies:
    Corgi, 55, 67, 71, 75, 210, 289, 296,
        311, 332
    Corgi Candle Holder, 75

Corgi Pipe Stand, 52
Corgi Puppy, Lying, Dish, 53
Corgi Puppy, Seated, Dish, 53
Corgi Tray, 71
    Mother, 51
    Puppy, Lying, 51
    Puppy, Seated, 51
Cornish Tin Mine Pixie, 179, 188
Coronation Street Houses, 257
Corythosaurus, 49
Cotswold Collectables, 242
Cougar, 68
Cow, 57, 62, 81, 86, 116, 205, 296, 321
    Clara, 105
    Clarence the Cow, 145
Cowardly Lion, 165
Crackle, 194
Cricket Design Incorporated, 243
Crocodile, 46, 65, 171, 206, 289
Cross-eyed Bear, 110, 149, 179
Crumpton, E. and A., 249
Crunchie the Foal, 109

D

Dachshund, 64, 312
Dack, 4
Daddy Bear, 179, 186
Dalmatian Key Chain, 160
Darling, Mrs., 286
David Trower Enterprises, 247
Deer:
    Fawn, 54, 61, 118, 204, 250, 289, 310
    Fizzy the Fawn, 109, 179
    Leaping Fawn, 63
    Reindeer, 171, 226, 259, 328
    Rud"E", Reindeer, 226
Dennis the Menace, 208
Devil's Hole, Bermuda, Tortoise, 130
Dick Whittington's Cat, 38, 179, 186
Digger the Mole, 109
Dilly, 4
Dino, 206
Dinosaur Collection: 49
Dinosaurs:
    Bronti, 206
    Brontosaurus, 207
    Camarasaurus, 49
    Corythosaurus, 49

Dino, 206

Dinosaur, 207

Dinosaur Collection, 49

Euoplocephalus, 49

Nodosaurus, 49

Protoceratops, 49

Saurclephus, 49

Scutellosaurus, 49

Spinosaurus, 49

Tyrannosaurus Rex, 49

Vulcanodon, 49

Dismal Desmond, 31

Display Stand (Circus), 105

District Bank, 93

Diver, 279

Dixie (mouse), 252

Doggy Family, 243

Dogs:

Alsatian, 50, 52, 56, 67, 71, 74, 205, 289, 314, 332, 343

Alsatian Candle Holder, 74

Alsatian Mother, 50

Alsatian Pipe Stand, 52

Alsatian Puppy, Lying, 50

Alsatian Puppy, Lying, Dish, 53

Alsatian Puppy, Seated, 50

Alsatian Puppy, Seated, Dish, 53

Alsatian Tray, 71

Antique Bully, 152

Arundel Puppy, 145

Basset Hound, 62

Beagle, 65, 121

Beau the Greyhound, 160

Bengo, 29

Bernie and Poo, 132

Black Terrier, 281

Border Collie, 121

Boxer, 62, 67

Boxer Candle Holder, 74

Boxer Tray, 71

Brand"E" the St. Bernard, 226

Brandy the St. Bernard, 160

British Bulldog, 161

Bruno Junior, 29

Bulldog, 174, 325, 332

Keychain, 146

Cairn Mother, 50, 243

Cairn Pipe Stand, 52

Cairn Puppy, Lying, 50, 243

Cairn Puppy, Lying in Dish, 53

Cairn Puppy, Standing, 50, 243

Cairn Puppy, Standing in Dish, 53

Cairn Terrier, Sitting in basket, 246

Cairn Terrier, Standing in basket, 246

Chee-Chee, 29

Chief, 88

Christmas Puppy, 139, 177, 184

Christmas Snoopy, 142

Circus Poodle, 137

Collie, 57, 205, 296, 310, 321, 331, 345

Corgi, 55, 67, 71, 75, 210, 289, 296, 311, 332

Corgi Candle Holder, 75

Corgi Mother, 51

Corgi Pipe Stand, 52

Corgi Puppy, Lying, 51

Corgi Puppy, Lying, Dish, 53

Corgi Puppy, Seated, 51

Corgi Puppy, Seated, Dish, 53

Corgi Tray, 71

Dachshund, 64, 312

Dalmatian Key Chain, 160

Dismal Desmond, 31

Dog, 118

Dog Family, 14

Dog Sitting, 48

Dog Waggs, 122

Dogs and Puppies, 99-101

Dougal, 235

Dribbles the Dog, 163, 179

Droopy Junior, 29

Ella, 151, 181

English Bull Terrier, 62, 162

Pearl Lustre), 82

Fifi, 29

Foxhound, 69

German Shepherd, 311

Mother, 243

Pup, lying, 243

Pup, sitting, 243

Sitting in a Basket, 246

Standing in a Basket, 246

Gnasher, 252

Golden Retreiver, 121

Goodnight Spot, 161

Great Dane, 62

Henry, 167

Huckleberry Hound, 44, 252

Hungry Dalmation, 161

Husk "E", 226

Husky, 61, 66, 332

Husky Blow Up, 83

Husky Candle Holder, 75

Husky Tray, 72

Irish Setter:

lying, facing right (In a Basket), 246

Mother, 243

Pup, lying, facing left, 243

Pup, lying, facing right, 243

Jack Russel Terrier, 121

Jem, 105

Jenny the Black Poodle, 167

Labrador, 306

Maisie, 147, 161

Mongrel, 54, 205, 284, 290, 310, 325, 332, 343

Mother, 14

My Dog Skip, 341

PA Pup, 172

Peg, 81, 88

Pepi, 29

Percy, 29

Pongo, 26

Poodle, 63, 290, 303, 319, 325, 332,

Poodle Candle Holder, 76

Prairie Dog, 164, 181

Pup, Front Paws Up, 92

Pup, Looking Back, 92

Pup Lying on Back, 92

Pup Sitting, 92

Pup, Sniffing Ground, 92

Pupp "E", 226

Puppy, 85, 169

Arundel Puppy, 145

Pearl Lustre, 82

Puppy Key Ring, 88

Puppy, Lying, 14

Puppy Play, 121

Puppy, Standing, 14

Puppy Tray, 88

Puppy Whimsie, 152, 161

Puppies, 306

Red Setter Mother, 51

Red Setter Pipe Stand, 52

Red Setter Puppy, Lying Facing Left, 51

Red Setter Puppy, Lying Facing Left, Dish, 53

Red Setter Puppy, Lying Facing Right, 51
Red Setter Puppy, Lying Facing Right,
    Dish, 53
Retriever, 64, 85, 312
Retriever Candle Holder, 76
Rufus, 155, 182
Rufus on Tour, 164
Saint Bernard, 67
    Brand"E", 226
    Brandy, 160
Scottie, 226
Scooby-Doo, 252
Scrappy Doo, 252
Sergeant Tobbs, 83
Setter, 55, 62, 210, 291, 310, 343
Shelby, 164, 181
Shep the Sheepdog, 151
Sidney, 156, 181
Simon, 29
Smudger, 182, 184
Snoopy, 225
Snoopy Happy Holidays, 225
Snoopy Hugging Woodstock, 225
Spaniel, 54, 62, 82, 109, 148, 205,
    291, 311, 332
Spaniel Candle Holder, 76
Spaniel, Pearl Lustre, 82
Spaniel Puppy, 79, 257, 300, 301, 320
Spaniel Tray, 73
Spaniel with Ball, 63, 77
Spot the Dalmatian, 147
Spotty's Feeding Time, 146
Steino, 144
Sweep, 235
Toby, 254
Truly the Puppy, 184
West "E," 226
West "E" and Scottie, 226
West Highland Terrier, 67. 332
West Highland Terrier Candle Holder, 76
West Highland Terrier Tray, 73
Westie, 164
Whisky, 29
Woofit, 240
Yorkie Terrier Puppy, Sitting, Dish, 53
Yorkie Terrier Puppy, Standing,
    Dish, 53
Yorkshire Terrier Mother, 52
Yorkshire Terrier Pipe Stand, 52

Yorkshire Terrier Puppy, Seated, 52
Yorkshire Terrier Puppy, Walking, 52
Doleful Dan, 2
    Posy Bowl, 3
Doll "E" the Sheep, 226
Dolphin, 59, 213, 322, 331
    Pearl Lustre, 82
    Whimsie, 161
Donald Duck, 78
Donkeys:
    Cheerful Charlie, 2
    Cheerful Charlie Salt Pot, 3
    Cheerful Charlie Posy Bowl, 3
    Comic Donkeys, 2
    Doleful Dan, 2
    Doleful Dan Pepper Pot, 3
    Doleful Dan Posy Bowl, 3
    Donk"E", 226
    Donkey, 58, 78, 118, 159, 205
    Dora, 105
    Pedro the Donkey, 258
    Seaside Donkey, 269
Dora, 105
Dormouse, 189, 316
Dorothy and Toto, 165
Dougal, 235
Dr. Foster, 38, 47, 260, 282, 292, 329
Dr. Healer, 276
Dr. Healer's House, 91
Dracula, 245, 286
Dragon Whimsies, 265
Dribbles the Dog, 163, 179
Droopy Junior, 29
Drum Box Series, 105
Ducks:
    Arundel Chick, 144, 177
    Arundel Duck, 143, 177
    Cheeky Duckling, 22
    Comic Duck Family, 4
    Dack, 4
    Dilly, 4
    Duck, 48, 55, 61, 62, 81, 86, 158,
        210, 250, 280, 289, 306, 311,
        315, 325, 331, 343, 345, 346
    Duck Family, 4
    Duck Key Ring, 88
    Duck, Mr., 4
    Duck, Mrs., 4
    Duck Tray, 88

    Duckling, head back, beak closed, 23
    Duckling, head forward, beak open, 23
    Lil' Bit Duck, 172
    Quackers on his Sleigh, 139
    Quackers on Ice, 139
    Quackers the Duck, 163, 181
    Swimming Duck, 321, 325, 331, 345
Duckworths, No. 9, 256
Dunstable Fairs, 1996-1999, 203
Dunstable Leisure Centre, 2002-2003, 204
Dunstable Travelhare, 216
Dunstable Whimble, 261
Dustbin Cat, 132

E

E. and A. Crumpton, 249
Eagle, 280, 315, 328, 346
    American, 169
    American Patriotic Eagle, 175
    Bald, 174
    Golden, 87, 305
    Whimsie, 174
Easter Bunn "E", 226
Easter Bunny, 161
Edward Fox, 214
Edward Town Mouse, 147
Elephants:
    Baby Elephant, 65
    Baby, Trunk Down, 15
    Baby, Trunk Up, 15
    Elephant, 46, 56, 79, 86, 95, 105, 212,
        295, 298, 303, 310, 320, 345, 346
    Elephant (Circus), 105
    Elephant Family, 15
    Elephant, Seated, 303, 319
    Elephant, Standing, 303, 319
    Female, trunk down, 305
    Jumbo Jim, 33, 132
        Calendar, 132
    Large Elephant, 131
    Lil' Bit Elephants, 171
    Male, trunk up, 305
    Medium Elephant, 131
    Miniature Elephant, 131
    Mother, 15
    Pink Elephant, 250
    Small Elephant, 131
    Sumo the Elephant, 145

Tiny Elephant, 131
Tray, 131
Trunky, 105
Tusker, 122
When Elephants Fly, 340
Y2K Pink Elephant, 250
Elizabeth Tedwing, 179
Ella, 151
Elson, Peter and Robert Williamson, 342
Emily the Doll, 179, 187
Enchanted Witch, 193
Endangered North American Animals, 305
England Catkins, 336
English Boy, 104
English Bull Terrier, 62, 162
    Pearl Lustre, 82
English Inns Collection, 251
English Whimsies 54-61, 250
English Whimtrays, 61
Enrol a Friend, 185
Eskimo and Igloo, 141, 233
Eskimo Girl, 360
Euoplocephalus, 49
Event Figures, 223-228
eWade, 226

F

Fairies:
    Collectania, 239
    Collectus, 239
    Collecteenie, 239
    Collect It!, 239
Fairy Godmother, 191
Fairytale Friends, 244
Family Favourites, 210
Family Pets, 320
Fantail Goldfish, 210, 289, 314
Fantasy Series, 265
Fantasyland, 228
Farmyard Whimsies, 62
Fat Controller, 232
Father Abbot, 262
Father Christmas Catkins, 336
Father's Collection, 250
Fawn, 51, 54, 61, 118, 204, 250, 289,
    310
    Fizzy, 109, 179
    Leaping, 63

Felicity Squirrel, 179, 214
Felix the Cat, 106, 152, 162, 184, 199,
    241, 338
    Left Arm Raised, 106
    Carpet Bag, 106
    Cocktail Felix, 106, 162
    Halloween, 106, 162
    Seasonal Greetings, 106, 199
    Miniature, 106
    Heart in His Hands, 106
Field Mouse, 56, 87, 311, 325, 343
Fifi, 29
Fire Station, 93
Fireman Catkins, 157
Firm Friends, 185
First Whimsie Blow Up Spaniel, 77
First Whimsies, 63-77
First Whimsies English Animals, 312
First Whimsies Zoo Lights, 74-76
Fish:
    Angel Fish, 59, 185, 296, 322
    Arundel Salmon, 144
    Fantail Goldfish, 210, 289, 314
    Goldfish, 133, 179
    Shoal of Fish, 151
    Sturgeon, 304
    Tropical Fish, 306, 320
    Trout, 55, 61, 210, 291, 343, 346
Fish Waiter, 107
Fishmonger's Shop, 94, 276
Fizzy the Fawn, 109, 179
Flamingo Whimsie, 166
Flintstones Collection, 338
Flo: 211
Floppy the Penguin, 142
Florida Panther, 304
Florist Shop, 89
Fluff, 9
Fluffy Cat, Miss, 33
Flying Birds, 108
Flying Flowers, 341
Foals:
    Crunchie the Foal, 109
    Foal, 65
    Foal, Lying, 111
    Foal, Sitting, 111
    Foal, Standing, 111
Football Bear, 152
Football Crazy, 128

Footed Oblong Bowl, 130
For You, 229
Foster, Dr., 38, 47, 260, 282, 292, 329
Fox, 48, 55, 87, 96, 210, 258, 259, 289,
    296, 316, 327, 343
    Arundel, 146
    Edward Fox, 214
    Huntsman, 242
    Tufty, 295
    Whimsieland, 146
Fox Cub, 64
Foxhound, 69
Frankie, 123
Fred, 338
Fred at Forty, 274
Fred Blow Ups, 272
    Hungry Fred, 272
    Souper Fred, 272
Fred at Your Service, 271
Fred's Big Bandstand, 273
Fred's Christmas Pudding, 271
Fred's Christmas Surprise, 271
Fred's Easter Egg, 271
Fred Holding a Carrot, 272
Fred Holding a Leek, 272
Fred Holding a Mushroom, 272
Fred Holding an Onion, 272
Fred Holding a Pepper, 272
Fred Holding a Tomato, 272
Fred's Little Blue Book, 271
Fred's Tasting Time, 271
Fred the Conductor, 273
Fred Playing
    The Double Base, 273
    The Drums, 273
    The Keyboard, 273
    The Saxophone, 273
    The Tuba, 273
    The Violin, 273
Free Wade Miniatures, 283
Friar Tuck, 287
Frisco Coffee, 250
Frogs:
    Baby, Singing, 15
    Baby, Smiling, 15
    Boy Frog, 5
    Bulgie, 171
    Bullfrog, 60, 314
    Comic Frog Family, 5

Frog, 171, 210, 289
Frog Family, 5, 15
Frog, Mr., 5
Frog, Mrs., 5
Girl Frog, 5
Hip Hop, 122
Hopper, 240
Mother, 15
Smiling Frog, 148
Toad of Toad Hall, 184, 190, 284
Travelling, 149
Frost"E", 226
Frost "E" the Snowman, 226
Frost Flake, Mr., 120
Fudge Collectables, 251
Fun, Miss, 119
Funny, Mr.,195

G

G & G Collectables, 252
Gaffer, 84
Gaffer and Sydney, 184
Gamble and Styles (see Peggy Gamble)
Gamble, Peggy, 254
Garfield, 229
Gargoyle, 265
Geese:
Goose, 280, 315, 321
Goose, female, preening, 305
Goose, male, feeding, 305
Goosey Goosey Gander, 35, 38, 47,
244, 248, 256, 282, 292
Mother Goose, 38, 47, 181, 186, 255, 282,
293
Snow Goose, 258, 321
General Foods, 255
Miscellaneous Animals, 255
Miniature Nursery Rhymes, 255
Gengar, 124
Gentleman Rabbit, 242
Georgina Town Mouse, Miss, 147
German Shepherd, 311
Mother, 243
Pup, lying, facing left, 243
Pup, sitting, facing right, 243
Sitting, 246
Standing, 246
Giant Panda, 68

Candle Holder, 75
Tray, 71, 72
Giggles, Little Miss, 119
Ging "E" Trick or Treat, 226, 229
Gingerbread Children, 342
Gingerbread Girl, 173
Gingerbread Man, 38, 80, 282, 292, 342
Tree Ornament, 166
Gingie Bear, 229
Gingy the Bear, 127
Giraffes:
Baby, Awake, 16
Baby, Sleeping, 16
Baby, Lying, 245
Baby, Upright, 245
Giraffe, 46, 56, 82, 86, 207, 257, 289
297, 299, 301, 311, 343
Giraffe Family, 16
Mother, 16, 245
Pearl Lustre, 82
Stretch, 122
Whimsie, 152
Girl Frog, 5
Girl Pig, 8
Gnasher, 208
Goat, 62, 81, 86, 321, 331
Goat, Italian, 69
Gold Book Ted "E" Bear, 226
Gold Jesthare, 217
Gold Star Gifthouse, 257
Gold Teapot, 272
Golden Eagle, 87, 304
Golden Retriever, 120
Goldfish, 133, 179
Goldie (cat), 168
Goldilocks, 32, 186
Goldilocks and the Three Bears Series, 32,
186
Golliwogs, 261
Golly Gosh Bear, 110, 149, 179
Gone Fishin' Bear, 196
Goodie Boxes, 109-110
Goodnight Spot, 161
Goose (see Geese)
Goosey Goosey Gander, 35, 38, 47, 244,
248, 256, 282, 292
Gordon, 84
Gorilla, 58, 79, 204, 259, 297, 299, 301,
323, 328

Granada Television, 256
Great Dane, 62
Great Universal Stores (GUS), 257
Green Man, The, 179, 188
Green Sea Turtle, 304
Greengrocer's Shop, 91, 308
Gretel, 127
Grey-haired Rabbit, 148
Greyhound, Beau, 160
Grizzly Bear, 68
Candle Holder, 75
Tray, 72
Grizzly Cub, 68
Tray, 72
Grumpy, Mr, 119
Guinea Pig, 168, 320
Squeak, 109
Gypsy Catkins, 158, 337

H

Halloween, Felix the Cat, 106, 152
Halloween (Gingie Bear), 229
Halloween Fred, 270
Hanna-Barbera Cartoon Characters, 44, 252
Hansel, 127
Hansel and Gretel, 127
Happy Birthday Fred, 270
Happy Families, 13-20
Happy Family, 245
Happy Mr., 307
Happy New Year Fred, 270
Hare, 64, 298, 312, 316, 322, 323, 324,
331
Arthur Hare, 169, 214
Brown Hare, 196
Candle Holder, 75
Snowshoe, 258, 327
Tray, 72
Harelloween, 217
Harestronaut, 215, 217
Harpy, 105
Hattie the Squirrel, 163, 179
Hazelnut, 234
Healer, Dr, 276
Healer's House, Dr., 91
Heart in his Hands, Felix the Cat, 106
Hector the Owl, 158

Hedgehog, 56, 87, 96, 206, 290, 296, 311, 346
   Baby, 146
   Holly Hedgehog, 214
   Mother, 146
   Santa Hedgehog, 242
Hedgerow Crackers, 280
Hen Pepper Pot, 333
Henry Engine, 232
Henry, Puppy Love, 167
Hermit Crab, 133
Hickory Dickory Dock, 38, 80, 260, 282, 292, 323, 324, 326, 329
Hip Hop (Frog), 122
Hippos:
   Baby, Asleep, 16
   Baby, Awake, 16
   Baby, Eyes Closed, 245
   Baby, Eyes Open, 245
   Born to be a Big Brother, 134
   Born to be Cool, 134
   Born to be a Daydreamer, 134
   Born to be Friends, 134
   Born to be Loved, 134
   Born to be Naughty, 134
   Born to be Sleepy, 134
   Born to Slide, 134
   Born to be Wild, 134
   Family, 16
   Hippo, 56, 79, 95, 207, 290, 295, 298
   Mother, 16, 245
   Paddles, 122
Holly Hedgehog, 214
Holstein Calf, 264
Homepride Fred, 270-275
   Annual Figures, 270
   Big Band, 273
   Blow Up, 272
   Fortieth Birthday, 274
   Halloween, 270
   Miniatures, 272
   Whimsies, 273
   World Cup, 274
Honey Brown Bo-Peep, 309
Honey Brown Smiling Rabbit, 309
Honey Bunch Bears, 110, 149, 179
"Hopper" the Frog, 240
Horse of a Different Colour, 263
Horses:

Arundel Pony, 145
Baby Pegasus, 82
Bluebell the Pony, 160
Buttercup, 151
Colt, 65
Crunchie the Foal, 109
Foal, 65
Foal, Lying, 111
Foal, Sitting, 111
Foal, Standing, 111
Horse, 57, 63, 205, 297, 311, 313, 321, 325
Horse of a Different Colour, 263
Horse Sets, 166
Mare, 65, 111
Mare and Foal Dish, 70
Mare Candle Holder, 75
Mare Tray, 72
Pantomime Horse, 181, 186
Pegasus, 228
Pon "E", 226
Pony, 62, 81, 85, 105, 257, 303, 306, 319
Pony Tray, 88
Pony Whimsie, 145
Sets, 111
Shetland Pony, 64, 184, 257, 300, 301 320
Shire Horse, 69
House that Jack Built, 38, 282, 292
Huckleberry Hound, 44, 252
Hugging Bear Cubs, 141
Human Cannonball, 303
Humpback Whale, 304
Humpty Dumpty, 34, 38, 80, 244, 248, 260, 282, 292, 323, 326, 329, 346
Hungry Dalmatian, 161
Hungry Fred, 272
Hungry Spot, The Dalmatian, 161
Huntsman Fox, 242
Husk "E", 226
Husky, 61, 66, 332
   Blow Up, 83
   Candle Holder, 75
   Tray, 72

I

Igor Jr., 123
I'm On My Way, 238
In The Forest Deep Series, 242
Internet Guide Ted "E" Bear, 226
Irish Comical Pig, 182
Irish Girl, 104
Irish Setter
   lying, facing right, 246
   Mother, 243
   Pup, lying, facing left, 243
   Pup, lying, facing right, 243
Italian Goat, 69
I've a Bear Behind, 43, 44

J

Jack, 34, 38, 47, 244, 247, 255, 282, 293
Jack (salt), 256
Jack Horner, 244
Jack the Ripper, 363
Jackpumpkinhead and the Sawhorse, 267
Jack Russel Terrier, 121
James Robertson & Sons, 261
James Engine, 232
Jekyll and Hyde, 123
Jem, 105
Jenny the Black Poodle, 167
Jerry, 42, 339
Jesthare, 215, 217
Jet Set (Gingie Bear), 229
Jigglypuff, 124
Jill, 34, 38, 47, 244, 247, 255, 282, 293
Jinks, Mr., 44, 252
John, 192
Jolly Potter Collecthare, 216
Jonah in the Whale, 132
Jonno Bear, 161
Jubilee Terrace, 89
Judy, 254
Judy's Ghost, 254
Jumbo Jim, 33, 132
   Calendar, 132

K

K.P. Foods Ltd., 262
K.P. Friars, 262
KS Wader, 263
Kangaroo, 59, 155, 299, 301, 324, 326, 331
Keith Langford, 280
Keenan, Patty, 268
Key Kollectables, 269
King Aquariums Ltd., 279
King Arthur, 179, 187
King Canute, 188
King Cobra, 197
King Cole, 244
King Penguin, 66
    Candle Holder, 75
    Tray, 72
King Velveteen, 125, 179
Kingfisher, 161
Kissing Bunnies, 112
    Ashtray, 113
    Mustard Pot, 113
Kitten, 14, 54, 64, 205, 290, 300, 311, 312
    346
    Key Ring, 88
    Lying , 14, 85, 317
    Mitzi (kitten), 29
    On the Keys, 132
    Persian, 301, 320, 345, 346
    Rosie, 109, 181
    Seated, 14, 79, 205, 250, 311, 317, 343
    Whimsie, 141
Kittens, 306
Kneeling Angel, 99
    Candle Holder, 100
    Dish, 101
Koala Bear, 59, 151, 204, 259, 299, 301, 324, 325, 326, 331
Kodiak Bear, 344

L

Labrador, 306
Lady of the Lake, 179, 187
Lady Town Mouse, 146

Lamb, 57, 64, 205, 297, 311, 312
    Arundel Lamb, 146
    Blow Up Lamb, 184
Landlord Barley Mow, 276
Langford, Keith, 280
Langur, 59, 204, 257, 297, 299, 301, 326
Latka, Sharon, 281
Laughing Rabbit, 24
Laughing Squirrel, 24
Lawyer, 103
Lazy, Mr, 119
Leaping Fawn, 63
Left Eye Open (Homepride Fred), 273
Right Eye Closed (Homepride Fred), 273
Leopard, 58, 79, 204, 259, 297, 299, 301, 317, 331
Leprechaun on a Rock, 171
Leprechaun Riding a Snail, 168
Leprechaun / Wheelbarrow, 169
Leprechaun with Sign, 172
Lever Rexona, 282
Li'Bear'ty (bear), 203
Library, The, 94
Library Bear, 136, 179
Lighthouse, 279
Lightning (cat), 168
Lil' American Footballer, 171, 179
Lil' Bit Cat, 174
Lil' Bit Duck, 172
Lil' Bit Elephants, 171
Lil' Bit Mice, 218
Lili Bit Mouse, 169
Lil' Bit Pig, 173
Lil' Cricketer, 151
Lil' Devil, 158, 181
Lil' Easter Bear, 159
Lil' Footballer Bear, 160
Lil' Uncle Sam, 169, 175
Lil' Witch, 151
Linesman Fred, 274
Linus, 225
Lion, 46, 56, 65, 86, 105, 204, 251, 290, 298, 303, 311, 317, 319, 326, 343
    African, 197
    Born Free, 290
    British Lion, 151
    Circus, 105
    Cowardly Lion, 165

Cub, 68
Cub Candle Holder, 75
Cub Tray, 72
Female, lying, 305
Major the Lion, 158
Male, with mane, 305
Safari Park Lion, 79
Lion (The), 251
Little Bo-Peep, 35, 36, 38, 80, 244, 248, 255, 260, 282, 293, 323, 324, 326, 329, 346
Little Boy Blue, 35, 80, 260, 282, 293, 329
Little Bunnies (Lil' Bits), 168
Little Jack Horner, 34, 36, 37, 47, 248, 255, 260, 282, 293, 329, 345
Little Laughing Bunny, 11
Little Miss Giggles, 119, 307
Little Miss Muffett, 34, 37, 38, 47, 248, 282, 293
Little Miss Splendid, 195
Little Miss Sunshine, 119
Little Miss Tiny, 195
Little Red Riding Hood, 38, 80, 253, 255, 282, 293
Little Tommy Tucker, 35
Lizzie, 123
Llama, 68
    Candle Holder, 75
    Tray, 72
Locomotive Joe, 102, 154, 318
Lois Lane, 285
London Train, 98
Long Arm of The Law, 249
Long-neck Cat, 181
Looby Loo and Ted, 335
Lord Whimsie, 276
Lugsi, 123
Lucky the Bear, 140
Lux Soap, 283

M

Ma Straw, 277
Mabel Lucie Attwell Figures, 39
Mabel Lucie Attwell Series, 230
    Mad Hatter, 230
Mad Hatter, 181, 189
Madison Mouse, 164, 181
Maid Marian, 287
Major the Lion, 158
Mama Bear, 32

Mama Otter, 212
Mama Seal and Pup, 140, 233
Manatee, 304
Manor, 92
Maple the Canadian Bear, 218
Mare, 65
    Candle Holder, 75
    Tray, 72
Mare and Foal Dish, 70
Market Hall, 93
Mary and Baby Jesus, 78
Mary Had a Little Lamb, 34, 247
Mary Lamb, 244
Mary Mary, 35, 244, 256
Maisie (the Puppy), 147, 161
Master Howard Town Mouse, 146
Maurice, 84, 162
Mayflower, 126
Membership Figures, 184
Membership Series, 185-197
Memories Collection, 335
Memory Jars, 283
Merlin, 181, 187
Mermaid, 181, 188, 228, 279, 286
Merryweather Farm, 92
Mice:
    Arundel Town Mouse, 145
    Baby, eyes closed, 17, 245
    Baby, eyes open, 17, 245
    Cheesy, 122, 240
    Christmas Mouse, 141
    Dixie, 252
    Dormouse, 189, 316
    Edward Town Mouse, 147
    Field Mouse, 56, 87, 311, 325, 343
    I'm On My Way, 238
    Jerry, 42, 339
    Lady Town Mouse, 146
    Lil' Bit Mouse, 169
    Madison Mouse, 164, 181
    Master Howard Town Mouse, 146
    Miss Georgina Town Mouse, 147
    Mother, 17, 245
    Mouse, 58, 117, 322
    Mouse Family, 17
    Pixie, 252
    Sleeping, 320
    Stilton the Mouse, 109
    Timid Mouse, 151

Tiny the Mouse, 163, 182
Michael, 192
Michelin Man, 334
Millennium Catkins, 157
Millennium Teddy, 157, 181
Miller, 276
Mini Mansions, 237
Miniature, Felix the Cat, 106
Miniature Nursery Rhymes, 47, 255, 292-294
Minikins, 114-118
    Minikins Shop Counter Plaque, 114
Minnie the Minx, 208
Miscellaneous Animals (General Foods), 255
Miscellaneous Christmas Cracker Boxes, 280
Mischief the Chimp, 169, 175, 181
Miss Bossy, 119
Miss Fluffy Cat, 33
Miss Fun, 119
Miss Georgina Town Mouse, 147
Miss Muffet, 244
Miss Prune's House, 93
Miss Splendid, Little, 195
Miss Tiny, Little, 195
Mitzi, 29
Mole, 79, 190, 316, 322
    Digger, 109
    Morris, 242
Mongrel, 54, 205, 283, 290, 310, 325, 332, 343
Monkey and Baby, 65
    Tray, 72
Morgan's the Chemist, 91
Morris Mole, 242
Mother and Baby Bear, 140
Mother Badger, 146, 181
Mother Goose, 38, 47, 181, 186, 255, 282, 293
Mother Hedgehog, 146
Mother Turtle, 246
Mother Polar Bear and Cubs on Ice, 233
Mouse (see Mice)
Mr. and Mrs. Snowman Cruet, 207
Mr. Bump, 119, 307
Mr. Chill Flake, 120
Mr. Christmas Flake, 120
Mr. Cold Flake, 120
Mr. Duck, 4
Mr. Frog, 5

Mr. Frost Flake, 120
Mr. Funny, 195
Mr. Jinks, 44, 252
Mr. Jinks, Pixie and Dixie, 252
Mr. Grumpy, 119
Mr. Happy, 307
Mr. Lazy, 119
Mr. Magoo, 230
Mr. Men and Little Miss, 119, 195
Mr. Men Collection, 307
Mr. Noisy, 119
    All Aboard, 119
Mr. Penguin, 6
Mr. Penguin Pepper Pot, 7
Mr. Pig, 8
Mr. Pig Salt Pot, 8
Mr. Plod, 33, 339
Mr. Punch, 254
Mr. Punch and Judy, 254
Mr. Rabbit, 9
Mr. Rabbit Salt Pot, 10
Mr. Rush on his Skateboard, 195
Mr. Small, 195
Mr. Snow, 307
Mr. Snow Flake, 120
Mr. Snowflake and his Family, 120
Mr. Snowman Pepper, 155
Mr. Winter Flake, 120
Mrs. Darling, 286
Mrs. Duck, 4
Mrs. Frog, 5
Mrs. Penguin, 6
Mrs. Penguin Salt Pot, 7
Mrs. Pig, 8
Mrs. Pig pepper Pot, 8
Mrs. Rabbit, 9
Mrs. Rabbit Pepper Pot, 10
Mrs. Snowman Salt, 155
Mummy Bear, 181, 186
Musical Marco, 102, 154, 318
Musk Ox, 326
Mustard Pot (Rabbit), 12
My Dog Skip, 341
My Pet, 121

N

Nanny Fluffins and Baby Velveteena, 125, 181

Narrow-Eared Rabbit, 115
Nativity Whimsies Set, 78
New Colourway Whimsies, 79-81
New Whimtrays,
New Victoria Theatre, 284
New York Tourist, 164, 181
Newark, Collect It! Travelhare, 216
Nennie Scottish Terrier,
Nibbles the Bunny, 168
Noah and Wife, 305
Noah's Ark, 305
Nod, 43, 44
Noddy, 33, 339
Noddy Set, 33, 339
Nodosaurus, 49
Noisy, Mr, 119
    All Aboard, 119
North American Bear, 171
Novelty Animals and Birds, 22-26
No. 9 The Duckworths, 256
Nursery Crackers, 280
Nursery Favourites, 34-38, 256
Nursery Rhymes, 37
Nursery Rhyme Miniatures, 36
    Blow Ups, 38
Nursery Rhyme Collection, 247-248
Nursery Rhyme Crackers, 326
Nursery Rhyme Models, 283

O

Oblong Pavilion, 209
Octopus, 133
Old Buck Rabbit, 25
Old Father Time Catkins, 336
Old King Cole, 34, 36, 255, 282, 294, 323,
    324, 326
    with blue hem, 36
    without blue hem, 36
Old Smithy, 93
Old Woman in a Shoe, 35, 36, 38, 80, 244,
    255, 256, 282, 294, 323, 326, 345
Olive Oyl & Swee'pea, 247
Olympia Incentive Exhibition, 1998, 153
One-of-a-Kind Models, 177-182
Oops! The Bear, 138, 149, 181
Orang-outan, 59, 204, 259, 297, 299, 301,
    326, 331
Orca (Killer Whale), 176

Orinoco Womble, 231
Oscar the Christmas Teddy Bear, 164, 181, 199
Oswald Owl, 242
Otter, 55, 87, 96, 145, 210, 290, 296,
    298, 322
    Mama Otter, 212
Our Little Angel, 199
Out For A Duck Catkins, 336
Out of the Blue Ceramics (Collectables
    Magazine), 285
Owls:
    Baby, wings closed, 18
    Baby, wings open, 18
    Barn Owl, 58, 304, 315
    Hector the Owl, 158
    Mother, 18
    Oswald, 242
    Owl, 55, 87, 158, 210, 250, 255,
        280, 290, 298, 311
    Family, 18
    Tray, 88
    Specs, 122
    Snowy Owl, 68, 197, 212, 258, 327
        Tray, 73
    Spotted, 304
    Toots the Owl, 109
Ozma, 165

P

Pa Straw, 277
PA Dragon, 173
PA Pup, 172
Paddington Bear, 235
Paddington's Snowy Day, 235
Paddles (Hippo), 122
Painted Ladies, 237
Palm Cockatoo, 197
Panda Bears:
    Blow Up, 212
    Giant Panda, 68
    Giant Panda, Candle Holder, 75
    Giant Panda Tray, 71, 72
    Keyrings, 88
    Panda, 46, 86, 212, 255
    Plaque, 137
    Whimsie, 212
Panther, Florida, 304
Pantomime Dame, 181, 186

Pantomime Horse, 181, 186
Pantomime Series, 186
Papa Seal, 140, 233
Partridge, 87, 140, 280, 315, 316
    Whimsie, 140
Patty Keenan, 268
PC Gotchare, 215, 217
Pearl Bunny, 159
Pearl Dolphin, 82
Pearl English Bull Terrier, 82
Pearl Giraffe, 82
Pearl Lustre Whimsies, 82
Pearl Penguin, 82
Pearl Puppy, 82
Pearl Seahorse, 160
Pearl Snail, 151
Pearl Spaniel, 82
Pearly King, 103
Pearly Queen, 103
Pebbles, 338
Pedro the Donkey, 158
Pegasus, 228
Peggy Gamble, 254
Pelican, 59, 118, 280, 297, 315
Penguin, The, 331
Penguins:
    Benny, 6
    Comic Penguin Family, 6
    Floppy the Penguin, 142
    King Penguin, 66
    King Penguin Candle Holder, 75
    King Penguin Tray, 72
    Pair of Penguins, 156
    Penguin, 48, 61, 82, 156, 255, 258,
        327, 331, 385
    Penguin Family, 6
    Penguin, Mr., 6
    Penguin, Mr., Pepper Pot, 7
    Penguin, Mrs., 6
    Penguin, Mrs., Salt Pot, 7
    Penguin (Pearl Lustre), 82
    Penguin Whimsie, 152
    Penny, 6
    Whimsie, 152
    Wonderland Penguin, 233
Penny, 6
People From Whimsey-on-Why, 275
Pepi, 29
Percy, 29

Percy the Small Engine Miniature, 40, 232
Percy Engine, 232
Peregrine Falcon, 304
Persian Kitten, 301, 320, 345, 346
Peter Pan, 184, 192, 286
Peter Pan Series, 192
Pet Shop Friends, 306
Pet Shop, 306
Pheasant, 87
Picture Palace, 93
Pied Piper, 255, 282, 294
Pig Styles, 159
Pigs:
    Arnie, 159
    Arundel Pig, 147
    Baby, asleep, 18
    Baby, awake, 18
    Boy Pig, 8
    Brick House Pig, 177, 185
    Ceasar, 159
    Comic Pig Family, 8
    Girl Pig, 8
    Lil' Bit Pig, 173
    Mother, 18
    Pig, 57, 62, 69, 81, 86, 205, 320, 321
    Pig Family, 8, 18
    Pig Large, 297
    Pig Medium, 297
    Pig, Mr., 8
    Pig, Mr., Salt Pot, 8
    Pig, Mrs., 8
    Pig, Mrs., Pepper Pot, 8
    Pig Small, 297
    Piglet Tray, 72
    Poppy the Pig, 158
    Priscilla the Pig, 163, 181
    Straw House Pig, 182, 185
    Topsy-Turvey, 159
    Truffle, 122, 240
    Twirly Whirly, 159
    Whimsieland, 147
    Wood House Pig, 185
Pikachu, 124
Pin trays (see listing under model name)
Pine Marten, 56, 204, 210, 257, 297, 299,
    301, 311, 314, 346
Pink Elephant, 250
Pink House, 330
Pink Lady, 237

Pipe stands (see listing under model name)
Pirate, 286
Pixie (mouse), 252
Pixie on a Mushroom, 228
Plaque, Camtrak, 235
Plaques, Membership, 231
Plod, Mr., 33, 339
Pocket Horrors, 123
Pocket Pals, 181
    Series One - Animals, 122
    Series Two - Horrors, 123
    Tango, 231
    1999-2005, 240
Pokemon, 124
Polar Bears:
    Mother Polar Bear and Cub on Ice, 233
    Polar Bear, 61, 66, 72, 79, 95, 151,
        204, 258, 259, 295, 299, 301,
        304, 326, 327, 328
    Polar Bear Cub, 66, 73, 75, 139, 140,
        141, 233
        Blow Up, 83
        Candle Holder, 75
        Hugging, 235
        Seated, 140, 233
        Standing, 140
        Walking, 233
        Tray, 73
    Polar Bearcubs on Ice, 233
    Polar Bear Mother and Cub on Ice, 233
    Polar Bear Mother Blow Up, 83
    Polar Bear Tray, 72
Polar Blow Ups, 83
Police Station, 94
Policeman, 249
Policeman Catkins, 336
Poliwhirl, 124
Polly Kettle, 244
Polly Put the Kettle On, 34, 256
Pon"E", 226
Pongo, 26
Pony, 62, 81, 85, 105, 257, 303, 306, 319
    Arundel, 145
    Tray, 88
    Whimsie, 145
Poodle, 63, 290, 303, 319, 325, 332
    Candle Holder, 76
    Circus, 137
Poor Man, 41

Pop, 194
Popeye, 247
Popeye Collection, 247
Poppa Bear, 32
Poppy the Pig, 158
Pos-ner Associates, 287
Postman, 276
Post Office, 90, 91, 308
Pretty-in-Pink Budgie, 340
Prairie Dog, 164, 181
Prince, Arthur of England, 338
Prince, 193
Prince Charming, 191
Prince George Tedward, 125, 181
Princess Elizabeth Tedwina, 125, 179
Princess Plushette, 125, 181
Priscilla the Pig, 163, 181
Prisoner, 249
Protoceratops, 49
Prune's House, Miss, 93
Psyduck, 124
Puck, 181, 188
Puff, 9
Pump Cottage, 91, 308
Punch, Mr., 254
Pup, Looking Back, 92
Pup, Lying on Back, 92
Pup, Sitting, 92
Pup, Sitting, Front Paws Up, 92
Pup, Sniffing Ground, 92
Pupp "E", 226
Puppy, 85, 88, 169
    Arundel, 145
    Christmas, 139, 177, 184
    Key Ring, 88
    Pearl Lustre, 82
    Lying, 14, 50, 51
    Maisie, 147, 161
    Play, 121
    Seated, 50, 51, 52
    Spaniel, 79, 258, 301, 302, 321
    Standing, 14
    Tray, 88
    Truly, 184
    Walking, 52
Puppy Love:
    "Ella," 151, 181
    "Henry," 167
    "Shelby'" 164, 181

"Sidney," 156, 181
"Steino," 144
Whimsie, 152, 161
Puppy Play, 121
Puppies, 306
Pups-in-a-Basket, 246
Puss in Boots, 35, 80, 244, 282, 294, 317

Q

Quackers:
On His Sleigh. 139
On Ice, 139
The Duck, 163, 181
Queen Beatrice, 125, 181
Queen Guinivere, 181, 187
Queen Mum, 125
Queen of Hearts, 35, 38, 80, 189, 244, 260
282, 294, 329

R

R & M Collectables, 287
Rabbits:
Arthur Hare, 214
Arthur Hare Teenies, 215
Arthur Hare Wizhared, 168
Arthur Hare Wizhared Whimsie, 215
Arundel Bunny, 143, 177
Arundel Travelhare, 216
Baby, seated, 19, 245
Baby, standing, 19, 245
Big Chief Bravehare, 217
Boots the Rabbit, 163, 177
Bravehare, 215
Bounce, 122, 240
Brown Hare, 197
Buffalo Travelhare, 216
Bunn"E", 226
Christmas Bonanza, 216
Christmas Rabbit, 141
Comic Rabbit Ashtray, 12
Comic Rabbit Family, 9
Comic Rabbit (Little Laughing Bunny), 11
Comic Rabbit Mustard Pot, 12
Dunstable Travelhare, 216
Ears open, 297, 310

Easter Bunny, 161
Easter Bunn "E", 226
Family, 19
Fluff, 9
Gentleman, 242
Grey-haired Rabbit, 148
Hare, 64, 298, 312, 316, 322, 323, 324, 331
Hare Candle Holder, 75
Hare Tray, 72
Harestronaut, 215, 217
Harelloween, 217
Honey Brown Smiling Rabbit, 309
Jesthare, 215, 217
Jolly Potter, 216
Kissing Bunnies, 112
Ashtray, 113
Mustard Pot, 113
Laughing Rabbit, 24
Little Bunnies (Lil' Bits), 168
Little Laughing Bunny, 11
Memory Jar, 283
Mother, 19, 245
Mustard pot, 12
Narrow-Eared Rabbit, 115
Nibbles the Bunny, 168
Newark Travelhare, 216
Old Buck Rabbit, 25
PC Gotchare, 215, 217
Pearl Bunny, 159
Puff, 9
Rabbit, 54, 85, 109, 117, 250, 255, 283, 291, 300, 301, 306, 310, 320, 322, 345, 346
Rabbit Family, 9, 19
Rabbit, Mr., 9
Rabbit, Mr., Salt Pot, 10
Rabbit, Mrs., 9
Rabbit, Mrs., Pepper Pot, 10
Rabbit Sitting, 115
Rabbit Whimsie, 174
Roly Poly Rabbit, 156, 181
Santhare Paws, 217
Shareriff, 215, 217
Snowshoe Hare, 258, 327
Special Edition Travelhare, 216
Trentham Travelhare, 216
Uxbridge Travelhare, 216
Wade's World, 216

Whimsieland, 173
Whimsies, 266
White, The, 182, 189
Wide-Eared Rabbit, 117
Wizhared, 217
Racoon, 60, 68, 79, 96, 257, 295, 299, 301, 326
Tray, 70, 73
Raisin, 234
Ram, 58, 205
Ratty, 181, 190
In a Row Boat, 190
Red Riding Hood, Little, 38, 80, 253, 255, 282, 293
Red Rose Tea (Canada) Ltd., 288-297
Red Rose Tea Fair, Connectcut, 166
Red Rose Tea (U.S.A.) Ltd., 164-182, 298-307
Red Setters:
Mother, 51
Puppy, Lying Facing Left, 51
Puppy, Lying Facing Right, 51
Red Setter Pipe Stand, 52
Red Setter Puppy, Dishes, 53
Referee Fred, 274
Reindeer, 171, 258, 327
Rud"E", Reindeer, 226
Retriever, 64, 85, 312
Candle Holder, 76
Revenge, 126
Rhino, 58, 206, 207, 259, 297, 299, 301, 331
Rhinoceros, 65, 305
female, head down, 305
male, head up, 305
Rich Man, 41
Ride a Cock Horse, 80, 260, 329
Ringmaster, 105, 303
Ripley Village Fete / Teddy Bears' Picnic, 154
Robell Media Promotions Ltd., 307
Robert Williamson and Peter Elson, 342
Robertson's Jam Gollies and Bandstand, 261
Robin Whimsie, 142
Robin Hood, 287
Rocking Horse, 268
Roly Poly Rabbit, 156, 181
Rose Cottage, 90
Rosie the Kitten, 109, 182
Rovers Return, 256

Royal Guard, 125, 182
Rud"E" Reindeer, 226
Ruffles the Bear, 185
Rufus, 155, 182
Rufus on Tour, 164
Rule Beartannia, 125
Rule Beartannia Plaque, 125
Rupert and the Snowman, 235
Rupert Bear, 235
Rush, Mr. (On his Skateboard), 195

S

S-shaped ashtray, 12, 113
Sailor, 41
Saint Bernard, 67
    Brand"E", 226
    Brandy, 160
St. George and the Dragon, 182, 188
St. John Ambulance Brigade (U.K.), 308
St. John's School, 89
St. Lawrence Church, 89
St. Sebastian's Church, 91, 275
Safari Park Lion, 79
Safari Whimsies, 46
Salada Tea Canada, 308
Salmon, Arundel, 144
Sam, 39, 230
San the Fat Slag, 209
Santa:
    And Snowman, 286
    With Open Sack, 199
Santa Claus, 253, 286
Santa Hedgehog, 242
Santa Maria, 126
Santa's
    Flight, 138
    Little Helper, 199
    Sleigh, 268
    Train, 268
Santhare Paws, 217
Sarah, 39, 230
Saurclephus, 49
Saxophone Golliwog, 261
Scarecrow, 267
School Teacher's House, 94
Scooby-Doo, 252
Scottie, 226

Scots Boy, 104
Scrappy Doo, 252
Scutellosaurus, 49
Sealife Crackers, 280
Sea Lion, 303, 319, 328
Sea Turtle, 328
Seahorse, 59, 133, 213, 279, 297, 322
    Pearl, 160
Seaside Donkey, 269
Seasonal Greetings, Felix the Cat, 106
Seasonal Snow Greetings, 199
Seals:
    Baby Seal, 66
    Baby Seal Candle Holder, 74
    Baby Seal Tray, 71
    Mama and Pup, 140, 233
    Papa, 140, 233
    Pair of Seals, 151
    Seal, 79
    Seal Blow Up, 83
    Seal on Rock, 210, 291, 298, 322
    Seal Pup, 61, 185, 258, 327
Setter, 55, 62, 210, 291, 310, 343
Shareriff, 215, 217
Sharon Latka, 281
Sharps Chocolate, 309
Sheep:
    Arundel Lamb, 146
    Baa Baa Black Sheep, 38, 282, 292, 333
    Doll "E" the Sheep, 226
    Female, head down, 305
    Lamb, 57, 64, 205, 297, 311, 312
    Lamb Blow Up, 184
    Male, head up, 305
    Ram, 58, 205
    Sheep, 333
Shelby, 164, 181
Sherwood Forest, 287
Shep the Sheepdog, 151
Shepherd, 78
Shetland Pony, 64, 184, 257, 300, 301, 320
Shetland Pony Blow Up, 184
Ships:
    Mayflower, 126
    Revenge, 126
    Santa Maria, 126
Shire Horse, 69

Shoal of Fish, 151
Sid the Sexist, 209
Sid the Sexist and San the Fat Slag, 209
Sidney, 156, 181
Silent Night, 199
Simon, 29
Simons Associates, Inc., 310
Sir Lancelot, 187
Sitting Angel, 99
    Candle Holder, 100
    Dish, 101
Sleepy Bear, 110, 149
Slinky (Cat), 122
Slow Fe, 238
Slow K, 238
Small, Mr., 195
Smiling Frog, 148
Smudger, 182, 184
Snack Tray, 70
Snail, Pearl, 151
Snap, 194
Snippets, 126-127
Snoopy, 225
    And Woodstock, 225
    Christmas, 142
    Happy Holidays, 225
    Hugging Woodstock, 225
Snow, Mr., 307
Snow Children, 182, 199
Snow Flake, Mr., 120
Snow Goose, 258, 327
Snow Woman, 199
Snowshoe Hare, 258, 327
Snowman, 199, 286
    Frost "E," 226
    Silent Night, 199
    Snowball Fight, 199
    Snowman, Mr. (Cruet), 155
    Snowman, Mrs. (Cruet), 155
Snowy Owl, 68, 197, 212, 258, 327
    Tray, 73
Soldier, 41
Sooty, 235
Souper Fred, 272
Souvenir Tortoises, 130
Spaniel, 54, 62, 82, 109, 148, 184, 205, 291, 311, 332
    Blow Up with Ball, 77

Candle Holder, 76
Pearl Lustre, 82
Tray, 73
with Ball, 63, 77
Spaniel Puppy, 79, 257, 300, 301, 320
Special Edition Travelhare, 216
Specs (Owl), 122
Spillers Dog Foods Ltd., 312
Spinosaurus, 49
Spook "E" (cat), 226
Spooky, 123
Spot the Dalmatian, 147
Spotted Owl, 305
Spotty's Feeding Time, 146
Spring Train Set, 278
Squeak the Guinea Pig, 109
Squirrels:
Felicity Squirrel, 179, 214
Hattie the Squirrel, 163, 179
Laughing Squirrel, 24
Squirrel, 56, 63, 87, 291, 298, 310, 316, 322, 324, 331
Squirrel Candle Holder, 76
Squirrel Tray, 73, 88
Squirrel Whimsie, 166
Tailwarmer, 242
Tufty, 242
Staffordshire House Gifts, 312
Stag Hotel, 91
Standing Angel, 99
Candle Holder, 100
Dish, 101
Standing Bear Cub, 141
Star Player, 128
Steino, 144
Stilton the Mouse, 109
Stoat, 64, 96, 296
Storybook Figures, 27-44
Straw Family, The, 277
Straw House Pig, 182, 185
Stretch (Giraffe), 122
Strongman, 105, 303
Stoke Fairs, 155, 156
Sturgeon, 304
Summer Train Set, 278
Summer Wade Fest (2003-2006), 171-174
Sumo the Elephant, 145
Sun, Sea and Sid, 269
Sunny Bear, 110

Sunshine, Little Miss, 119
Superman, 285
Supergirl, 285
Swallows, 108
Swan, 69, 77, 145
Blow Up, 77
Tray, 73
Sweep, 235
Sweet Shop, 92
Swifts, 108
Swimming Duck, 321, 325, 331, 345
Sydney, 84, 162

T

TV Pets, 29
Tabby Cat Dish, 53
Tailor, 41
Tailwarmer Squirrel, 242
Tales From the Nursery, 280
Tango, 231
Ted "E" Bear, 182, 226
Gold Book, 226
Internet Guide, 226
Wade Handbook, 226
Teddy Bear Plaque, 143, 154, 164
Teddy Bear Show, The, 136
Teddy Bears Picnic, 154, 196
Teen Straw, 277
Teenies, Arthur Hare, 215
Terrapin, 171, 206, 291, 314, 343
Terrier Dog, Black, 281
Tessie Bear, 339
Tetley Tea Folk Whimsies, 84
Thatched Cottage, 330
Thief, 41
Thisbe (Ugly Sister), 191
Thomas the Tank Engine, 232
Thomas the Tank Engine Miniature, 40, 232
Thomas Waide & Sons, 313
Three Bears, 35, 38, 244, 282, 294
Thunder (cat), 168
Tigers:
Baby, awake, 20
Baby, sleeping, 20
Mother, 20
Tiger, 46, 59, 86, 95, 204, 206, 207, 259, 295, 299, 301, 303, 317, 319, 326

Tiger Family, 20
Timber Wolf, 304
Timid Mouse, 151
Tin Woodman, 267
Tinker, 41
Tinker, Tailor, Soldier, Sailor, 41
Tinkerbell, 192
Tinker's Nook, 92
Tiny Clanger, 235
Tiny the Mouse, 163, 182
Tiny Treasures, 285-286
Tobacconist's Shop, 91, 308
Toad of Toad Hall, 184, 190, 284
Toby, 254
Toco Toucan, 197
Togetherness, 182
Tom, 42, 339
Tom and Jerry, 42, 339
Tom Piper, 244
Tom Smith and Company, 314-332
Tom Tom the Piper's Son, 34, 80, 255, 256, 260, 282, 294, 329
Tommy Tucker, 244
Tony the Tiger, 128
Tony Tiger Surfing, 194
Toots the Owl, 109
Top of the World, Betty Boop, 102
Topsy-Turvey (pig), 159
Tortoises:
Ash Bowls, 130
Baby Turtle, 246
Bahamas, 130
Bermuda, 130
Bermuda Triangle, 130
Devil's Hole, Bermuda, 130
Footed Oblong Bowl, 130
Green Sea, 304
Jumbo, 129
Large (Father), 129
Medium (Mother), 129
Mother Turtle, 246
Sea Turtle, 328
Slow Fe, 238
Slow K, 238
Small (Baby), 129
Souvenir Tortoises, 130
Terrapin, 171, 206, 291, 314, 343
Tortoise Family, 129
Town Mouse (Arundel), 145

Turtle, 59, 297, 298, 306, 322
Turtle Family, 246
Town Crier Catkins, 336
Town Garage, 90
Toy Box Series, 187
Toy Soldier, 182, 187
Trains:
    Alphabet Train, 98
    Autumn Train Set, 278
    Christmas Train Set, 278
    London Train, 98
    Percy the Small Engine Miniature, 40
    Spring Train Set, 278
    Summer Train Set, 278
    Thomas the Tank Engine Miniature, 40
    Winter Train Set, 278
Training Fred, 274
Traufler, 333
Traveller (Gingie Bear), 229
Travelhare Collection, The Arthur Hare, 216
Travelling Badger, 155, 182
Travelling Frog, 149
Trays (see listing under name of model)
Treasures Set, 131
    Derivative, 131
Trentham Gardens 1997, 155
Trentham Gardens 1998, 155
Trentham Gardens 1999, 156
Trentham Gardens Travelhare, 216
Tropical Fish, 306, 320
Trout, 55, 61, 210, 291, 343, 346
    Tray, 111, 121
Trower, David, Enterprises, 247
Truffle (Pig), 122, 240
Truly the Puppy, 184
Trumpet Golliwog, 261
Trunky, 105
Tubby the Bear, 163, 182
Tufty, 242
Tufty and His Furryfolk Friends, 242
Turtles (see Tortoises)
Tusker (Elephant), 122
21st Century Keepsakes, 335
21st Century Collectables, 334
Twirly Whirly (pig), 159
Tyrannosaurus Rex, 49

U

U.K. International Ceramics Ltd., 336
U.K. Wade Collectors Fairs, 136-163
U.S.A. Wade Collector Shows, 164-182
    Buffalo, New York - 1998, 164
    Kansas City, Kansas - 2001-2002, 165
    Mini Wade Fair, York,
        Pennsylvania - 1999, 167
    Oconomowoc, Wisconsin - 1997, 164
    Red Rose Tea Fiar, Connecticut, 166
    Rosemont Trade Show - 1999, 167
    San Antonio, Texas - 1999, 164
    Seattle, Washington - 1996, 164
    Summer Wade Fest - 2000-2001, 168
    West Coast Wade Collectors Fair -
        2002-2003, 175-182
Uncle Sam (Gingie Bear), 229
Usherette, 276
Unicorn, 265, 266
    Blow Up, 266
    Whimsies, 266
Union Bear, 151, 218
United Caves of Bearica, 203
Unknown Companies, 343-346
Uxbridge Travelhare, 216

V

Vale Farm, 90
Various Novelty Models, 132
Vera (Pepper), 256
Vicar, 276
Vicarage, 92
Victor "E" Bear, 218, 226
Village of Broadlands, 330
Village People Arthur Hare Series, 217
Village Store, 330
Vulcanodon, 49

W

Wade Baby, 182, 184
Wades By Peg, 254
Wade Handbook Ted "E" Bear, 226
Wade Watch USA, 340
Wadeusa.com 2003, 340
Wade Christmas Extravaganza 2000, 163
Wade's World Collecthare, 216
Waggs (Dog), 122
Wakey, Wakey! Bears, 196
Walrus, 61, 258, 322, 326, 327
Warner Brothers, 341
Water Life Collection, 133
Water Snail/Whelk, 279, 322
Watermill, 91
Weasel, 190, 316
Wee Willie Winkie, 34, 47, 244, 247, 255,
    282, 294, 323, 324, 326
Welcome Home, 182
Welsh Girl, 104
Wendy, 192
We're Hungrey Bears, 196
West "E," 226
West Highland Terrier, 67, 332
    Candle Holder, 76
    Tray, 73
    Westie, 164
Whale, 133, 176, 182, 258, 259, 322,
    327, 328
    Humpback, 304
    Jonah, 132
    Orca / Killer Whale, 176
Whelk/Water Snail, 279, 322
When Elephants Fly, 340
Where's My Mummy, 123
Whimsical Waders, 341
Whimsie
    Bluebird, 162
    Bulldog, 174
    Dolphin, 161
    Dragon, 265
    Eagle, 174
    Flamingo, 166
    Giraffe, 152
    Penguin, 152
    Puppy, 152, 161
    Rabbit, 174, 266
    Squirrel, 166
    Whimsie, (Gingie Bear) 229
    Wren. 172
Whimsies 2007, 197
Whimsey School, 91
Whimsey Service Station, 91
Whimsey Station, 92, 308
Whimsey-in-the-Vale, 89-90

Whimsey-on-Why, 91-94, 275, 308

Whimsie-land Series, 85-88

Whimsieland

    Fox, 146

    Pig, 147

    Rabbit, 173

Whimsies Dogs and Puppies, 99-103

Whisky, 29

White Lady, 237

White Rabbit, 182, 189

Whoppas, 95-96, 295-296

Why Knott Inn, 91

Wide-Eared Rabbit, 117

Wild Boar, 60, 207, 291, 298, 314, 331

Williamson, Robert, 342

Williamson, Robert and Peter Elson, 342

Willie Winkie, 244, 247

Wilma, 338

Wimpy, 247

Wind in the Willows Series, 190

Windmill, 91

Winter Flake, Mr., 120

Winter Wonderland, 233

Wiseman, 78

Witch Catkins, 336

Witch Hazel, 123

Witch Snoopy, 225

Wizard of Oz, 267

Wizard Merlin, 187

Wizhared, 217

Wizhared Whimsie, 215

"Woofit" the Dog, 240

Wolf, 79, 96, 295

    Beast, 193

    Timber, 304

Wolf, Big Bad, 177, 185, 253

Wolfy, 123

Wonderful World of Animals Series, 204

Wonderland Penguin, 233

Wood House Pig, 185

Woodstock, 225

Work's Cat "Burslem," 184

World Cup Fred, 274

Wren, 172, 280, 315

Wynken, 43, 44

Wynken, Blynken, Nod and I've A Bear Behind, 43, 44

Y

Year of the Rabbit, 283

Yellow Lady, 237

Yogi Bear, 44, 252

Yogi Bear and Friends, 44

Yorkshire Terriers:

    Mother, 52

    Pipe Stand, 52

    Puppy, Seated, 52

    Puppy, Walking, 52

    Yorkie Puppy, Seated, Dish, 53

    Yorkie Puppy, Standing, Dish, 53

Yum-Yum Bear, 196

Y2K Pink Elephant, 250

Z

Zebra, 58, 79, 207, 255, 257, 297, 299, 301, 310, 331, 343

    Female, lying, 305

    Male, standing, 305

Zoo Light Candle Holders, 74-76

Zoo Mazing, 134

If you want to know what is going on in
the world of Wade then you must join the

Official International
Wade Collectors Club

Membership offers, besides the pleasure of sharing the hobby, such intangibles as greater appreciation of Wade collectables through initiation into techniques of designing, modelling and production. You can find out about new products - designed to charm and capture the heart. The 2007 membership picece is Felix the Cat.

ANNUAL MEMBERSHIP BENIFITS

Membership figurine: exclusive to club members only.

Membership Pin: designed to compliment the membership figurine

Membership Certificate: personalised, complete with date of membership

Membership Card: entitles you to 10% discount at fairs and at the Wade shop on selected items.

Quarterly Magazine: full of news on limited editions, club news, fairs and events, articles on old Wade, and sales and wants. PLUS the opportunity to purchase member only limited editions.

Members only offer: exclusive to club members for 2007 a limited edition set of whimsies

MEMBERSHIP APPLICATION FORM

Simply photocopy this form and send it to: The Offical International Wade Collectors Club, Westport Road, Burslem, Stoke-on-Trent, ST6 4AG, England
Tel: +44 (0)1782 255255; E-mail: club@wadecollectorsclub.co.uk; www.wadecollectorsclub.co.uk

Please enrol me as new a member
- ❏ Annual Membership (12 mos. from receipt)   £ 30.00 ; US$ 52.00
- ❏ Two Year Membership (24mos. from receipt)   £ 54.00 ; US$ 98.00
- ❏ Family Membership (12 mos. from receipt - 4 family members) £ 100.00 ; US$ 185.00

❏ My cheque for............£ payable to Wade Collectors Club is enclosed or debit my credit/charge card

Title............First Name.........................
Last Name...
Address..
....
Post/Zip Code......................................
Tel. No...

❏ Visa   ❏ Mastercard   ❏ Switch

card no ❏❏❏❏❏❏❏❏❏❏❏❏❏❏❏❏

The sum of..
Card expires on month ❏❏ year ❏❏ security no ❏❏
Issue number (switch only)..............................
Signature...

❏ Please tick the box if you would like us to automatically renew your membership using your nominated card.
Please allow 28 days for processing your membership.   Membership prices are correct at time of printing, Jan 2007.

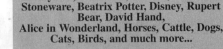